Longman Guide to World Science and Technology

LONGMAN GUIDE TO WORLD SCIENCE AND TECHNOLOGY

Series editor: Ann Pernet

Titles already commissioned:

Science and Technology in the Middle East
by Ziauddin Sardar

Science and Technology in Latin America
by Latin American Newsletters Limited

Science and Technology in the USSR
by Vera Rich

Science and Technology in Eastern Europe
by Vera Rich

Science and Technology in Israel
by Vera Rich

Science and Technology in the UK
by Anthony P. Harvey and Ann Pernet

Science and Technology in China
by Tong B. Tang

Science and Technology in Japan
by Alun M. Anderson

Science and Technology in South-East Asia
by Ziauddin Sardar

Science and Technology in the Indian Subcontinent
by Ziauddin Sardar

Science and Technology
in the Middle East

A guide to issues, organizations and institutions

Ziauddin Sardar

Longman
London and New York

SCIENCE AND TECHNOLOGY IN THE MIDDLE EAST

Longman Group Limited,
6th Floor, Westgate House, Harlow, Essex CM20 1NE, UK

© F.H. Books Limited 1982

Distributed exclusively in the USA and Canada by Gale Research Company,
Book Tower, Detroit, Michigan 48226, USA

First published 1982

British Library Cataloguing in Publication Data

Sardar, Ziauddin
   Science and technology in the Middle East.
   – (Longman guide to world science and technology)
   1. Science – Near East
   2. Technology – Near East
   I. Title
   508.56   Q127.N/

ISBN 0-582-90052-2

Printed in Great Britain by
Butler and Tanner Ltd, Frome, Somerset

Contents

List of Principal Abbreviations

ABEGS   Arab Bureau of Education for the Gulf States
AERCGS Arab Educational Research Centre for the Gulf States
AID   United States Agency for International Development
ALECSO Arab League Educational, Cultural and Scientific
        Organization
AOPEC   Organization of Arab Petroleum Exporting Countries
BOSTID Board on Science and Technology for International
        Development
ECWA   United Nations Economic Commission for Western Asia
IFSTAD Islamic Foundation for Science and Technology for
        Development
OPEC   Organization of Petroleum Exporting Countries
UAE   United Arab Emirates
UNCSTD United Nations Conference on Science and Technology for
        Development
UNCTAD United Nations Conference on Trade and Development
UNDP   United Nations Development Programme
UNEP   United Nations Environmental Programme
UNESCO United Nations Educational, Scientific and Cultural
        Organization

Introduction

Science and technology in the Middle East received a tremendous boost in the 1970s. Oil-rich Arab States, such as Saudi Arabia and Kuwait, poured in a large proportion of their oil revenues in building up an indigenous scientific and technological capability. These countries now have precise, aggressive science policies based on rapid industrialization following the classical, Western patterns of development. Countries lacking financial resources, such as Pakistan and Egypt, have devoted the second half of the decade in the pursuit of a single goal such as building up expertise in nuclear technology and remote sensing. New technical colleges and universities have emerged almost overnight and the enrolment of science and engineering students has increased rapidly. In addition, a number of regional organizations, such as the Conference of Arab Ministers Responsible for the Application of Science and Technology to Development (CASTARAB) and the Islamic Foundation for Science and Technology for Development (IFSTAD), devoted to the promotion of science and technology in the region, have emerged. All this means that scientific and technological activity in the Middle East – involving transfer, planning, institutional building and developing manpower resources – has never been greater.

Along with the upsurge in scientific activity, a number of cultural, social and ideological issues have come to the fore. The development of science and technology in the Middle East cannot be divorced from these issues. The efforts to rediscover and reconstruct the nature and style of science and technology under Islam, the numerous projects to 'Arabize' science and technology so that it could be taught in Arabic and can be 'internalized' by students and researchers, the concern over pollution that the rapid transfer of technology has produced, and greater emphasis on regional cooperation are all an integral part of the efforts to give science and technology an indigenous base in the region. At the same time, the old problems have developed a new significance, like the problems of brain drain and adaptation of imported technology to local needs.

But what constitutes the Middle East – the developing but politically important region which is the subject of this book? 'Middle East' is one of the most imprecise terms in geography: usually the region includes Turkey, Iran and other countries of south-west Asia, but often it is used with reference only to the region's Arab states. However, no definition of what does or does not constitute the Middle East has ever proved perfect. For the purpose of this book, the Middle East includes the region from Morocco to Pakistan – that vast stretch of land that is dominated by distinct historical and cultural themes. It is not geography – although there are obvious similarities in landform and climate – that makes the region distinct but the world view, history, culture and life-styles of Islam. The region includes Afghanistan, Algeria, Bahrain, Egypt, Iran, Iraq, Jordan, Kuwait, Lebanon, Libya, Morocco, Oman, Qatar, Pakistan, People's Democratic Republic of Yemen, Saudi Arabia, the Sudan, Syria, Tunisia, Turkey and Yemen Arab Republic. If that does not appear as the Middle East to some, it is because the term applies a European or at least a Western view of the world. Looked at from Islamabad, the region would be more accurately described as Near and Middle West.

This book is a reference guide to the scientific and technological activity in this region. It is divided into three sections: overview, regional organizations and country profiles.

The part entitled 'Overview' is a critical description of scientific and technological developments in the region since 1975; it is also a signpost for the developments of the next decade. It covers the major scientific and technological issues in the Middle East as well as recording the pace of development in the area. As the overview is concerned only with contemporary issues and development, historical background and analysis is presented only where it is essential. Emphasis is placed on delineating future trends and developments. (A more historical and analytical discussion of science in the region will be found in *Science, Technology and Development in the Muslim World* (Z. Sardar, Croom Helm, London, 1979) and *Science and Science Policy in the Arab World* (A. B. Zahlan, Croom Helm, London, 1980).) A resource bibliography of science and technology in the region from 1975 to 1981 provides references for further study.

The part entitled 'Regional Organizations' described the origins, projects and programmes of major science and technology organizations in the Middle East. Only one of these organizations, the Arab League Educational, Cultural and Scientific Organization, can be considered to be truly established. The others have yet to make an impact on the region: the charters of these organizations are reproduced to give an indication of their legitimacy and power base and how they may develop and influence the region.

Finally, the part entitled 'Country Profiles' gives a comprehensive account of the organization and administration of science and technology, government and academic research institutions and their research projects for each country of the region. This information has been gathered from a number of sources – official government agencies and private institutions, national papers submitted to the United Nations Conference on Science and Technology for Development (UNCSTD), held in August 1979 in Vienna, and from the personal visits of the author to some of the leading research institutions in the region. It has been critically examined and can be relied upon for a high degree of accuracy. The main exceptions to this rule are inevitably Iran and Afghanistan.

By providing a critical overview to science and technology issues in the region, it is hoped that this reference guide will become equally useful to students and researchers working on science development in the Middle and Near East, scientists seeking cooperative ventures, decision-makers who need detailed references to organization and administration of science in the area, journalists seeking background material to contemporary scientific and technological issues related to the region, and to those who are simply interested in keeping abreast of international developments in science and technology.

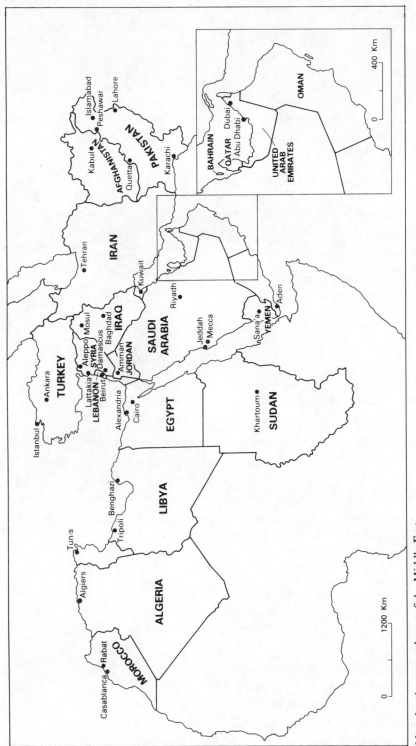

Map showing general area of the Middle East.

PART I

OVERVIEW

Science in the Middle East is in a state of flux. It is simultaneously looking back, far back, to a glorious past, experiencing an energetic and slightly productive present, and looking towards a future with the hope of capturing something of its past splendour. It is, moreover, a future that, given the present dominant trends of over-reliance on imported technology, is by no means certain.

There are two somewhat contradictory trends that characterize contemporary scientific and technological activity in the region: while expenditure on science and technology continues to increase, technological dependency, in both oil-producing and non-oil-producing countries, becomes more overt, more acute and much more apparent. Like most developing countries, the countries of the Middle East manifest their dependency in a range of economic and technological relationships with North America and Europe. The dominant features of these relationships include: trade structures based on import of technology and export of primary resources; limited national technological capability reflected in low levels of research and development related to local needs and requirements; over-reliance on foreign assistance, advisers and consultants for selection and management of imported technology; a lack of awareness as to the choices of technologies available; and weak technology-negotiating capabilities.

These features of technological dependency are the major obstacles to the indigenous flowering of science and technology in the Middle East. This dependency has had a profound impact on the scientific communities of the region: a whole generation of scientists and technologists has grown up taking dependency for granted and accepting the paradigm that without foreign scientific expertise nothing can be achieved. Since the beginning of the 1950s, when most of the Middle East countries obtained their independence, scientists and policy-makers in the region have lived in one system, the local cultural milieu, and thought in another, fundamentally opposed, system, which has led to a lack of confidence in their own abilities and resources.

This, in essence, is the main problem regarding science and technology in the Middle East. Science and technology can play their role in development only when the integrity of the whole enterprise – research institutions, universities, publications, research priorities and emphasis – as well as those active in science is preserved. Science policy-makers in the Middle East, however, still tend to accept the priorities of Western science policies, and organize their science, both education and research, on Western patterns, to serve the needs of societies that are radically different from the Western societies. The whole system is thus geared to imitation rather than originality.

This situation is largely due to an enduring colonial legacy. However, a number of social and cultural trends, due to a few unique characteristics of the region, may change the shape of science and technology in the Middle East quite radically. Apart from the obvious peculiarities of the region – the rather wide economic gap which exists between the oil-producing countries and the others, the diversified patterns of social development in different countries, the uneven distribution of population density over the region, and the tremendous growth rates of many commercial and State enterprises, particularly in the rich Arab states – the Middle East is going through a unique historical experience: a cultural reawakening. The rediscovery of their Islamic identity by the people of the Middle East is a fact that henceforth cannot be ignored by any government in the region, however determined it may be to continue the unchecked import of technology without due consideration to local social and cultural needs. Moreover, the cultural revival has produced a number of countertrends in Middle East science which, as discussed later in this volume, are geared towards a genuine, indigenous growth of science and technology. For scientists and technologists the cultural reawakening has meant that they are regaining confidence, although rather slowly, in their own society, traditions, culture, and institutions and hence in themselves as scientists and technologists. The impact that such a regeneration of confidence can have is obvious.

Science Planning and Organization

The cultural reawakening is now beginning to have an impact on science and technology policies of the Middle East countries. Governments are becoming much more sensitive to the social and cultural impact of science and technology. In the last five years there have been shifts in the science policies of Egypt, Pakistan, Turkey, and to some extent Saudi Arabia, from grand, far-reaching goals towards emphasis of local problems and development of indigenous scientific capability. In Egypt, for example, there has been a swing, at the National Research Centre in Cairo, away from the more leisurely pursuits of 'pure science' which has little bearing on Egypt's immediate problems, towards concentration on problems with direct relevance to national needs. Egyptian agricultural and rural needs, persistently ignored over the years, have received a major emphasis in the 1980–84 development plan. After being shelved for over six years, the plan to reclaim 12 million ha of the Nile Delta by piping the Nile has been revived. There are impressive plans to boost the fertilizer industry and reduce the import of nitrogen and phosphates. In short, Egypt's science planners are showing a new concern about her agriculture and rural population.

On the whole, Middle East governments are becoming conscious of the importance of science policy and planning. This, perhaps, is one of the most important outcomes of UNCSTD, held in Vienna in August 1979. UNCSTD forced the countries of the region to take a closer look at their science and to produce national papers that described their science policy and planning process. While most Middle East countries produced papers of uniformly poor quality, the exercise forced these countries to think seriously about science policy. The post-UNCSTD period produced a certain amount of reorganization of science in Syria, Egypt and Pakistan and a concerted effort to create a coherent science policy in most other countries.

Moreover, as the intellectual and educated segment of the population becomes more aware of the social and cultural impact of science, it seeks active participation in the discussions on issues of science policy. In Pakistan, for example, scientists, engineers, doctors, journalists and other intellectuals refused to have a science policy imposed on the country from above. A draft of national science policy prepared by the Ministry of Science and Technology was severely criticized by professional organizations of scientists and engineers, Pakistan's Council for Scientific and Industrial Research, and the national press. A debate on national science policy was conducted in the pages of *Dawn* and *Pakistan Times* for over a year. The government reviewed a number of drafts before the final document emerged in mid-1981. Such intense commitment, from both the scientific community and the educated public, and pressure to produce a viable science policy, in the face of a military government, would have been inconceivable only a few years ago. In Algeria, Tunisia, Saudi Arabia and Kuwait scientists and concerned intellectuals are gradually becoming more articulate in expressing their opinion on matters of science policy.

In a region that is dominated by dictatorships, benevolent or otherwise, public awareness of science policy issues is crucial if science is to take social roots. Science policy and politics, much to the displeasure of many scientists, are closely linked in the Middle East. The long-range, sustained efforts required for science to take indigenous roots, come into conflict with the emotional, volatile and unstable nature of the politics of the region. Active participation by the scientists and the educated population, as for example in the case of Pakistan, in the issues of science policy and planning would introduce an element of reality and stability that science in the region acutely needs.

In most Middle East countries science planning forms a part of development planning. In Saudi Arabia and Algeria, for example, science forms an important part of the new national development plans. In Sudan science planning is seen as an integral part of the Six Year Plan for Economic and Social Development (1977/78–1982/83) which constitutes the first phase of an eighteen-year 'prospective plan' whose basic objective is to put the economy on a pattern of self-sustained growth and to achieve a regionally balanced, self-reliant and accelerated development that would triple real per capita income by 1995 and ensure its equitable distribution. The problem in this case is that science and technology becomes engulfed in a host of economic goals and does not receive the individual attention that is essential for a viable national science and technology plan; and eventually the economic goals become an end in themselves and the statements about science and technology are either forgotten or shelved.

Moreover, because science planning is linked to national development plans it becomes inflexible and rigid. No provisions are made for continuous feedback into the plan itself. The exception here is Saudi Arabia: the Saudi development plan, and its science and technology components, are reviewed annually. But the momentum of the plan is such that the change in direction in national science planning and policy is not feasible without abandoning the whole development plan. The end result is that even though the plan is reviewed annually, negative feedback cannot really be taken into account.

Throughout the Middle East science administration is centralized. Science is administered by ministries such as Algeria's *Ministère de l'Enseignement Supérieur et de la Recherche Scientifique (MESRS)* and Pakistan's Ministry of Science and Technology, which channel funds to national science organizations such as the *Conseil National de la Recherche Scientifique (CNRS)* and the Pakistan Science Foundation. In most cases science ministries are junior ministries with very little power; they are also rather bureaucratic institutions. In fact, it is sometimes argued that centralized administration of science would be more effective were it not for the bureaucracy. In Saudi Arabia, Egypt, Pakistan and Libya it is suffocating new initiatives as well as alienating scientists from decision-makers. Much valuable time is spent by senior scientists in the bureaucratic procedures involved in obtaining equipment vital to their research.

Centralized administration has also laid scientific circles in the Middle East open to charges of corruption. There are accusations of influence-peddling through personal channels and of political vendettas against scientists. It is apparent that funds are usually channelled towards scientists who follow the government line and not necessarily towards those who deserve them.

Despite rigid centralization, science has been recently reorganized in some countries. Egypt, perhaps, has experimented more with various forms of science organization than any other developing country. Egypt first formed a national science policy and planning body in 1939. The Fouad I National Research Council was formed to control and coordinate all scientific activity in the country, conduct research, and establish research institutes. After the Suez crisis in 1956, the Fouad I National Research Council was abandoned in favour of a Science Council. The council produced a five year plan for scientific research (1960–64), which presented a multi-disciplinary attempt to strengthen the scientific base and infrastructure in Egypt. However, the experiment did not last long as in 1961 a Ministry of Scientific Research was established. Then followed a decade of organizational chaos: 1964 saw the creation of the Council for the Promotion of Scientific Research; 1965 the Supreme Council of

Scientific Research and 1968 the re-emergence of the Ministry of Scientific Research. Then, in 1971, the Academy of Scientific Research and Technology was created with fourteen specialized research centres under its control. A fresh research programme was worked out and emphasis was given to research-industry linkage. The academy has had considerable success in science planning and policy-making. However, there are complaints that it has not been able to integrate science planning with national economic plans – and this could mean that Egypt may undergo another reorganization.

In the last few years both Syria and Kuwait have attempted to reorganize their science. Syria has a science plan prepared by the Supreme Council of Sciences in cooperation with the Ministry of Planning. This new plan envisages a diversification of Syria's research and development activities. Traditionally, Syrian science policy was unique in that it concentrated on agriculture and 'Arabization' of science. Now, however, the country is moving into electronics, chemicals and nuclear energy and a number of new research institutes, such as the Centre for Industrial Research and Development and the Centre for Nuclear Energy and Research, have been set up. This suggests that the old administrative structure, where research organizations were under the Ministry of Higher Education and agricultural research was under the Ministry of Agriculture, has proved to be inefficient and ineffective. Whether Syria opts for a Ministry of Science or a Science Council with ministerial powers remains to be seen.

In Kuwait, the entire development planning process has been halted, even before the 1976–80 development plan had a chance to run its full course, and is undergoing reappraisal. Kuwait's development plan has nothing to say about science and technology, but in view of the prestige and impact on government thinking of the Kuwait Institute for Scientific Research (KISR), a science plan for Kuwait should emerge soon. The KISR is already working on the role of science and technology in diversification of Kuwait's economy.

Science planning and policy-making in Iraq and Jordan is reasonably well established. Iraq has had a strong national science institution since 1963. The Foundation for Scientific Research, attached to the national Planning Board, is responsible for the planning and coordination of scientific and technological activities and has its own science policy unit. It also runs seven research centres and the Directorate-General for the Welfare of Young Scientists. The Royal Scientific Society of Jordan is a much younger institution, having been established in 1970, but it is a much more dynamic and expanding institution than Iraq's Foundation for Scientific Research. It has only recently added national science planning and policy-making to its role as a promoter of scientific research and industry-research linkage, and organizer of scientific and technological information services. The bulk of its activities are focused on education, economic research, electronic engineering, mechanical engineering, and computer systems. Both organizations are operating at less than full efficiency; and both have a long way to develop as thriving, national science institutions.

Algeria provides the only exception to single, all-dominant, centralized science policy and planning institutions. The responsibility for scientific activity in Algeria is shared by three institutions: the *Organisme National de la Recherche Scientifique (ONRS)* is the executive agency responsible for implementing science policy through research grants and contracts; the Ministry of Higher Education and Scientific Research is responsible for research in Algerian universities; and the *Conseil National de la Recherche Scientifique (CNRS)* acts as an advisory body, promoting the development of science policy in Algeria. For Arab institutions, there is a surprising amount of communication and collaboration between the three bodies. Moreover as a method of organizing national science policy and planning, the Algerian system appears to be as effective as those of Egypt and Iraq.

The youngest science planning organization in the region is the Saudi Arabian National Centre for Science and Technology (SANCST). It is the central body responsible for promoting science policy and scientific research and coordinating the activities of research organizations in the Kingdom. Established in November 1977 and run in cooperation with the United States National Science Foundation, SANCST has an independent ᵢₑgal identity but is administratively attached to the office of the prime minister. Its policy and programmes are based on two basic objectives: to 'provide assistance to the private sector in the development of productive

Table 1.1 Science policy making in selected countries

Country	Institution	Projects/programme	Staff
Algeria	CNRS	Science policy envisaged	Professional
Iraq	FSR, Science Policy Unit	Sectoral science and technology plans, overall plan envisaged	Professional, technical
Jordan	RSS	Initiatives taken for formulation of national science policy and plan	Professional, technical
Kuwait	KISR, Techno-economics Division	Long-term technological requirements studied	Professional, technical, foreign
Lebanon	NCSR	Science plan included in 1972–77 development plan	Professional, technical
Pakistan	Pakistan Science Foundation	Science policy developed after lengthy national debate	Professional, technical
Saudi Arabia	SANCST	National science and technology plan part of the third development plan (1981–85)	Professional, technical, foreign
Syria	SCS to be integrated in National Council for Science Policy	National science and technology plan envisaged	Professional, technical
Turkey	TUBITAK	Sectoral science and technology plans	Professional, technical

Table 1.2 Roles and functions of national science and technology institutions in selected countries

Institution	Long/short-term planning	Coordination of research and development	Promotion of research and development	Execution of research and development	Advise consultation services	Advocacy of science and technology
Academy of Scientific Research and Technology (Egypt)	Yes	Yes	Yes	Yes	Yes	Yes
Foundation for Scientific Research (Iraq)	Yes	Yes	Yes	Yes	Yes	Yes
Royal Scientific Society (Jordan)	–	–	–	Yes	Yes	–
Kuwait Institute for Scientific Research (Kuwait)	–	–	Yes	Yes	Yes	–
National Council for Scientific Research (Lebanon)	Yes	Yes	Yes	–	Yes	Yes
Supreme Council of Sciences (Syria)	–	–	Yes	–	Yes	Yes
Saudi Arabian National Centre for Science and Technology (SANCST)	Yes	Yes	Yes	–	–	Yes
Conseil National de la Recherche Scientifique (CNRS)	–	–	Yes	Yes	Yes	Yes
Pakistan Science Foundation (PSF)	Yes	Yes	Yes	Yes	Yes	Yes
The Scientific and Technical Research Council of Turkey (TUBITAK)	Yes	Yes	Yes	Yes	Yes	Yes

agricultural and industrial research that will help to increase the gross national product' and 'to support joint research programmes between the Kingdom and international scientific foundations in an effort to keep pace with scientific development in the world by awarding research grants and undertaking joint research projects'. As Saudi Arabia has no urgent need to increase its GNP, SANCST seems to have concentrated its efforts on the latter objective.

Expenditure on science in the Middle East varies sharply between the oil-producing countries and others. On the whole less than 1 per cent of the GNP is devoted to research and development in the poorer countries of the region. Egypt and Pakistan fare better than others but a considerable proportion of their research and development budget actually goes to administration and maintaining the bureaucracy. In the case of Egypt, the bulk of research and development funding comes as foreign assistance from the United States and West Germany. (Foreign assistance is discussed at greater length later in this volume.) In the case of oil-producing countries the exact expenditure on science is difficult to pin down: but it is safe to say that over 5 per cent of the GNP is devoted to building universities and research institutes and in promoting local research and development activities, if there are any. On the whole, figures for countries such as Saudi Arabia and Kuwait become meaningless when the expenditure is actually compared with results. The 1980/81 budget for the University of Riyadh was SR 3,128 million (approximately, US$1 billion), much of which would have been spent on research and development activities at the University! It is not so much the lack of finance that is the problem; it is the manpower needed to transform such an expenditure into hard research and development that is lacking.

In addition to government funding, independent foundations are also beginning to fund research and development activities in the region. Two philanthropic organizations were formed in 1976: the King Faisal Philanthropic Foundation (KFPF), which is based in Riyadh, and the Kuwait Foundation for the Advancement of the Sciences (KFAS). The KFPF, which awards annual prizes for Islamic scholarship, including the scholarship of science and technology, is backing research projects on solar energy, desalination, iceberg studies, agriculture, housing, and the history of Islamic science. The KFAS, which was formed on the initiative of the Amir of Kuwait, Sheikh Jaber al-Ahmad (then crown prince and prime minister), and with the backing of the Kuwait Chamber of Commerce and Industry, supports pure and applied research in the natural sciences, health and medicine, and a whole range of engineering disciplines, and also awards grants and prizes to Arab scientists for internationally recognized contributions. The KFAS also promotes links and cooperative programmes between Kuwait and other Arab countries. One of the KFAS's most successful projects has been the development of the Arabic 'Smart' typewriter and an Arabic telex machine. Other successful projects include evaluation of Kuwait clays for use in ceramics and pottery, studies of Kuwait's sand and soil for utilization in glass and glass fibre manufacture, and studies on recycling of industrial wastewater.

Pakistan too has produced an independent funding organization: the Agha Hasan Abedi Foundation for Advancement of Science and Technology, which has its head office in Lahore. Established in 1981, the foundation is named after the founder and president of the Bank of Credit and Commerce International (BCCI). It will provide financial assistance to scientific institutions and give research grants to talented students. A second foundation for the advancement of learning is likely to be established with the help of the Karachi Chamber of Commerce, which has decided to devote 1 per cent of its annual profits (estimated to be US$4 million) to scientific research. Financial resources of Pakistani foundations cannot compare with those of KFPF and KFAS, but they do provide a glimmer of hope that independent funding for scientific research may increase not just in the oil-rich states, but also in the other countries of the region.

Scientific Manpower and the Brain Drain

The financial resources of the oil-rich Arab states have attracted a great deal of scientific and professional manpower from the poor countries of the Middle East. In the 1960s and early 1970s the flow of scientific and technical manpower was almost exclusively from the Middle East to the industrialized countries. As science could not be 'consumed' at home or bring adequate financial rewards, the only satisfying career for the Muslim scientists was in the universities and industries of the West. This classic pattern of brain drain has now changed significantly. Restrictive immigration policies and mounting unemployment in the West has meant that scientists from Egypt, Turkey and Pakistan are now going to the oil-rich countries. Although reliable figures are not available, the brain drain to the oil-rich states is thought to be much higher than the drain to the West has ever been. On certain poor Arab countries the effect of this new pattern of brain drain has been considerable.

Following an Organization of Islamic Conferences (OIC) study on brain drain in the Muslim world, three types of brain drain can be identified. The first is the migration of scientists to industrialized countries. This seems to be on the decline and is now relatively unimportant. The second is the movement of scientists from the poor countries to capital-rich states. Such transfer of talent is looked upon favourably as a net increase, but this migration does aggravate the manpower problems of the poorer Muslim countries. The third type of brain drain is the internal waste caused by the poor use of native talent; this is perhaps the most serious loss of the three categories.

In practice, the migration of scientists to oil-rich Arab countries has worked out both to the benefit of some countries (Egypt, Syria, Pakistan), and to the detriment of some others (Sudan and the Democratic Republic of Yemen).

Egypt actually encourages brain drain to oil-rich states. This is certainly a better option than the old policy of absorbing newly trained scientists in Egypt's vast bureaucracy – a policy that stifled original minds and created

the worst type of internal brain drain. The new policy of educating graduates for the technical manpower market of oil-rich states has brought dividends for Egypt. Egyptian universities have courses on petrochemicals,
desalination and high-technology agriculture, and its output of skilled
manpower in these areas is much more than the Egyptian economy or
scientific institutions can absorb. The manpower needs of the oil-rich
states, therefore, constitute a true blessing. Some of these special education
programmes are recognized only in the Arab world and a few particular
qualifications are recognized only in specific countries. Certain Egyptian
medical degrees and doctorates, for example, are valid only in Saudi
Arabia.

Unlike Egypt, Syria faces an acute shortage of scientific manpower, but
it manages to provide facilities for its scientists who wish to work in other
Arab states. The government allows up to four years leave of absence; and
in many instances, the government actually helps in locating employment
in the oil-rich states.

Although some scientists in Pakistan have expressed concern over the
migration of Pakistani scientists to the oil-rich states, it is a problem which
does not worry Pakistan's Science Foundation. There are two basic reasons
for this: it is not a permanent brain drain and the Pakistani economy does
benefit from the remittance of its expatriates. Pakistani scientists do not
appear anxious to settle down in the oil-rich states, even if the governments
of these countries were to allow long-term settlement. Invariably, they
return to Pakistan after four to five years.

However, for Sudan and South Yemen the story is considerably different.
Emigration of scientific manpower was practically non-existent in Sudan
prior to 1975. However, from 1976 onwards, there was a very sharp increase
in the migration of scientists. As far as the Third World is concerned,
both Egypt and Pakistan have a highly developed science infrastructure;
Sudan, in contrast, has an embryonic scientific community. The migration
of about 29 per cent of academic staff of the University of Khartoum, about
50 per cent of engineers of the country's major institutions and 60 per cent
of medical doctors by the end of 1979 would have had very serious consequences for the growth of science and technology in Sudan.

South Yemen faces a similar problem, but because the scientific community there is so small that it has not yet reached critical mass, the loss
of its scientists to Saudi Arabia and Kuwait could in fact do irreparable
damage to scientific development. Unless there is a sufficient number of
scientists in South Yemen, for example, research at the University of Aden
is not a viable proposition.

In French-speaking countries the pattern of brain drain has not changed
significantly. Scientists from Morocco, Algeria and Tunisia still tend to
migrate to France, with which these countries have colonial links, and to
some extent to Switzerland. Considering the immigration policies of France,
one would expect a decline here too, and a consequent increase, in the
near future, in the migration of scientists from these countries to the oil-
rich Arab states.

The last few years have also seen a number of attempts by Middle East countries to woo their scientists back from the West. Both Turkey and Pakistan have had considerable success with their respective schemes.

In 1977, the Turkish government, with the help of the United Nations Development Programme (UNDP) initiated the Project for Transfer of Know-How Through Expatriate Nationals (TOKTEN) with the aim of securing the expertise gained abroad by the many expatriate Turkish scientists and technologists. The TOKTEN scheme has proved to be ingenious and highly workable. Its main objective is for specialists of Turkish origins resident in the West to provide specific technical help. It gives preference to scientists of international standing whose services are obtained for short assignments of one week to a maximum of three months. The visiting scientist transmits his knowledge through training seminars, consultations, reports and proposals on policy issues, and other advisory services. The UNDP meets the travel costs and living expenses, but pays no salary; the host institution pays an honorarium. This method of consultancy by expatriates has proved far superior to traditional methods of seeking technical assistance. The consultant does not need a period of adaptation, adjustment, or acquaintance with local conditions, or to establish his credibility; his cultural affinity to Turkey improves his acceptance and effectiveness. Moreover, the Turkish expatriate provides a faster response to an institution's problems than is possible through traditional technical cooperation. Sometimes the character and confidentiality of the desired advice requires a privileged relationship, which is easier to ensure with a trusted expatriate. Often the full value of a training programme or a seminar can be ensured only if it is conducted in Turkish. Scientists visiting Turkey under the TOKTEN scheme have been responsible for directing the country's solar energy programme and have been involved in advising Turkey on its nuclear energy programme. Of course, the government hopes that some of them will become so involved that they will either return or will be motivated to spend a number of years working for a Turkish institution.

Pakistan has initiated a similar programme. The TOKTEN scheme in Pakistan started in January 1980 with the aim of bringing fifty experts to Pakistan to work and advise on projects ranging from agriculture, animal husbandry, civil and electrical engineering, and medical research to education and industrial management. It is too early to judge the impact of the scheme on Pakistan. However, since early 1978 Pakistan has been operating another similar scheme under the title 'National Talent Pool, Manpower and Overseas Pakistani Division', known popularly as 'Regular Visits of Qualified Pakistani Experts Positioned Abroad to Pakistan', which has had considerable success. The National Talent Pool not only allows Pakistani expatriates to visit Pakistan for a period of six to eight weeks, for which the Pakistani government meets all expenses and provides, by Pakistani standards, a generous honorarium, but also keeps a register of Pakistani experts abroad so that they can be tapped when the need arises. In some cases a regular link is developed between an expatriate scientist and a Pakistani institution, which ensures a certain amount of continuity.

In some cases, Pakistani expatriate scientists have themselves taken initiatives and approached institutions in Pakistan with advice and research proposals. One example is the Canadian Association for the Promotion of Research and Education in Pakistan (CANPREP), a group of Canadian scientists and academics of Pakistani origin, which since its inception in 1973 has made significant inputs in research and development in Pakistan. CANPREP's aim is to channel professional and material assistance to individual scientists as well as institutions in Pakistan. CANPREP's members, through their own resources and with some help from the local community have made a modest but consistent contribution to science education and research in Pakistan. The association has established a Mutagenecity Research Centre at Faisalabad, a Drinking Water Research Institute at Karachi and is now working to set up a Biotechnology Research Centre also at Karachi. It has held a number of joint conferences between Canadian professional societies and their Pakistani counterparts and regularly provides current literature, scientific books and journals and samples of rare chemicals and cultures to Pakistani scientists. A number of CANPREP's research and development proposals, e.g. establishment of a basic facility for the *in vitro* fertilization and maintenance of mammalian cells, studies on the microbiological and chemical hazards of Karachi's potable water supply and their alleviation, and an investigation to develop an optimum pesticide-use model for the cotton crop of Pakistan, are being considered both by Canadian international agencies and Pakistani institutions. As a model of expatriate input into national science education and research, CANPREP is likely to be adopted by expatriates of other Middle East countries. Certainly it is one way to reduce the impact of brain drain on a developing country.

Science Education and Arabization

One of the main causes of the brain drain is the dissatisfaction of many scientists with the quality of education and research as well as the acute lack of adequate research facilities in the countries of the Middle East. None of the Muslim countries has an adequate system of higher education and they still place heavy reliance on sending students abroad. Many of these students have traditionally tended to get jobs and settle down in the host countries. However, that pattern too has now changed: difficulties in finding jobs in the industrialized countries and tighter immigration laws means that almost all Muslim students who do their higher studies or are trained abroad are now forced to return home. Moreover, higher fees in Britain and other European countries have meant that the number of students coming to study from the poorer Middle East states has dropped substantially.

The continuous reliance on European and American universities for the training of their scientists has meant that the universities in the Middle East have not had adequate opportunity and government support to develop research infrastructures and the skills and resources necessary for postgraduate teaching. As most of the teaching staff are educated abroad, the little research that is carried out tends to bear no relationship to local needs and requirements. A. B. Zahlan has noted that:

1. The quality of research on problems of vital importance to the Middle East countries is extremely modest; and research and scholarship within the framework of local value systems and thought processes is virtually non-existent.
2. A good portion of the dissertations earned at home and abroad are on irrelevant or trivial topics.
3. A significant proportion of research on Middle East countries is by non-natives: 90 per cent of all books and papers on the Arab world are by non-Arabs. Thus the major sources of information and analysis available to native scholars and researchers in the Middle East is foreign – and often ethnocentric – scholarship and writing.
4. Areas of research of vital importance to the cultural, social and economic needs of these countries are untouched.
5. A great deal of vital and useful technical and non-technical information is not being absorbed and utilized by Middle East scientists for unknown, and a variety of known, reasons.

This situation is likely to continue as long as Middle Eastern countries rely on Western universities to train their scientists and the educational system itself remains an embodiment of Western culture and values, priorities and emphases. The educational system of most Middle East countries has been transferred *ex occidente* in a way rather analogous to the transfer of technology, with the basic assumptions of the Western educational system as well as the traditional Western dogmatic conceptions. This means that universities in the Middle East have been serving the interests not of their own societies but those of Western culture – the main reason why original initiatives in institution building, curricula development and research programmes have been so conspicuously absent.

Science and engineering education in the Middle East started in technical colleges founded by the colonial powers. The oldest of these is the School of Engineering of the *Université Saint-Joseph* of Beirut, established in 1913 by French Jesuits. It was followed in 1925 by the School of Engineering of *Maison Carré* (now al-Harrach), near Algiers which, after the independence of Algeria, became *l'Ecole Nationale Polytechnique*. Both schools are fully functional today.

These colleges were followed by a host of others, many of which, such as the University of Damascus and the University of Khartoum, have now become fully-fledged universities. These universities tend to exemplify middle-class European culture and the norms and values that go with it. The institutions teach European-type science courses, which are strongly examination oriented. Often the medium of instruction is a European language and the students rely almost exclusively on learning by rote and memorizing. Examinations requiring exact recitation of material are the rule. There is emphasis on premature specialization and students barely exposed to science at the undergraduate level are plunged into research, which is little more than mastering of elementary experimental techniques. There is also a strong prejudice against experimental work, which is considered akin to manual labour. The students produced by these educational institutions have little real understanding of science, much less experience of doing science. The complete absence of the history, philosophy and methodology of science in the curricula means that the students cannot relate science to anything real or appreciate the importance of history, philosophy and methodology for science policy and management. Science does not touch their lives and they can see no relationship between science, their immediate environment and their society. Scientists with such a non-functional understanding of science and a remarkably narrow area of competence are in no position to make a genuine contribution to scientific productivity or make the connection between innovation and technological development.

The Universities of Rabat, Algiers, Khartoum, Tripoli, Cairo, Damascus, Baghdad, Tehran and Karachi have all been producing such non-functional scientists for the last three decades. Moreover, because of the pressures of rapidly increasing student enrolment - e.g. an average class at the University of Cairo has anything up to 500 students - and lack of experimental equipment, standards are dropping consistently.

In contrast, the situation at the new universities which have emerged over the last ten to fifteen years, is considerably better. The new universities, on the whole, are free from colonial links. They have emerged at a time of growing consciousness in Muslim societies of their traditional heritage and distinct cultural identity. Some of these universities, such as the Quaid-i-Azam University, Islamabad, were founded either exclusively as post-graduate research universities or with a strong research bias, to attract expatriate scholars back. However, what makes the new universities, such as the King Abdul Aziz University of Jeddah, the University of Kuwait, and the *Centre Universitaire* at Oran and Constantine in Algeria, radically different from the universities inherited from the colonial period, is their vitality, freshness, ready acceptance of technological change and a strong bias towards science and technology. Moreover, some of these universities are firmly committed to the need to set scientific and technological education within the cultural and intellectual heritage of Islam. Along with the faculties of science, engineering, and medicine, many new universities also have strong departments of Islamic studies.

The attempt by the new universities to give Islamic orientation to scientific and technical education has created local consciousness in other institutions of learnings and research, and reforms are now starting to be made in some countries to tailor technical education to pressing local needs. A certain amount of confidence has been generated in local research and efforts have started to develop links between universities and both industry and society at large. There have even been efforts at institutional innovations such as the development of the University of Juba in Sudan and the attempt to set up a Peoples' University in Pakistan.

A further outcome of these developments is the current intense discussion on the methods of tackling the problems faced in Arabization of science and technical education.

The hitherto dominant view that the Muslim lag in science and technology is so tremendous that it is pointless and even harmful to try and develop

Arabic as a means of teaching science and engineering, is now being challenged strongly. Proponents of this view argue that there is no modern science and technology literature in Arabic and since Muslim scientists and engineers should know foreign languages, they might at least be educated in these languages; French in North Africa (except Libya) and English in the rest of the Middle East. The argument now gaining ground is that it is not possible for the Middle East countries to develop, and for science and technology to take social root in Muslim societies, without making Arabic the language of science and technology. True development can be achieved only within a distinctive cultural heritage. If Arabic has been lacking in technical terminology and literature, it is more because of backwardness and lethargy among Muslims than because of any inherent weakness in the Arabic language.

Attempts to Arabize science and engineering education have been going on since the beginning of the century. But these early attempts were isolated, conflicting, and in fact produced a certain amount of confusion. However, recently the problem has really caught the imagination of the Arab world and efforts at Arabization have been consolidated, due largely to the efforts of the Arab League Educational, Cultural and Scientific Organization (ALECSO).

Contemporary attempts at Arabization began in 1961 in Rabat at the first Arabization congress. The purpose of the meeting was to coordinate Arab efforts to standardize the scientific and technical terminology of the language and keep it up to date. The congress recommended setting up the Permanent Bureau of Coordination of Arabization in the Arab World (PBA), which was eventually set up in Rabat in 1967. Since its formation, the PBA has succeeded in developing a methodical inventory of the linguistic heritage of Arabic, and through a monumental historic analysis and some contemporary innovations, over fifty trilingual (Arab, English and French) technical glossaries, the latest of which is on informatics, have been produced in addition to a number of technical and scientific dictionaries.

However, a number of key problems still remain. The foremost among these is the problem of duality: there are deep differences in conceptual perception and modes of thinking between the Maghrib, with its French colonial legacy, and the rest of the Arab world which is entrenched in a web of British colonial ideology. Both sides consider themselves to be linguistically close to classical Arabic but there are subtle differences in the way they perceive and use the language. The different approaches to Arabization can be seen in, for example, the technical glossaries produced in Rabat and Cairo: in one case there is a systematic invention of neologisms and in the other a straightforward adoption in Arabic of foreign terms. Both are sometimes incomplete and inconsistent. This divergence is purely artificial: and overcoming it requires shaking off the alien colonial outlooks of the two segments of the Arab world. Some of the basic differences will perhaps be resolved in the PBA's efforts to produce a mechanized information retrieval system for scientific and technical terminology in Arabic, which requires standardization, simplicity and a consensus on universally accepted scientific meanings of certain Arabic terms. However, marginal and partial measures will not produce a true Arabization of science and technology; that requires a common perception and serious coordination between the two regions of the Arab world.

Despite this problem, considerable success has been achieved in Arabization: the University of Damascus, for example, has been teaching medicine in Arabic for over fifty years and has produced a store of medical literature, both translations and original works, in Arabic. Its experience is now being utilized in Algeria, Kuwait and Saudi Arabia. Such cooperation is likely to spread and progress in Arabization would be rapid if the old and new universities could find ways of working together.

Islamic Science

Along with Arabization, discussions on various issues of Islamic science, science that is a true embodiment of the values, culture and civilization of Islam, have also been intense. In recent years, the history of Islamic science has been enjoying a modest revival. The subject itself has been receiving considerable scholarly attention; and attempts are being made to remedy some of the misconceptions, deliberate omissions, and misrepresentations in the history of Islamic science and technology.

In the history of Islam, science occupies a central position. Although known to the West largely for its historical influence on the development of European scientific thought, it also had a powerful effect on the development of Muslim civilization itself. Islamic science is considered to be one of the basic ingredients that provided the drive for the 'Golden Age of Islam'. So it is now being realized that science which takes its nourishment from the culture and social values of Islam is even more essential for a Muslim civilization of the future. This realization is obviously related to the cultural reawakening of the Muslim people. There are, however, a number of particular factors that have helped create this scientific consciousness. The first was the publication of Seyyed Hossein Nasr's book, *Science and Civilisation in Islam* (Harvard University Press 1968). This was the first serious attempt to examine Islamic science within the context of the civilization of Islam. But more than that, because Nasr, an Iranian scholar now in exile in the United States, commanded attention and respect in the West, he made it possible for many Muslim scientists to speak about Islamic science. His second, somewhat distorted overtly Sufi examination of the subject, in *Islamic Science: An Illustrated Study* (World of Islam Festival Trust, London 1976), took the discussion to the popular and student level. Despite many serious flaws in the book, it is responsible for generating excitement and discussion on the campuses of the universities of Muslim countries.

The Islamic Solidarity Conference on Science and Technology, sponsored by the University of Riyadh and held in Riyadh in March 1976, was the second catalyst. The conference spent a great deal of its time discussing Islamic ways of conducting science. At the conclusion of the conference it was declared that the future of the Muslim world was closely linked to the revival of Islamic science and putting into effect its concepts and principles.

The third major boost came with the publication of Fuat Sezgin's *Geschichte des arabischen Schrifttums* (Frankfurt-am-Main 1972–76) – a massive survey of the early history of Islamic science and technology. Sezgin, a Turkish scholar who won the first King Faisal Foundation Prize for Islamic scholarship in 1979, took thirty years to complete six of the planned twenty volumes and surveyed 1.5 million Arabic manuscripts that he located throughout the world. He stops in the middle of the twelfth century and shows how even for those first four-and-a-half centuries of Islam, the depth and scope of Islamic scientific scholarship is truly staggering.

These events triggered off a host of conferences and have produced a number of institutions devoted to the history of Islamic science. First among these was the Institute for the History of Arabic Science set up at the University of Aleppo, which in 1976 began the publication of the *Journal for the History of Arabic Science*, the only journal completely devoted to the subject. The institute has already held two major international symposia on the history of Arabic science; and the third one is planned for September 1983.

In November 1979, the Technical University of Istanbul established the Institute of History of Science and Technology, which is devoted to the history of Turkish–Islamic science and technology with particular emphasis on the history of Ottoman technology. In September 1981, the institute held the First International Congress on the History of Turkish–Islamic Science and Technology, which has produced four volumes of papers on basic sciences, the history of medicine, pharmacy and dentistry, the history of engineering and building technology, and Turkish scientific relations with the rest of the world.

This emphasis on the history of Islamic science is not without purpose. Only through an analytical examination of the historical literature can the true nature and style of Islamic science be discovered and realized.

Until very recently, much of the discussion on the contemporary aspects of Islamic science was confused, and understandably so. In its practical form Islamic science existed in a distant past and the Muslim civilization has been out of touch with science for over four centuries. During this period the Muslim civilization degenerated to reach its nadir, was consequently colonized, and has only recently re-emerged to face what are probably the biggest fundamental material changes human life has ever experienced. However, after almost a decade of discussion on the subject, the contemporary ideas on Islamic science are crystallizing and a modern definition of the term is emerging.

A recent survey of the thinking of Muslim scientists on the subject published in *Nature* revealed four distinct points of view. A majority of Muslim scientists still regard science as value-free and free from ideological bias. A second group believes that while science is neutral, the attitude with which science can be approached can be secular or Islamic; it is the attitude that determines both the direction of science and research priorities and emphasis. A third group suggests that Islamic science is more a matter of philosophy than science, but at the same time it argues that both modern science and technology are distinctively occidental, that throughout the world all significant science is Western both in style and content. For this group, Islamic science is that science which reflects the needs and aspirations of Muslim people: it is a goal-oriented activity that cannot be isolated from true Islamic wisdom. The fourth group, which up to now has been a very small minority, argues that Islamic science is based on a set of entirely different assumptions about the relationship between man and man, man and nature, the universe, time and space. Because the axioms of Islamic science are different from those of Western science, and its methods of knowing are more open and all-encompassing, it is a science with its own identity and character.

The analysis of the last two groups now seems to be converging. The main reason for this convergence is that concerned scientists in the Middle East are now beginning to realize that there is a certain amount of ideological bias in science and that there is an acute crisis in science itself. This crisis is evident from the vast literature on science, technology and society that is now beginning to filter through to the Middle East. Among all the interactions of science and technology with the natural environment, there are problems. These grow in scale and complexity, sometimes quite suddenly, and their individual practical solution seems to recede with environmental, economic and political constraints. Indeed, one of the most significant problems facing mankind at present is the onset of so many problems and dilemmas altogether, from the impact of technology on the environment and societies, rapid depletion of resources, and increasing production of frightening arsenals of nuclear, chemical and biological weapons, to the complex moral and ethical issues of genetic biology and engineering. These developments represent a crisis in the system of science – both research and application – as a means of controlling the natural world for the satisfaction of human purposes.

Moreover, the crisis of science as it reveals itself in the social practice of science, means that the image of the scientist as a dedicated lone researcher is now dangerously obsolete. It now seems obvious that, in the absence of any preparation in the social and ethical aspects of science, scientists are ill-equipped to resist, even recognize, the danger to their integrity. The areas where searchers after knowledge are becoming party to its distortion or suppression are rapidly multiplying. Genetic engineering is promised to be intensely powerful for industry but yet so harmless as to need no serious regulations. Microprocessors will assuredly lead to the redundancy of humans on a mass scale, and the convulsion of all industrially-based societies; yet the scientific community permits only anodyne reassurances to reach the public.

These realizations have forced those Muslim scientists who agree that science has certain ideological bias to define Islamic science and explore its themes in terms of Islamic values – the very basis of an Islamic society. If that society is to preserve its cultural and traditional heritage, science and technology must promote its values. Thus a truly living and dynamic Islamic society is inconceivable without an operational model of Islamic science.

A multi-disciplinary study, organized by the International Federation of Institutes for Advanced Study (IFIAS), Stockholm, attempts to produce just such a model of Islamic Science. Entitled, *Science and Technology in Islam and the West: A Synthesis*, the study aims to synthesize the growing awareness of the crisis in science with the various attempts to rediscover the spirit of Islamic science. It attempts to identify the impact science and technology are having on contemporary Muslim societies and the possible future impact that science and technology can have if the present direction is maintained. It also attempts to produce a contemporary understanding of the way science and technology have been historically used and developed in Muslim societies and hence produce a model of Islamic science that could be used to develop science policies for Muslim countries and provide an insight for Muslim scientists in their own research and development work.

The primitive model of Islamic science produced so far relates science and technology to a set of basic Islamic values. There are ten such values: *tawheed* (unity), *khilafah* (trusteeship), *ibadah* (worship), *ilm* (knowledge), *halal* (praiseworthy) and *haram* (blameworthy), *adl* (justice) and *zulm* (tyranny), and *istislah* (public interest) and *dhiya* (waste). Those who developed this model argue that this set of values embraces the nature of scientific inquiry in its totality: it integrates facts and values and replaces the linear, enlightenment thinking which is the basis of modern science with a system of knowing that is based on accountability and social responsibility.

What do these values actually mean in relation to science and technology?

Usually, the concept of *tawheed* is translated as unity of God. It becomes an all-embracing value when this unity is asserted in the unity of mankind, unity of man and nature and the unity of knowledge and values. It is the essence of Islamic thought and social behaviour. From *tawheed* emerges the concept of *khilafah*: that man is not independent of God but is responsible and accountable to God for his scientific and technological activities. The trusteeship implies that man has no exclusive right to anything and man is responsible for maintaining and preserving the integrity of the abode of his terrestrial journey. Thus the Heroic concept of science, the lone scientist out to conquer and dominate nature at all costs, has no place in this framework.

However, although man is not to seek knowledge for the outright exploitation and domination of nature, he is not simply reduced to a passive observer. On the contrary, contemplation (*Ibadah*) is an obligation, for it leads to an awareness of *tawheed* and *khilafah*; and it this very contemplation that serves as an integrating factor for scientific activity and a system of Islamic values. *Ibadah*, or the contemplation of the unity of God, has many manifestations of which the pursuit of knowledge is the major one.

The concept of knowledge, *ilm*, which becomes a value when it is pursuit within an Islamic framework, is one of the most written-about and discussed concepts of Islam. There are over 1,200 definitions of *ilm*; and almost all Muslim classical authors from al-Kindi (801–873), al-Farabi (d. 950), and al-Baruni (937–1048) to al-Ghazzali (d. 1111) and ibn-Khaldun (1332–1406) have produced major classifications of knowledge. In general, *ilm* is divided into two categories: revealed, which provides the ethical and moral framework, and non-revealed, the pursuit of which is an obligation under the dictates of *Ibadah*. Non-revealed knowledge is further subdivided into two categories: *fard-ayan*, which is essential for individuals to survive, such as ethics and morality, and *fard kifayah*, which is necessary for the survival of the whole community. In this framework, the pursuit of knowledge for the benefit of the individual or the community is *ibadah*. There is no place here for the notion of science for science's sake. Also rejected is the purely utilitarian science as an end in itself.

The concepts of *halal* and *haram* come into play in the determination of the social responsiveness and non-utilitarian nature of science. When closely examined *haram* includes all that which is destructive for man as an individual, his immediate environment and the environment at large. The word 'destructive' should be understood in its physical, mental and spiritual sense. On the other hand, all that is beneficial for an individual, his society and his environment is *halal*. Thus an action that is *halal* brings all-round benefit. But an action that may bring benefits for the individual may have harmful effects either on society or the environment or both. This is why *halal* operates on the premise of the distribution of *adl* (social justice). *Haram* propagates *zulm* (tyranny). Within the framework of Islamic values, *zulm* is of three categories: between man and God, between man and man, and between man and himself. Thus, scientific and technological activity that seeks to promote *adl* is *halal*, while that science and technology which promotes alienation and dehumanization, concentration of wealth in fewer and fewer hands, unemployment and environmental destruction is *zalim* (tyrannical) and therefore *haram*. A major characteristic of *zalim* science and technology is that they destroy human, environmental and spiritual resources and generate waste. It is therefore categorized as *dhiya* (wasteful) science. Scientific and technological activity that promotes *adl* – distributive technologies, science for the people – draw their legitimacy from *istislah* (public interest), which is the chief supplementary source of Islamic law.

A definition of Islamic science can now be formulated in terms of the framework of these Qur'anic values. The paradigms of Islamic science are the concepts of *tawheed*, *khilafah* and *ibadah*. Within these paradigms, Islamic science operates through the agency of *ilm* to promote *adl* and *istislah*. Thus the accountability of a Muslim scientist is both social and spiritual. Therefore, Islamic science promotes God-consciousness, harmonizes the ends and means in the pursuit of knowledge, emphasizes social relevance in both the pursuit and the application of knowledge, and rejects the neutrality of objective knowledge.

It might be asked how close Islamic science has come in its history to this model. Certainly, in the works of individual scientists, such as ar-Razi (865–925), al-Biruni and ibn-Haitham (d. 1038), this model of science can be seen in operation to a considerable extent. But the historians of Islamic science have provided insufficient evidence on these aspects of the evolution of Islamic science for such a judgement to be made. However, it is clear, even without the support of historical evidence, that institutions which derive their legitimacy from the paradigms of Islamic science can be developed and Islamic science realized, because the elements of this model can be internalized and can take social roots in the Muslim world. Thus institutionalization of Islamic science can become an effective weapon in countering *dhiya* and *zalim* (tyranny) science and technology and its social and political consequences. How such institutions can be developed and promoted is a question that needs much research and deliberation.

From the definition of Islamic science, it can be seen that not all occidental science and technology is outside the framework of Islamic values. For example, the ideas of appropriate technology, indigenous resource management and renewable energy resources all fall within the Islamic purview. Moreover, all scientific and technological activity pursued to promote *adl*, such as medical research to alleviate sickness and human misery, agricultural research and development to combat world hunger, environmental conservation and technology assessment for the prevention of *zalim* effects of technology, would automatically form a part of Islamic science. But scientific and technological development pursued with an intent to perpetuate certain bigotry, like eugenics and sociobiology, are certainly outside the framework of Islamic values. It is the intent which makes this science *haram*.

The IFIAS study will use this primitive model of Islamic science to develop more specific policy-oriented models of Islamic medicine, environment, agriculture and industry and modes of production. The end product of this study would be a model science policy for the Muslim countries to adopt and follow.

Already a considerable amount of work has been done on Islamic medicine – due largely to the efforts of the Hamdard National Foundation of Pakistan. Hamdard's research and development work on traditional medicine has brought a new respectability to Islamic medicine: it is now given a professional status in Pakistan and Kuwait; and teaching and training of traditional doctors has now been standardized and upgraded. The moral and ethical problems of contemporary medical and genetic research has been uppermost in the minds of those who have been working on Islamic medicine. One of the major outcomes of the First International Conference on Islamic Medicine, held in Kuwait in January 1981, was the production of an *Islamic Code of Medical Ethics*, which deals with such issues as social responsibility of doctors and medical researchers, mercy killing, and the ethics and morality of contemporary biotechnical advances. Work has also started on setting up a major international institute of Islamic medicine devoted both to contemporary and historical research and located in Kuwait. Islamic medicine seems set to make an important contribution to health policies and the physical and mental environment of Muslim countries.

Medicine and Health

Undoubtedly, medicine is the most neglected research area in the Middle

East. Yet, despite the eradication of smallpox, which repeatedly altered the course of history in the region, other diseases such as malaria and schistosomiasis have reached an almost epidemic level. Malaria seems to reappear in Afghanistan, Egypt, Iran, Saudi Arabia, Sudan and Syria every few years. With thirteen of the region's most notorious malaria mosquito species now resistant to hydrocarbon insecticides, a critical increase in malaria's potential has been reported, over the last few years, from areas under intense irrigation. Large irrigation projects, such as Egypt's Aswan Dam, Syria's Euphrates Dike and Sudan's 810,000 ha Gezira scheme, are also responsible for the spread of schistosomiasis. In some areas of Egypt, up to 78 per cent of villagers may be affected with schistosomiasis. Increases in the disease, with infection rates of up to 60 per cent, are being observed in the newly irrigated area of Syria and the Yemen Arab Republic.

In addition to malaria, schistosomiasis and other diseases are prevalent in the region, such as cholera and tuberculosis (which is showing a disturbing sharp increase in infection rates from infancy to adolescence, so that every third adolescent in the Middle East is now statistically a potential tuberculosis threat to himself and others), increases have also been reported in diseases new to the area.

Among these, cancer, cardiovascular diseases and mental disorders are particularly on the increase. Apart from lung cancer, an oesophageal cancer in northern Iran, a frequently noted type of inflammatory breast cancer in Tunisia and a high occurrence of urinary bladder cancer have been reported by the World Health Organization. Hospital records reveal a whole range of troublesome cardiovascular disorders from hypertension associated with affluence in Kuwait to rheumatic fever and cardiac defects of infectious origin in Egypt. Environmentally induced mental disorders account for some 30 per cent of reported illness in the Middle East, and in certain countries, such as Saudi Arabia, Kuwait and Lebanon, mental disorders afflict 40 to 70 per cent of psychiatric patients admitted to hospitals.

For most countries of the region, sanitation and health education is top priority, although in some countries, such as Algeria, Egypt and Pakistan, an equal emphasis is being given to family planning. Egypt, for example, has a free health service and is the only country in the area to have a surplus of doctors and nurses. But its health care problems could not be more basic: overcrowded and insanitary city life kills a high number of children and nurtures diseases such as cholera and malaria. Lack of sewage disposal and unsafe drinking water had made diarrhoea, which is blamed for nearly a million deaths so far of under-fives in the region, endemic. Schistosomiasis costs Egypt $300 million annually in lost production through workers' incapacity. Moreover, intestinal diseases now account for 43 per cent of Egypt's deaths of under-fives.

Similar unsanitary conditions in Jordan lead to regular outbreaks of cholera. The disease is endemic and thrives in insanitary conditions, while public awareness lapses. Given the appalling sanitation facilities in some areas of Jordan, the task of eliminating the disease is almost impossible.

Considering these formidable problems, there are relatively few noteworthy institutes for medical and health research. Only Cairo's Theodor

Bilharz Institute (TBI), the Institute of Radiotherapy and Nuclear Medicine (IRNUM) at Peshawar, Pakistan, and the King Faisal Specialist Hospital in Riyadh, Saudi Arabia, have earned international recognition. All three have been established only recently.

Operating under the National Research Centre and the Academy of Scientific Research, the TBI is Egypt's foremost medical research institute. Although on the drawing board since 1962, TBI could not materialize, due to various political problems between Egypt and its financial backers, West Germany, until 1978. Research at the TBI began at the end of 1978 with scientists on secondment to the institute from different Egyptian universities. In early 1980, a hospital with 120 beds and an outpatient clinic was added to the institute. Research at the TBI is exclusively on schistosomiasis and emphasis is on the discovery of a vaccination which may protect against infection or prevent severe complications. A chief goal of the TBI is to coordinate the efforts of researchers working on schistosomiasis throughout Egypt. Research at the TBI is therefore guided and planned by a council consisting of heads of research groups in universities and research centres working on schistosomiasis. This council has also produced a general long-term plan for research on schistosomiasis; while most of the research under the plan will be carried out at the TBI, the institute will also give research assignments to universities and other research centres with experience of research on schistosomiasis.

IRNUM was established in 1975 as a teaching and research centre with facilities for treating outpatients. The institute works in close collaboration with the Medical College of the University of Peshawar as well as the Pakistan Medical Research Council, and in conjunction with them runs a postgraduate course leading to a PhD degree. Research at IRNUM is mainly concerned with various types of cancer, including mouth cancer caused by chewing *Naswar* (a chewing tobacco), and those non-malignant complicated diseases which are amenable to nuclear techniques for diagnosis and treatment. In conjunction with the Pakistan Council for Scientific and Industrial Research (PCSIR), IRNUM is conducting a major research project on early detection, prevention and eradication of *Naswar*-induced mouth cancers. A second project, also in collaboration with the PCSIR, focuses on the use of indigenous drugs in the treatment of various types of advanced cancerous diseases, such as leukaemias and squamias and squamous cell carcinomas.

While both the TBI and IRNUM suffer from lack of funds, the King Faisal Specialist Hospital in Riyadh is one of the world's most highly financed and well-equipped research hospitals. The hospital boasts a spectrum of technology rarely amassed anywhere, from LARC (to count white blood cells) and a nuclear accelerator (for treating cancer) to a total-body scanner. The hospital has its own cancer therapy centre and a team from Baylor University in Houston is on call to perform open-heart surgery. There is a satellite link to some of America's better-known specialists for instant advice. The King Faisal Specialist Hospital was established in 1975 and since then it has been administered and run by American expatriates. Most of the scientists at the hospital, in complete contrast to the TBI and

IRNUM, are also American and European expatriates. It is the essential core of a future medical city which will provide health services to the whole of Saudi Arabia. Already, the King Faisal Specialist Hospital has made its mark in medical research. Researchers at the hospital have established a link between diabetes and viral hepatitis, offering promise of a new line of inquiry into the cause of diabetes. An initial survey has shown that 4.5 per cent of the Saudi population suffer from diabetes – four times the world average and markedly higher than many of the African and Arab communities. The King Faisal Specialist Hospital researchers also discovered that chronic hepatitis (disease of the liver) invariably formed the most serious complication of diabetes, and that the hepatitis B virus, endemic in many parts of the region, could be a major cause of the disease. Liver studies at the hospital have revealed an incidence as high as 10 per cent of hepatitis B carriers in some parts of Saudi Arabia. Research at the King Faisal Specialist Hospital is now focused on establishing a link between diabetes and the hepatitis B virus.

Saudi Arabia is establishing another research and teaching hospital of the same magnitude as the King Faisal Specialist Hospital. The King Abdul Aziz Medical City is being built on a 1.2 million m² site in Jeddah. It will be completed by 1986.

In addition to the above centres, the WHO has also set up a number of research institutes such as the Biomedical Centre for Infectious Diseases in Cairo. The WHO has also involved the countries of the region in its Special Programme for Research and Training in Tropical Diseases, the Biomedical Research Programme and the Tehran-based WHO Regional Medical Library whose services are maintained throughout the region through WHO's own Regional Office library in Alexandria.

Agriculture and Irrigation

Compared to medicine, agriculture and irrigation have received much more attention in the Middle East. While agriculture has never been considered by the region's policy-makers to be as important as industrialization, most countries have evolved agricultural research institutions and some even have agricultural universities.

Despite some differences, a majority of the countries in the Middle East have three agricultural policy goals in common: increasing the productivity of land and labour, achieving a more equitable distribution of income in the rural sector, and accomplishing these objectives while ensuring that human, physical, and biological resources are not excessively exploited. Three strategies have been employed to this end: the exclusive use of modern high-technology agriculture, as, for example, in Saudi Arabia and the Gulf; concentrating on a particular cash crop, as is the case with cotton in Syria; and what has come to be known as 'walking on two legs', i.e. supporting both modern and traditional agricultural systems, as in Algeria, Tunisia, and Iraq. Each strategy can be illustrated by examining recent developments in agriculture in Saudi Arabia, Syria and Algeria.

Saudi Arabia has invested huge resources in developing modern agriculture. Saudi Arabia's third development plan includes major projects – to conduct detailed soil surveys in agricultural development areas; to prepare a base map depicting general soil conditions for the entire country; to implement a land-allocating and record-keeping system for the Kingdom; to initiate native range and grazing improvement projects; to install a computerized water data base; and to oversee the collection and analysis of water supply data for a national water plan. The government has set up agricultural centres in Jizan, Medina, Qasim, Riyadh and Hufuf to provide technical advice for the farmers. Programmes to make the country self-sufficient have been launched in dairy production, meat, poultry and horticulture. These involve turnkey agreements with the United States (cattle), Australia and New Zealand (sheep), Sweden, West Germany and the United Kingdom (poultry), and France and Japan (horticulture).

However, Saudi Arabia's major ally in agricultural development is the United States. Under the United States–Saudi Arabia Joint Commission on Economic Cooperation, the United States is currently implementing three projects worth over US$170 million in total: establishing the Agriculture and Water Research and Training Centre (AWRTC); an overall plan for the preservation of the Asir National Park and an ambitious plan for the development of advanced desalination technology to make the country self-sufficient in water. The AWRTC, set up in April 1979 in a Riyadh suburb, aims to find methods of increasing agricultural productivity and to provide analytical and diagnostic services for water, soil, plant and animal life to the Ministry of Agriculture and Water Resources.

Extensive surveys have also been carried out on all the fertile land – some 12 per cent of the total area of Saudi Arabia – with the aim of converting it to cultivated land. The Ministry of Agriculture and Water Resources has carried out a comprehensive survey of underground water resources in six regions of the kingdom with a total area of 1.2 million km^2. Similar surveys are now being carried out for North and South Tihama, Quwayiyyah, al-Khraj, Qasim, Ar'ar and Wadi Sirhan. The third development plan allocated an unprecedented US$13 billion for developing water resources.

As part of the plan for conserving water in areas which depend mostly on rain the ministry intends to build dams. The first, located in Wadi Najran in the south, with a storage capacity of 68 million m^3, is expected to be completed in early 1982. The ministry has set up a model farm near the dam to experiment with the cultivation of sorghum, beans, sesame and fodder. If the combined dam–farm experiment is successful a network of dams will be constructed in the south.

Agricultural research has already had some success in Saudi Arabia. Pilot projects for cultivating the 'Maxipak' varieties of wheat and rice, the latter in cooperation with Taiwan, have proved successful enough for full-scale production. But undoubtedly the most successful agricultural project has been the Hasa irrigation scheme developed in conjunction with the United Kingdom. This scheme, started as long ago as 1960, has developed a 1,500 km network of irrigation canals from thirty-two springs at the oasis of al Hasa. More recently a demonstration farm has been set up on 120 ha of very poor land near the oasis. This farm has become the centre for demonstrating the most modern methods of agriculture and irrigation. The al-Hasa project has also generated an important innovation in techniques of removing salt from high-salinity soil. Alongside the underground irregation network of pipes are drains that take off the excess water along with the salt. The irrigation system is based on hydrants in the ground to which portable pipes can be attached, so there are no obstacles for the tractors and other machines that cultivate the soil.

In contrast to Saudi Arabia, Syria has concentrated its agricultural research on a single cash crop: cotton. Under the Ministry of Agriculture and Agrarian Reform, the Syrian Cotton Bureau, in Aleppo, has considerably extended the cotton-growing area over the last five years, and perfected a particular variety of cotton known as Aleppo 1, which is virtually immune to the most prevalent cotton disease, verticillium wilt. Until 1980, some 97 per cent of the cotton grown in Syria was Aleppo 1, the remainder being another Cotton Bureau variety called Aleppo 4; and some 200,000 ha of cotton-growing land was under irrigation. However, under the Fifth Five Year Development Plan (1981–85), the whole cotton-growing area will be producing Aleppo 1 glandless cotton, which is suitable for making seed cake fit for human and animal consumption. The plant protein thus obtained will make a valuable contribution to Syrian food production, since leguminous crops are rarely grown and animal production is not sufficient for local consumption. Here lies the dilemma of the Syrian strategy; while some genuine gains have been made in cotton production, other areas of agricultural research and output have suffered acutely.

Algeria has opted for a policy of backing both the traditional and the modern agriculture. Traditional Arab agriculture covers about three-quarters of all Algerian arable land and employs nearly 80 per cent of the rural labour force. While its method of production appears primitive, the traditional sector does seem to be slowly increasing its production. But there has been no research input in improving the productivity and techniques of traditional agriculture, despite the existence of an active research centre, the National Institute of Agronomy, at the University of Algiers.

The socialist system of agriculture which has been established on large modern farms formerly owned by the French settlers and enlarged later with the addition of all other foreign-owned land, was faced from the outset with serious problems of organization and management. Under the principle of self-management, the administration of farms was entrusted to a committee and a president elected by all the workers. The system was based on the reasonably successful Yugoslavian model. However, the low level of technical competence and leadership, and the lack of research into producing productive varieties and better irrigation schemes, has meant that the modern agricultural sector has been a major drain on the Algerian economy.

The new five year development plan, covering the period 1981–85, lays a great deal of stress on making Algeria self-sufficient in agriculture. By the year 2000, the plan envisages, the population will have risen to some

35 million and much of the heavy industrialization that Algeria has embarked on will be complete. Some 11 to 12 billion m³ of fresh water will then be required for drinking and for industrial and agricultural purposes. To meet this demand, the Environment, Soil Improvement and Hydraulic Ministry, created in 1977, is planning to build 100 dams in the next two decades, most of them in the neglected high plateau region. Among the larger agricultural development schemes is an ambitious irrigation plan for the Sidi bel-Abbes plain, a land reclamation scheme near Batna, an agro-industrial complex in the *wilaya* (local administrative unit) of Tebessa, and a feasibility study of the Setif area. The government also plans to reorganize Algerian agriculture, putting much more emphasis on the modern sector.

Both Tunisia and Morocco have similar plans to expand their modern agricultural sectors. Tunisia plans a number of major projects to upgrade agricultural production. One of the most important schemes is the integrated water development land conservation plan in the Medjerda river basin, which includes: the construction of a dam at Sidi el-Salem and a 126 km canal linking el-Aroussa, some 60 km downstream, to the Cap Bon area; the construction of a second dam on the nearby Djoumine river; filtration stations; and a canal linking this second dam to the Medjerda river. Another scheme aims at protecting the rich agricultural plains around the city of Kairouan, some 90 km south of Tunis, from periodic flooding. Here not only will run-off water erosion be checked, but an additional 5,000 ha of land are scheduled to be irrigated. Morocco has similar plans to modernize its water distribution network. The US$94.4 million Doukkala project, for example, financed by the World Bank, AID and the Kuwait Fund for Arab Economic Development, will open up 15,000 ha to irrigated farming. Another US$737 million will be spent in the next few years to improve the technological skills of 500,000 rural households.

Clearly, all three policies of agricultural development that are dominant in the region seem to emphasize rapid transformation of existing agricultural systems. With the exception of Syria, most of the countries in the region – Saudi Arabia, Iraq, Libya, Algeria, Tunisia, Morocco, and the Gulf states – are relying heavily on transfer of technology for agricultural development. Moreover, with the exception of Syria, Egypt, Pakistan and Saudi Arabia, there is no real agricultural research going on in these countries. Agricultural technologies which have developed in response to one particular set of environmental conditions and social factors, are being transferred to different situations. That failure rates for such projects are high is not surprising. The irrigation scheme at Abadla in the Bechar province of Algeria is a good example. Designed to turn this water-scarce region into an 'Algerian California', the scheme was to bring 10,000 ha under irrigation, with water being provided by the Djorf Torba Dam on Wadi Guir. In 1979, unprecedented heavy rains swelled the lake behind the dam to a dangerous level, and government officials decided to drain away 920,000 m³ of water. Poor rainfall in 1980 and 1981 has meant that the Djorf Torba lake is now practically dry.

However, the Abadla scheme is a minor example. The region provides

classic examples of high-technology irrigation projects causing considerable environmental, medical and irrigation problems. The Gezira scheme
in Sudan and the Aswan High Dam in Egypt, are often quoted in this
regard.

In terms of the functions for which it was built, the Aswan Dam has
been relatively successful. It holds back the Nile, making possible the use
of all its flood water, 40 per cent of which formerly flowed into the sea
unused. It provides half of Egypt's electricity needs through hydro-electric
power, and has made possible the reclamation of a theoretical 525,000 ha
of desert land from single-crop basin irrigation to multi-crop perennial
irrigation. It has also relieved the annual fear of flood or drought for the
first time in 7,000 years. But the dam has also spread schistosomiasis on a
wide scale, reduced the productivity of the Nile, completely killed off the
sardine industry, caused the erosion of the Mediterranean coastline, polluted the river, and raised the water table to such an extent that drainage
has now become the major problem in Egyptian agriculture. Fortunately,
the Egyptian scientific community has been alert to the side-effects of the
dam and considerable research under the Egyptian Academy for Scientific
Research, at the Department of Agriculture of the University of Alexandria and the National Research Centre has somewhat reduced the impact
of these side-effects. There is little doubt that the dam has increased agricultural productivity in Egypt; but it has also unleashed tremendous
ecological side-effects which will take up Egypt's agricultural research
efforts for decades to come.

Research is emphasized considerably in the new Egyptian plan to reclaim the desert and increase cultivable land by almost 50 per cent by the
year 2000. The plan is to use foreign investment in conjunction with
sprinkler irrigation to reclaim 61,000 ha a year, thus increasing the
250,000 ha now under cultivation by another 2.5 million over twenty years.
The plan has created a rift in Egypt's agricultural science community,
between those who back the new scheme acknowledging that it can take
anything from three to thirteen years to make reclaimed land productive
and those who see the path towards self-sufficiency in improving presently
cultivated land, whose productivity has dropped by 40 per cent since the
construction of Aswan. The present government aims to go ahead with
the plan.

Sudan's Gezira scheme, a 810,000 ha irrigation project, has a long history,
going back to 1899. The actual scheme came into operation in 1925 when
50,000 ha of crops were put under irrigation with the help of the Sennar
Dam and a network of canals. Since then, the area under irrigation has
been steadily increasing, so that the scheme now covers 840,000 ha. But
even after over fifty years of operation, it is difficult to classify the scheme
as a resounding success. Epidemics of schistosomiasis, malaria and yellow
fever have been linked to the scheme and development by any definition
has yet to be realized for the Gezira people. Since the 1950s, when the
scheme was taken over by the Sudan Gezira Board, it has received government spending of up to 77 per cent. Although large areas of Gezira have
been under wheat cultivation since 1970, the economics of the venture

are precarious and the soil needs heavy nitrogen application. Sudan's Agricultural Research Institute was established in 1918 and it is completely manned by Sudanese scientists. However, the Gezira scheme has meant that its research has been concentrated exclusively on cotton, the main output of Gezira, which is exported as raw material, while the country continues to import textile goods. As a result of this bias for cotton, Sudanese scientists have little information on other plant and animal production possibilities.

Until very recently, Sudan continued its bias towards big irrigation schemes. In 1977, the Rahad Irrigation Project, aiming to bring 300,000 ha of fertile land under irrigation, was inaugurated. There was a vast programme to turn the country, with the help of Arab aid, into 'the bread-basket of the Middle East'. For example, one scheme involved introducing mechanized sorghum and sesame production in 1 million ha of rain-fed areas in various parts of the country. However, these plans now seem to have been dropped and there are moves towards developing more moderate-sized schemes. A US$12 million integrated rural development project in southern Darfur, for example, will introduce mechanized farming to small-holders in a rain-fed area. In the southern region, another project, costing US$8 million, is designed to introduce agricultural services in the Kongor district. The United States is backing four such projects, costing a total of US$30 million. Agricultural research too is now being diversified: a programme to find high-yielding crop varieties which would perform well even on low inputs of water and fertilizers, both of which are scarce in Sudan, has been launched. Other programmes on conservation of soil and moisture in rainland farming, soil fertility, the exhaustion rate of the Sudan's share of the Nile water, and remote sensing have also been introduced.

Unlike Sudan, Pakistan has a diversified agricultural research base, even though wheat has been the focus of research. During the mid–1960s, following several years of widespread experimentation on farms, Pakistan introduced a high-yield wheat production technology. The complete package included the introduction and use of the high-yielding Mexican dwarf resistant varieties, extensive use of chemical fertilizer, the adoption of improved cultural practices such as better levelling of land, better sea bed preparation, improvements in planting methods and in irrigation practices, and heavy bias towards inter-disciplinary wheat research. The support for improved irrigation came from the construction of the Tarbela Dam. As a result, Pakistan's wheat production increased from 3.75 million tonnes in 1965 to 6.5, 7.1, and 8.94 million tonnes in 1968, 1969 and 1977. During 1968–69 Pakistan reached self-sufficiency in wheat production. The loss of this self-sufficiency is blamed, by Pakistan's Agricultural Research Council, on population growth, government policies, which did not encourage wheat production, and the failure to provide seeds and fertilizers to the farmers at the appropriate time. However, decline in wheat research during the past few years and the consequent delay in developing appropriate technology packages for achieving high crop yield must also share some of the blame.

Its experience with wheat has led Pakistan to reorganize the country's agricultural research to a certain extent. The basic features of the new system include identification of major problems of communication between the scientists and the farmers, monitoring of all research programmes at regular intervals, identification of trained manpower needs, and strengthening of existing research institutions, particularly in the universities and agricultural colleges, by providing adequate equipment, manpower and other facilities. A nationally coordinated research programme on important crops, including wheat, rice and maize, has been launched. A major part of the agricultural area in Pakistan lies in the Barani Tract, where the productivity has been very low. Barani agriculture has therefore become a particularly important research programme. An Arid Zone Research Institute is to be established at Quetta with experimental substations at Bahawalpur, Dera Ismael Khan and Umerkot, to work on solutions to the peculiar problems of Barani areas.

Moreover, there is considerable emphasis on the use of nuclear techniques in agricultural research. Pakistan's Atomic Energy Commission has two agricultural centres employing nuclear radiation, one at Faisalabad and the other at Tandojam. Both centres are involved in plant breeding using radiation and chemically induced mutations, as well as conventional breeding techniques. Among the successes achieved during the last few years at Faisalabad is an early flowering mutant of rice, Kashmir basmati, which matures three weeks earlier than its parent, can be grown in altitudes of 1,500 m, and yields 30 per cent more than the local variety. Since it matures earlier, it escapes the onset of winter and can be grown in Azad Kashmir, where rice could not be grown before. Other advances include lines of rust-resistant wheat, a new variety of triticale (a cross between wheat and rye) for rainy areas, and erect, compact, higher-yielding mutants of chickpeas. Similarly the Tandojam centre has developed higher yielding mutants of cotton and a blight-resistant variety of potato. The success of these two centres has created interest in setting up a third centre, a Nuclear Institute for Food and Agriculture at Tarnab, near Peshawar, to concentrate on preserving the food and fruit which are grown abundantly in the North West Frontier Province.

Pakistan seems to be almost the only country in the region without any plans for developing new large irrigation schemes or constructing new dams. In most Middle East countries, national development plans for the first half of the 1980s contain a considerable number of such projects. In Saudi Arabia, Iraq, Syria and the Yemen Arab Republic, for example, harnessing of run-off water in desert areas and control of river-overflow are priority projects.

Many countries in the region have water research institutions, but genuine research on water resources is rare. The Water Resources Development Centre of Kuwait has a research and development section engaged in investigations of various types of desalination plants, including materials used and corrosion in desalination plants. Indeed, much of the water research in the oil-rich states is concentrated on desalination. However, non-conventional techniques and processes for discovering water are beginning to be used. Simulation models for forecasting productivity of aquifers have been used in Jordan. In Saudi Arabia, the Umm-er-Radhuma project is using radio-isotopes in tracing underground water. And Jordan and Oman have demonstrated the practical value of the ancient bedouin 'hema' system for rangeland management and conservation. Hema-style reserves could in the near future help to protect the endangered wild relatives of domestic crops, provide undisturbed sanctuaries for seed production, and help in the recovery of degraded rangelands.

On the whole, however, traditional agriculture in the Middle East is being ignored and, in some cases, discriminated against. The only institute where work on upgrading traditional agriculture is being conducted is the International Centre for Agricultural Research in the Dry Areas (ICARDA). ICARDA was set up in January 1977 by the Consultative Group on International Agricultural Research to provide research assistance to farmers in North Africa and West Asia. It is based in Aleppo and has regional offices in Beirut and Tabriz, although, due to political problems, its Beirut and Tabriz offices have not been operating fully. ICARDA, an organization which will play an increasingly important role in the Middle East, has demonstrated that increasing agricultural productivity does not necessarily mean disrupting the farmers' way of life. For example, ICARDA's researchers discovered that Syrian farmers traditionally plant lentils in February. However, planting in November gave a 30 to 90 per cent higher yield. A narrower row-spacing of 15 cm, with a higher sowing rate of 160 kg of seed per hectare for large seeded, or 80 kg of seed per hectare for small seeded cultivators, also resulted in higher yields. Early planting, however increased the likelihood of heavy infestation by weeds later on in the season. The use of safe herbicides, therefore, became necessary. As ICARDA discovered, it is much easier to pursuade Arab farmers to plant early and use a herbicide than to get them to adopt high-technology, intensive and extensive methods of production.

ICARDA is also developing varieties of broad beans, lentils, and chickpeas that are resistant to most prevalent diseases. Chickpeas, for example, are particularly susceptible to *Ascochyta* blight. Although it can be controlled by fungicides, a more appropriate method of controlling the disease is through the development of resistant cultivators. ICARDA has developed twenty-nine lines that show a high degree of resistance and seven lines that do not show any disease symptoms at all.

ICARDA's approach has many advantages over some of the other agricultural strategies in operation in the region. This approach emphasizes that agriculture in the fertile crescent is not just an economic activity: it is an active way of life.

Environment and Pollution

The effects of large dams and big irrigation schemes on the Middle East environment are relatively well studied. Over the last few years, environmental degradation and pollution in the region have been increasing at an alarming rate and the attention is now being focused on three areas: the Persian Gulf, which is now considered to be one of the most polluted expanses of water in the world; the Red Sea; and urban and atmospheric pollution which has almost reached a critical level throughout the Middle East.

The Gulf is surrounded by eight countries – Bahrain, Iran, Iraq, Kuwait, Oman, Qatar, Saudi Arabia and the United Arab Emirates (UAE) – all devoted to rapid industrialization. Population of the region is growing at 16 per cent a year, cities are doubling in size every four years, and the number of cars doubles almost every year. City growth outstrips sewage and garbage disposal systems. Industrial investment on the Gulf's shoreline has reached an unprecedented scale: in 1976, industrial investment on Saudi Arabia's Gulf shoreline alone reached US$100 million per kilometre. The region contains the world's biggest concentration of desalination plants. Pollution from refineries is particularly acute: the outdated equipment of Bahrain's refineries for example, emits twenty times more sulphur dioxide and hydrocarbons into the atmosphere than a modern factory. In Kuwait, a chlor-alkali plant discharges 1 ton of mercury catalysts into the Gulf every year – right next door to the intakes of a desalination plant. Heavy metal pollution of marine organisms is also causing particular concern. Some fish and molluscs can accumulate mercury up to 100,000 times the concentration present in sea water without harming themselves. Consumption of these fish, however, can produce nerve damage, malfunction in new-born children and even death. There are at least twenty large industrial zones at various stages of construction around the Gulf. If allowed to, many of them will soon be releasing toxic heavy metals into the Gulf.

The Gulf is a small, extremely shallow (its average depth is 35 m) and virtually landlocked sea. More water evaporates from its surface than is received from its rivers. Water pours in from the Indian Ocean through the Straits of Hormuz to compensate. Because of the high rate of evaporation, and little outflow to the Indian Ocean, pollutants are becoming concentrated in the Gulf.

Apart from industrial wastes, these pollutants include raw sewage, the enormous brine output of desalination plants and the discharge of oil from tankers. About 60 per cent of all the oil carried by ship anywhere in the world is loaded in the Gulf; and ballast water (which contains about 0.15 per cent of oil per metre^3) is continuously discharged into the Gulf. Saudi Arabia's waters alone receive an estimated 400,000 tons of oil a year from deballasting – a figure that is 150 times more than the estimated 2,737 tons of oil effluent discharged directly from the Saudi Ras Tanura refinery, one of the largest in the world.

Urban and air pollution is also becoming a problem in the Gulf states. Solid domestic refuse is present in the region in enormous quantities. Domestic refuse – waste food, cans, cartons, glass, plastic, rubber and so on can often be seen in large rubbish tips which become breeding grounds for flies, rats and disease. When the rubbish tips are set alight, their high content of rubber and plastic contributes to air pollution. Other common air pollutants in the region are sulphur dioxide, hydrocarbons and carbon monoxide – all of which can also contaminate the sea.

The chronic state of the Gulf marine environment led the countries surrounding its shoreline, with some urging from the United Nations Environment Programme (UNEP), to organize a regional conference on the protection and development of the Gulf marine environment, in April 1978 in Kuwait. The conference produced the *Action Plan for the Protection and Development of the Marine Environment and the Coastal Areas of Bahrain, Iran, Iraq, Kuwait, Oman, Qatar, Saudi Arabia and the United Arab Emirates* and the *Kuwait Regional Convention for Cooperation on the Protection of the Marine Environment from Pollution.* With the exception of Saudi Arabia, all states have ratified the treaty and pledged themselves to cleaning up the Gulf.

The Kuwait Action Plan (reproduced in Part II) includes seventeen major projects which involve surveys of existing scientific institutions, information sources, research programmes, manpower and environmental legislation; assessment of the sources and extent of oil pollution; assessment of pollutants other than oil, including sewage and industrial wastes; research into the Gulf's fish and shellfish stocks and their potential for exploitation; identification of new industrial developments which will have a major environmental impact, and ways of minimizing these impacts; forming contingency plans for industrial or shipping accidents and setting up a mutual aid centre; increasing the engineering expertise needed for environmental protection; strengthening public health services, including water supply and sanitation; looking at ways of combating pollution through regionally-coordinated port and transport development; and a publicity campaign to make people in the region aware of the importance of environmental protection.

Work to implement the plan has already started. A team of environmental experts has started to study the major onshore sources of pollution and the sea currents and winds of the region. The Gulf is scientifically a little-known region; and a number of important questions need to be answered. A lot of the oil dumped by tankers is sedimented by dust carried on the north-west-south-east 'Shamal' winds, but what happens to it then? Is it more important to control the ships or the terminals? Where is most of the plankton population of the Gulf, and how sensitive is it? A great deal of research needs to be done on the present ecology of the Gulf coastal waters: the Kuwait Action Plan can clearly motivate scientists in the region – work on some of the above questions has started at Kuwait's Institute for Scientific Research – it has already shown that the Gulf states are not just aware of the serious threat to the marine environment of the Gulf but are serious about solving the problem.

Similar developments have taken place at the other side of the Arabian peninsula – on the Red Sea and the Gulf of Aden. Much of the work on the Red Sea, both research and raising awareness of the pollutants, has been done by ALECSO. ALECSO's researchers have been monitoring pollution levels in the Red Sea for over a decade and have identified four main pollutants: domestic sewage in the coastal area; industrial wastes;

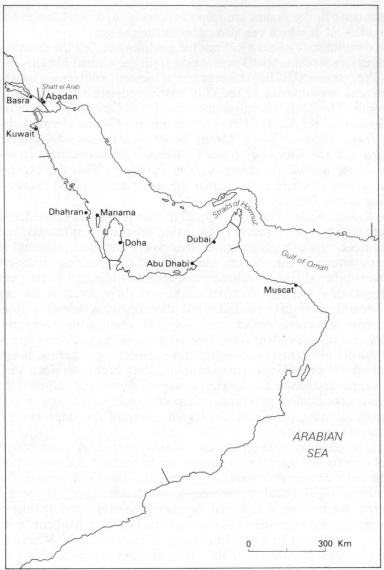

Fig. 1.1 The Kuwait Action Plan area includes both the Gulf area inside the Straits of Hormuz and the Gulf of Oman. Some of the main coastal cities are shown on this map.

pollution created by mechanical operations involved in dredging harbours and waterways; and oil contamination from tankers, pipelines and refineries. But there are even more serious threats to the Red Sea, in particular the threat of radioactive wastes from nuclear desalination plants and diluted muds from excavation operations. At present there are some twenty operational desalination plants and by the turn of the century these will be increased to fifty. Many will be atomic-desalination plants which will produce nuclear waste that may end up in the Red Sea. In addition, mining operations for the exploitation of metalliferous muds from the Red Sea produce two pollutants that could do serious damage to the Red Sea marine life: the chemicals which are used in the flotation process and the diluted muds that are pumped up from the sea bed. ALECSO has estimated that together the nuclear and mining wastes would raise the temperature of the sea by 5 °C which would do irreparable damage to the Red Sea marine life and ecosystems.

By 1974, ALECSO's researchers had done enough work to cause concern and, again with the help of UNEP, to bring together experts in marine science and government officials from the coastal states along the Red Sea and the Gulf of Aden, under the banner of the Jeddah I Conference. The Conference persuaded Jordan, Saudi Arabia, North Yemen, South Yemen, Somalia, Sudan and Egypt to monitor pollution in the Red Sea. It also produced the Jeddah Declaration, which called for cooperation in setting up a network for monitoring the level of pollutants in the Red Sea, adoption of a convention for the conservation and preservation of the Red Sea marine environment, setting up a network of national research stations, and setting up of joint interstate establishments to develop the natural resources of the Red Sea.

One outcome of the Jeddah Declaration was the establishment of the Saudi–Sudanese Commission for the Development of Red Sea Resources in May 1975. Under the commission's agreement, the Red Sea is divided into three zones: one extending westward from the Saudi coast to a line where the depth of water is continuously 1,000 m; one extending eastwards from the Sudanese coast to a line where the depth of water is continuously 1,000 m; and a common zone lying between the two others. Each country has exclusive rights over the area between its coastline and the common zone; in the common zone both countries have equal and exclusive rights. The agreement has paved the way for exploiting the mineral wealth in the Red Sea. Mining will start in a 60 km² area known as the Atlantis II Deep, which lies midway between Jeddah and Port Sudan in the central trough of the Red Sea. It is here that the metalliferous muds are found. These muds contain seventeen different metals in economic quantities ranging from zinc, silver, copper, cadmium, mercury, and gold to a great deal of iron. The system developed to mine the muds involves agitating it to dilute it with sea water, and then sucking it up with a hydraulic pump. Special shipborne flotation cells will collect a 5 per cent concentrate of mud in brine. The concentrate will then be carried off to the shore for further treatment and metal extraction. The method of separation and treatment developed is considered to be cost-effective with a recovery rate of 95 per cent. Provided some of the technical problems are resolved production will start in 1985.

By that time ALECSO hopes to establish several marine research stations around the coast of the Red Sea. Four stations at Aqaba, Ghardaga, Suakin and Jeddah are already functioning. Three long-standing marine institutes (at Suez, Port Sudan and Jeddah) will be developed further and ALECSO will coordinate their activities.

At the Jeddah II conference in January 1976, ALECSO persuaded the

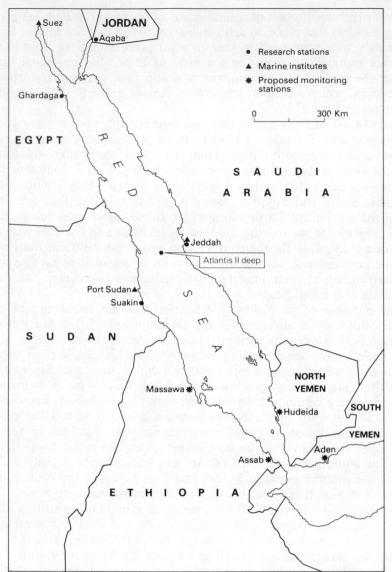

Fig. 1.2 The proposed monitoring and research stations around the Red Sea

countries concerned to monitor radioactive pollution in the Red Sea and the Gulf of Aden. The conference adopted a monitoring programme prepared by the Middle East Regional Isotope Centre for Arab States. An experimental station is planned to be set up in Jeddah that would eventually become the main centre for receiving and analysing field samples.

The Jeddah III conference of January 1981, accepted a *Convention on the Protection of the Marine Environment of the Red Sea and the Gulf of Aden* (reproduced in Part II) and established a regional organization for the protection of the Red Sea marine environment. The regional organization ⎯ludes a commission to settle disputes under the convention, a council to review the implementation of the convention and the state of the Red Sea and a secretariat to handle the organization's administration. The future Jeddah conferences are likely to set up a Marine Emergency Mutual Aid Centre to promote cooperation in combating pollution by oil and other substances caused by incidents such as ship collisions, oilwell blow-outs and failures of industrial plants. Among the cooperative programmes proposed so far are ones to establish protected aquatic areas, regional man-agement and exploitation of marine life, to strengthen the cooperation between national public health services, and to keep records of pollution incidents in the region. ALECSO will eventually turn these programmes into viable projects.

While both the Red Sea and the Persian Gulf are receiving considerable attention, little is done about the mounting urban pollution in the Middle East cities. Cities such as Casablanca, Cairo, Jeddah, Damascus, Ankara, Istanbul, Tehran and Karachi are facing a multitude of potentially, if not actually, harmful influences which, unless controlled or properly monitored, can become serious hazards – raw sewage, exhaust fumes, polluted drinking water and the occupational hazards of unplanned industrial growth. For the city populations of the Middle East, environmental decay has become a personal experience – a glass of water bitter with impurities, the acrid smell of industrial smoke or automobile exhaust, the noise of bulldozers or trucks piercing the 85 dB level beyond which noise can damage the ear. What they cannot see, hear, smell, taste or touch for themselves, they dis-cover in the grim list of food-poisoning casualties, cholera outbreaks and other environmental unpleasantness reported in the daily press.

Karachi, Pakistan's largest city and main port, presents a good example of the environment plight of the Middle East cities. The city's drinking water is heavily polluted with untreated sewage and industrial waste. Research at the Food Testing Laboratories of the Karachi Municipal Corporation shows that virtually the whole city's supply is contaminated by the bacteria *Escherichia coli*. But contaminated water is only one aspect of Karachi's pollution problem. Despite legislation against dumping dangerous industrial waste, local factories still discharge untreated mercury, lead compounds, chlorine and hydrochloric acid into rivers. An analysis of waste water flowing into the River Lyari showed that 70 per cent of the contaminants came from local factories; the rest was untreated sewage. Although the industrial area, unlike the rest of the city, does have a well laid-out sewage system, it has been overwhelmed by untreated waste from factories. Untreated industrial effluents and sewage from the city flow directly into the Lyari which now looks like a vast open drain.

Moreover, Karachi's problems do not end here. The Lyari drains into the harbour, which is also threatened by oil spills. In 1980, some 12,000 tonnes of oil were discharged into the stagnant water. The result is that faecal or-ganisms can be found on the beaches and in the salt produced by local fac-tories and the shellfish populations are almost on the verge of extinction.

Other Middle East cities face similar problems of drainage, industrial wastes and waterborne diseases. A number of major irrigation schemes such as Egypt's Aswan Dam, the Gezira irrigation scheme in Sudan, the

Jizam Dam in Saudi Arabia, the Indus Water Project in Pakistan, and the Helmend and Nangarhar irrigation networks in Afghanistan have brought tangible benefits in terms of reclaimed land and increased productivity but have also left a trail of vector-borne diseases which are affecting both urban and rural areas. As noted earlier, the list includes diseases such as malaria, schistosomiasis, ankylostomiasis, leishmaniasis and onchocerciasis (river blindness). On the Nile delta, water which was at a depth of 14 m fifty years ago is now less than 5 m deep. In much of Cairo, and in particular under the famous Citadel and the Giza Pyramids, the water table is only 3 m beneath the surface. Increases in air pollution in cities like Cairo has also meant an increase in respiratory diseases such as asthma, bronchitis, lung cancer and emphysema.

The challenge now facing environmental activists is to avert or control serious health risks through water- and air-monitoring systems, sound technology and realistic appraisals of the benefits and hazards involved in the introduction of new technology to urban–industrial complexes. Governments need to be made aware of environmental legislation that must be enforced.

An example of successful environmental legislation is provided, surprisingly, by post-revolutionary Iran. The pollution levels in Tehran have been so high that many citizens had taken to wearing masks at peak rush hours. The city supports some 1.3 million private vehicles, 20,000 buses, 33,000 small trucks and 60,000 lorries; together they produce enough exhaust fumes to make breathing uncomfortable during particularly bad days. Moreover, in the southern part of Tehran, which was largely neglected under the Shah, there is the serious dual problem of over-population and lack of sanitation. Nearly 1.6 million people, crowded together here in thirty-five districts, are facing chronic drinking-water shortage. They also lack electricity, schools, and hospitals – in sharp contrast to the affluent northern section of the city. Iran's Department of Environment attacked the problem in two steps: first of all bus routes were expanded and more buses were introduced. Then legislation was introduced to limit the use of heavily leaded and poor-quality petrol. Eventually, legislation requiring Iranian vehicles to have devices to reduce hydrocarbon and carbon monoxide will also be introduced. Bus and taxi lanes have already been introduced, and the Department of Environment intends to completely ban private vehicles from the centre of the city. An experimental one-week ban during August 1980 was considered very successful. Since the introduction of new clean-petrol legislation and the campaign to promote public transport, the number of public transport users has increased from 1.1 to 1.7 million and air pollution in the city has dropped considerably, according to the Department of Environment. To reduce incidents of water pollution, standards for the discharge of industrial effluents have been introduced – and they are enforced vigorously. New development plans for the city concentrate on removing the problems of the southern part of Tehran and include a project to provide extensive green areas. Although it remains to ʌe seen whether Tehran's environmental problems are completely eradicated ʌʌe initiatives, they are, nevertheless, a positive step forward.

Nuclear Energy

The ultimate environmental threat to the Middle East comes from nuclear power. Almost all countries in the region have nuclear power plants either in operation or under construction, or plan to have one within a few years. The regulatory organizations of countries with active nuclear programmes are sub-minimal; in many cases they consist of little more than fifteen full-time staff members connected with nuclear power activities. Furthermore, these individuals are quite often unfamiliar with the discipline of nuclear safety and need extensive training. Without good regulatory agencies, Middle East countries cannot ensure that they are being sold safe nuclear systems, or that they can operate them safely. And there is at least one example of new designs being tried out in a Middle East country; this is the case of design changes that had to be introduced, due to high seismicity at the site, in the two pressurized water reactors that were being built under the Shah in Iran near Ahwaz on the Karun river.

There is also the very rational concern over the military use of nuclear power in the Middle East. Nuclear power plants and nuclear weapons both ultimately evolve from the same physical phenomena. Virtually all reactors could produce some sort of low-grade weapon – and cheaply, if a few radiation safeguards are ignored. A nation with a commercial uranium enrichment plant or a fuel reprocessing plant is in a position to produce weapons-grade material if it wants to. The connection between peaceful and military nuclear technology is too close for comfort. The point, therefore, is not that Pakistan or Iraq or any other Middle East state is making the bomb, but that if these countries have a nuclear capability the temptation to develop nuclear weapons will be there.

Against the environmental and military case are the arguments for breaking the Western monopoly of nuclear technology and meeting the acute energy needs of certain Middle Eastern countries.

Perhaps the most articulate proponent of these arguments is Munir Ahmad Khan, chairman of Pakistan's Atomic Energy Commission. Khan's arguments are indeed powerful. The policies of the industrialized countries are reflected by the 1968 Nuclear Non-Proliferation Treaty (NPT), the 1978 Nuclear Non-Proliferation Act of the United States and the powerful Nuclear Suppliers Group (also known as the London Suppliers Group). Pakistan, along with India, Brazil and Argentina, claims that the NPT is an infringement of its sovereignty by the nuclear powers. They maintain that while the nuclear states reserve the right to continue vertical proliferation (the nuclear arms race), they wish to deny nuclear technology to the developing countries by placing obstacles in the way of the development of indigenous facilities for the peaceful utilization of nuclear energy. The object of the London Suppliers Group is to strengthen the non-proliferation regime by controlling the supply of nuclear-related equipment, materials, technology, and services. Most of the world's commercial reactors are fuelled by four commercial uranium enrichment plants run by the industrialized countries: URENCO, an Anglo–Dutch–German consortium, the United States Department of Energy, Russia's Tekhnoexport and

EURODIF, a France–Spain–Belgium–Italy–Iran facility. This is a very profitable and powerful oligopoly. Thus with the Western monopoly of technology and supplies, nuclear technology could become a tool of domination which would be directly challenged by any country that tried to develop an indigenous nuclear capability.

The energy needs of certain Middle East countries also feature strongly in the arguments for nuclear power. Pakistan, for example, is one of the poorest countries of the world as far as production and consumption of energy is concerned. Compared to the world average of 1,600 kWh per capita, its average per capita consumption of energy is below 150 kWh. Its total coal, oil, gas, hydro and fossil fuel resources correspond to 15 tons of coal equivalent (tce). This contrasts sharply with the fact that on an average a United States citizen uses 12 tce of energy in one year. Oil imports, even at concessionary rates, cost Pakistan some US$1,500 million a year, almost half of its foreign exchange earnings. By 1985 Pakistan would be spending 100 per cent of its export earnings if it did not have nuclear power.

Proponents of nuclear power in Turkey and Egypt produce similar statistics. Turkey's major source of energy is lignite, which supplies almost half of the domestic and industrial energy needs, and hydro-power. The Turkish Electricity Authority has calculated that hydro-electric energy will reach its maximum capacity around 1985; and by 1990 Turkey will face a minimum deficit of 10,000 MW in its energy demands. As the Turkish economy precludes any dependence on oil, nuclear power is seen as the only viable option.

Egypt's present power requirements are met by coal-fired stations, which are not considered practical because total coal reserves in Egypt are estimated at 100 million tonnes, only 35 million tonnes of which are economically exploitable, and hydro-electric power, over 80 per cent of which is already being harnessed. Hydro-electric power with 2,100 MW from the Aswan High Dam and 345 MW from the Aswan Dam, provides 55 per cent of Egypt's current power requirements. By 1990 another 350 MW will be harnessed by improving three barrages and extending the Aswan Dam. That means that if Egypt is to increase energy production significantly its only practical alternatives are thermal or nuclear power. However, the Ministry of Electricity and Energy has ruled out thermal power on the grounds that if Egypt continues to build thermal power stations by the year 2000 the country would be using 90 per cent of its oil production for power. Even at current prices of oil, nuclear power is claimed to be 40 per cent cheaper. The Egyptian government expects annual per capita power consumption to rise from the present 400 kWh to 700 kWh by 1985, 1,000 kWh in 1990, and 1,600 kWh in the year 2000. Most of this increase, according to the current plan, will be met by nuclear energy.

Such arguments form the basis for nuclear power in the Middle East. Egypt has already chosen three sites for nuclear plants: Sidi Kreir, at Zafran, 120 km south of Suez on the Red Sea, and at Dabaa, 160 km west of Alexandria. A series of eight nuclear power plants are planned for the next twenty years; and accords have been signed with the United States, France and West Germany for the supply of nuclear plants.

Turkey envisages that some 75 per cent of the country's energy needs will be supplied by nuclear power. Early in 1979, an agreement was signed with the Swedish firm ASEA–ATOM to build the first nuclear plant by 1987–88 at Akkuyu, 35 km from the town of Silifki, on the Mediterranean coast. That agreement came to an end and West Germany has stepped in to continue the work at Akkuyu. The Turkish Electricity Authority is actively looking for an appropriate site for a second plant which, it is hoped, will be operational by 1992. After that, eight more plants will be built in succession so that a network of ten plants will be operating by the year 2000. Each plant will cost Turkey an estimated US$1 billion; some 20 to 30 per cent of this cost will be met by the Turkish government, and the rest has to be secured in loans.

Under the Shah, Iran had similar plans. Iran's nuclear programme envisaged a network of twenty-three reactors, supplying 42 per cent of Iran's electricity needs by 1994. Before the revolution, work on four plants had started and nineteen were under negotiation. There was also a complicated plan for uranium enrichment: the Iranian government purchased vast quantities of uranium at inflated prices and directed it to West Germany for enrichment. Once enriched, the uranium had to be stored in West Germany until 1994, or until it would be needed by Iran. This programme was started in 1974 and since then until the programme was scrapped in 1979, the Iranian government was paying West Germany both for enriching its uranium and storing it. Of the four plants under construction, two pressurized water reactors of 900 MW near Ahwaz on the Harun river were being built at the cost of US$2.3 billion by the French company Framatome, and the other two, 1,200 MW plants near Bushehr on the Persian Gulf, were being built by the West German company Kraftwerk-Union, an engineering unit of Siemens, at the cost of US$3.2 billion. After the revolution, Kraftwerk-Union demanded US$7 billion to complete the work on the Bushehr plants. The differences between Kraftwerk-Union and Iran have now been settled. The Iranian government has decided to complete the unfinished plants using Iranian researchers and engineers.

Undoubtedly, Pakistan has a lead in nuclear expertise and technology in the region. Pakistan's first nuclear power plant, Karachi Nuclear Power Plant (KANUPP), a 137 MW heavy water reactor, was built in Karachi with Canadian assistance. It came into operation in 1972 and Canadians helped to run it until 1976. After a disagreement over renegotiations of nuclear cooperation accords, Canada withdrew. Since then KANUPP has been run and maintained by Pakistani engineers and is now fuelled with nuclear fuel produced indigenously. Besides running and maintaining the plant, Pakistani engineers have managed to fabricate a whole array of spare parts, including the specific alloys needed for some of the major components of the KANUPP. A new unit for upgrading heavy water, three times the size of the existing one and designed and built locally, has been added to the plant. Encouraged with its success with KANUPP, Pakistan is now constructing its own indigenously designed and produced 600 MW Chasma

Nuclear Power Plant (CHASNUPP) in Chasma in the Minawali District. The site has been prepared and construction is to start soon. CHASNUPP is a test case for Pakistan, and after its completion in 1983, Pakistan plans to set up more locally built nuclear power plants at a much faster rate.

Much of Pakistan's nuclear efforts are directed towards research. The Pakistan Institute of Nuclear Science and Technology in Nilore, near Rawalpindi, is one of the leading nuclear research institutes in the Third World. It has had a 5 MW pool-type research reactor in operation since 1965 and teaches a comprehensive postgraduate course in nuclear engineering. The Nuclear Institute for Agriculture and Biology, located at Faisalabad and established in 1972, has also established itself as one of the leading research institutes in the Muslim World.

The nuclear programmes of Saudi Arabia, Libya and Iraq also tend to emphasize research, although Iraq is the only country which has any capability for nuclear research. Saudi Arabia has plans to establish a large, multi-purpose national nuclear research centre which will study the possibilities of constructing nuclear reactors on the Gulf and Red Sea coasts and building a nuclear fuel facility. It will also study the applications of atomic energy in providing drinking water and electricity, and in such fields as medicine, industry and agriculture. Preparing the ground for Saudi capability in nuclear technology, the centre will work towards the creation of an institute of reactor technology and will assess domestic supplies of uranium and thorium and other radioactive minerals.

Libya already has a 440 MW VVER Russian reactor under construction. Early in 1981, the Libyan leader, Colonel Moamer Gaddafi announced the formation of a Ministry of Atomic Energy and made one of his closest associates, Abdul Majid al-Mabruk al-Gaud, the new Minister for Atomic Energy. The ministry will have executive powers of the country's Atomic Energy Commission, which was established in 1973. Libya has also signed nuclear cooperation agreements with Pakistan and Argentina.

In contrast to Saudi Arabia and Libya, Iraq has come a long way in nuclear research in the last ten years. Its Atomic Energy Commission, established in 1956, was one of the first in the Middle East and has had a Russian-built research reactor in operation since 1968. In 1975, it procured from France a more advanced research centre with a 70 MW Osiris reactor, called Tamuz 1, to be built near Baghdad at a cost of US$360 million. Since then France has agreed to supply a second, 600 MW Isis reactor to Iraq. Tamuz 2 is also part of a research centre in Baghdad and will be used to train 600 Iraqi scientists and technicians in nuclear technology. France has also agreed to supply 72 kg of 93 per cent enriched (weapons grade) fuel for this reactor. Iraq has nuclear agreements with Brazil, Italy and Portugal, for the supply of both nuclear technology and enriched uranium. Iraq has faced considerable opposition to its nuclear programme, including the sabotage of the French construction plant in April 1979 and the bombing of the Osirak reactor in June 1981, but is nevertheless continuing with its nuclear plans.

Unlike those of Iraq, Syria's nuclear plans have not received much attention. The Syrian Atomic Energy Commission was established in

1976 and since then it has been negotiating with Belgium and Switzerland for the construction of the country's first nuclear power plant. Eventually, Syria plans to build six 6,000 MW reactors at the cost of US$3.6 billion to meet the growing demand for electricity which is expected to rise sevenfold by 1990. Syria's first nuclear reactor will probably be built by Belgium and is expected to be operational by 1991.

Most Middle East countries have also developed big uranium exploration programmes. They have already produced some dividends for Pakistan and Saudi Arabia; and Algeria, Egypt, Morocco and perhaps Tunisia will start producing the mineral soon, while research is being carried out in Libya and Sudan. Algeria is likely to become the first major uranium producer in the Arab world. The Algerian mining company, the *Société Nationale de Recherche et d'Exploitation Minière (SONAREM)* has concentrated exploration in the Hogger mountains, about 100 km east of Tamanrasset and contracts for feasibility studies were awarded in 1978. According to the International Atomic Energy Agency, Algeria's uranium potential is 28,000 tonnes; but SONAREM estimates reserves of 50,000 tonnes or more. At the proposed output of 1,000 to 1,200 tonnes per year, Algerian uranium reserves are likely to last for over thirty years, and production can start as early as 1985.

Recent explorations in Egypt have revealed around 5,000 tonnes of crude uranium deposits between Qena and Safaya in the Red Sea governorate. Deposits of three more uranium fields remain to be estimated. A mobile unit is already producing between 20 and 30 tonnes a year from the first field, the capacity of which will be raised to 100 tonnes per year by the end of 1982. Other exploration teams are at work in the Qarun and Qatrani areas; and a US$5.7 million extraction plant is planned for the region.

Morocco's first uranium extraction plant at Safi started operation in July 1979. Recently, a number of processes have been developed which allow the recovery of uranium from phosphate. One of these processes, originally developed in the United States using Florida phosphate, is being used, under licence, in the Moroccan plant. Phosphoric acid made from marine phosphate rock commonly contains uranium at a concentration of 0.001 to 0.07 per cent, although the average is between 0.01 and 0.02 per cent. In the 'wet process' for producing phosphoric acid, sulphuric acid is used to break down the phosphate rock. The phosphoric acid which is subsequently filtered off, leaving waste gypsum, contains the uranium previously in the rock. This is extracted by using a solvent and the acid is made into fertilizer. This process will be used in Morocco to produce 500,000 tonnes of phosphoric acid per year, from which 600 tonnes of yellow cake will be extracted.

Libya too has been exploring for uranium since its Atomic Energy Commission was established in 1974. Libya's extensive Marzuk and Kufra basins are likely to have uranium deposits. Geological proximity to uranium-bearing zones in Niger and Algeria would indicate that Libya's potential for discovering uranium is relatively high. However, explorations so far have not yielded positive results.

Table 1.3 Nuclear technology in the Middle East

Country	Official body	Power plants			Other interests	Uranium resources	Research		Cooperation (official and unofficial)	NPT status	Remarks
		Built or under construction	Immediate plans	Long-term plans			Institutions	Reactors			
Algeria				Feasibility study under way		50,000 tons assured reserves. Mining in Hoggar Mts to begin mid-1980s. Annual production 1,000 tons expected	Institut d'Etudes Nucleaires (1958) Algiers			Not party	Uranium mining city is to be built at Tingapuina by consortium of Swiss, Belgian, and American companies
Egypt	Atomic Energy Establishment (1955)		600 MW at Sidi Kreir (Westinghouse) Joint plant with Israel in Sinai	10 plants of 6,600 MW by AD 2000 (39% electricity needs)		Reserves in phosphates	Radioisotope Centre (1957) Alexandria University	2 MW at Inchass (1961) Soviet-built. Seeking its expansion to 5 MW	America, Soviet Union	Signed	Financial problems are delaying the Sidi Kreir plant. Sina plant would be built with Israeli help and possible American finance
Iran	Atomic Energy Organization (1974)	2×1,200 MW at Bushehr (Kraftwerk Union) 2×900 MW on Karun river (Framatome) Plans to start construction using local expertise			10% holding in Eurodif enrichment plant (Tricastin, France), 25% holding in Coredif enrichment plant (France). *(Expected to be withdrawn)*	Occurrences reported. Big exploration programme now stopped	Tehran University. Radioisotopes Centre under construction	5 MW pool-type at Tehran University (1967) 1 MW TRIGA II on order from General Atomic *(may be cancelled)*	France, America, United Kingdom, West Germany, India, Sweden, Italy, Brazil. *Talks with:* Japan, Brazil	Ratified	
Iraq	Atomic Energy Commission (1956)		600 MW on order from France for Tigris river south of Baghdad (Framatome and Geusor-Loire)	3 plants 1,700 MW by AD 2000		Exploration under way	Nuclear Research Institutes (Tuwaitha) Research Centre bought from France (Baghdad)	IRT-2000 (1968) Soviet supplied 70 MW Osiris on order from France	Soviet Union, France, Italy, Brazil	Ratified	Osiris (Osirak) sabotaged and bombed by Israelis
Jordan	Atomic Energy Commission						Jordan University		West Germany		
Kuwait	Nuclear Energy Committee (commission planned)		500 MW training reactor *cancelled*	4 plants 3,600 MW by AD 2000 *shelved.* Regional reactor with Bahrain and Saudi Arabia mooted					United Kingdom, Saudi Arabia	Signed	
Libya	Ministry of Atomic Energy (1981), Atomic Energy Commission (1973)	440 MW VVER Soviet reactor (cooling system by Finland) on Mediterranean coast			Reports of contract with West Germany for heavy-water plant	Reserves in Aozou Strip (annexed from Chad) and in Marzouk basin	Soviet Building Centre, Fateh University (Tripoli)	10 MW in Soviet-built centre	Soviet Union, Argentina, India, France, West Germany, Sweden, Pakistan	Ratified	Students also training in America and Europe

Table 1.3 — *continued*

Country	Official body	Power plants Built or under construction	Immediate plans	Long-term plans	Other interests	Uranium resources	Research Institutions	Reactors	Cooperation (official and unofficial)	NPT status	Remarks
Morocco	Atomic Energy Commission			600 MW reactor under discussion with France	Uranium extraction plant under discussion with America (Westinghouse), France and Japan also interested	Reserves in phosphates (about 10,000 tons)	Rabat University		America	Ratified	Morocco also controls the phosphate mines in the former Spanish Sahara which it annexed in 1975
Pakistan	Atomic Energy Commission	125 MW KANUPP at Karachi (1972)	600 MW at Chashma	20 plants by AD 2000 including FBRs (50% of electricity needs)	Reprocessing plant (France). *Cancelled by France.* Enrichment plant (built by buying parts abroad)	Occurrences reported	Islamabad Institute for Science and Technology	5 MW at Islamabad	Canada (suspended 1976), France, Libya, China, United Arab Emirates (financial help), Saudi Arabia, Niger	Not party	
Saudi Arabia	Atomic Energy Commission to be formed			Considering reactors for Gulf and Red Sea coasts	Considering fuel-assembly plant and heavy-water plant	Occurrences reported. Big exploration programme (France, US, IAEA involved)	Atomic Energy Centre to be set up (Technicatome of France). Nuclear Medicine Centre (Riyadh)	Centre to have 5 MW reactor	France, Kuwait, Pakistan	Not party	
Syria	Atomic Energy Commission (1976)		6,000 MW plant by 1991	6 plants by AD 2000		Reserves in phosphates			India, Belgium	Ratified	
Tunisia			50 MW plant for Gulf of Gabes			Reserves in phosphates	*Institut de Recherches Scientifique et Techniques* (1969)			Ratified	
Turkey	Atomic Energy Commission (1956)		600 MW plant by 1988 near Akkuyu			3,500 tons assured reserves. Big exploration programme	Cekmece Nuclear Research and Training Centre. Ankara Nuclear Research and Training Centre. Technical University (Istanbul). Radiobiology Institute (Ankara)	1 MW AMF pool-type TR-1 at Cekmece (1959). Istanbul Technical University (1979)	America, Switzerland, Pakistan	Signed (IAEA safeguards)	

Source: Parera, J., 'Nuclear Plants Take Root in the Desert', *New Scientist*, **83**, 577–80 (23 Aug. 1979).

The Sudanese Geological Department has also had to face disappointments. Two areas were pinpointed for exploration, the Nuba mountain zone and the Hofrat-en-Hahas area in the south-west. Radioactive elements were discovered in the Nuba area as long ago as the early 1950s, and radioactive elements were discovered in copper deposits of the Hofrat-en-Hahas area recently. However, a comprehensive evaluation has still to be made.

In the Middle East, phosphate resources are mined or occur in Algeria, Egypt, Iraq, Jordan, Morocco, Saudi Arabia, and Turkey. A significant proportion of the mined phosphate is exported without processing. However, with the current drive for fertilizer production and recovery of contained uranium, not only will mine expansion and new mine programmes flourish, but there will also be greater emphasis on the construction of plants to process more and more of this ore within the national boundaries. The uranium extraction process is still quite expensive; but the desire for nuclear technology and the availability of capital in certain oil-rich Arab states means that this route for acquiring uranium will be developed rapidly.

With the strong desire of many Middle East countries to acquire nuclear technology, the availability of uranium and the development of an indigenous uranium enrichment capability in Pakistan, the stage is set for nuclear proliferation in the region, and the possibility of the emergence of a nuclear device is clear.

The decision as to whether to opt for nuclear power or not rests entirely with the individual countries in the Middle East, but there has been surprisingly little awareness of the hazards of nuclear technology among the scientists and intellectuals in the region. Some opposition to Turkey's nuclear plan, restricted to Akkuyu and Silifki, the site of the country's first nuclear plant, has come to the fore. The Silifki anti-nuclear group is quite vocal and has been able to raise some questions in the parliament before the present government took over. In Egypt, a major anti-nuclear lobby developed in Alexandria because the first plant was to be sited near that city. The lobby proposed that instead of a nuclear plant a conventional power station should be built at Abu Qir to utilize recently discovered gasfields there. However, the Alexandria anti-nuclear group has died down as the main force behind it, Alexandria's ex-governor Fuad Helmi, has retired. But nuclear protest in the region is limited to these two incidents, and there are no signs to indicate that there will be a major anti-nuclear movement in the Middle East in the near future.

Solar Energy

Solar energy in the Middle East is almost as important as nuclear technology. Two factors are responsible for the upsurge of solar technology activities in the region. The first is the success of American, French, West German and Swiss solar technology salesmen. The second is a genuine desire for developing alternative energy sources. As a result over thirty universities and twenty government institutions are now actively involved in solar energy research; solar conferences in the region have become a

Table 1.4 Phosphate and recoverable uranium resources of the Muslim world

Geographical area	Phosphate resource (millions of tons)	Typical P_2O_5 content of phosphate resource (%)	Potentially mineable phosphate product ($=30\% P_2O_5$) (millions of tons)	Estimated recoverable phosphate product ($=30\% P_2O_5$) (millions of tons)	Average uranium concentration of phosphate product ($=30\% P_2O_5$) (millions of tons)	Uranium contained in potentially mineable phosphate (thousands of tons)	Estimated recoverable uranium (thousands of tons)
Algeria	1,100	25	700	525	100	70	52
Egypt	1,645	20–26	1,000	750	100	100	75
Iraq	2,360	18	770	579	130	100	75
Jordan	16,000	15–33	4,000	3,000	120	480	360
Morocco	88,000	25–34	60,000	45,000	110	6,600	4,950
Saudi Arabia	1,000	18–23	300	220	100	33	26
Senegal	255	25–37	220	175	180	47	38
Syria	900	19–28	540	405	130	70	52
Tunisia	1,300	26–30	910	682	60	55	41
Turkey	350	10–25	70	56	40	2.8	2
Western Sahara	11,000	31–33	7,400	5,550	100	740	555
	123,910		75,910	56,942		8,298	6,226

Source: Rana, M. H., 'Phosphate (and Contained Uranium) Resources of the Muslim World', *The Muslim Scientist*, **9** (3–4), 30–51 (Sept.–Dec. 1980).

common sight and the annual Soltech exhibition in Bahrain draws record crowds.

The lead in solar research is taken by Saudi Arabia which is also the biggest spender on the solar energy project. The 1981 solar energy budget was a huge US$590 million. Saudi Arabia also has a US$100 million five-year cooperation agreement with the United States Department of Energy's Solar Energy Research Institute. Known as SOLERAS, the agreement was signed in 1977 and is due for review in 1982. The major projects under this scheme include the setting up of a 350 kW photovoltaic station and solar cooling laboratories, the establishment of a solar village in Saudi Arabia and studies on solar energy availability, solar desalination and solar cooling. SOLERAS is also coordinating solar energy research between the major Saudi universities and a number of universities in the United States – from research into solar generation of hydro- and helio-electricity to investigations of the uses of solar power in remote areas and agriculture. For example, US$8 million have been awarded to the University of Riyadh to study the provision of solar powered electricity to two villages near Riyadh. The university has pioneered solar research in Saudi Arabia and has been undertaking studies in heating and air-conditioning applications of solar energy for well over a decade. Research at other universities includes agricultural and industrial applications of solar energy at the King Faisal University, Dammam; water desalination research at the King Abdul Aziz University, Jeddah; and solar electric power generation and development of an information system for solar energy information in the Middle East. Saudi Arabia also boasts the largest solar heated building with the 30,000 m² Tabuk athletic centre. Private finance is also involved in the Saudi solar energy drive: Prince Nawaf bin Abdul Aziz, Minister of the Interior, has set up the Saudi Technology and Research Centre (STAR), a consulting firm on solar technology which has invested its own money in an Australian-developed solar collector.

Other oil-rich Arab states are not far behind Saudi Arabia. In Kuwait, a 100 kW thermal conversion station has been installed at the Kuwait Institute for Scientific Research (KISR), which also carries out other solar projects on desalination, housing and agriculture. Iraq recently established a Solar Energy Research Centre, which will work on solar thermal conversion, desalination, solar drying and solar housing. Libya too has established a Centre for Solar Energy Studies, which works on 'mission oriented' projects, such as supplying solar power to remote communities and determining heating and cooling loads on modern buildings.

In Algeria, work on solar energy started as long ago as the early 1950s. The solar station of Abu Zarriah was built by the French before Algerian independence. Its main feature is a solar furnace, which was built in the 1950s. It is now being used for studying solar heat and the development of locally produced thermal turbines. A solar village has been developed, almost from a clean site, in the province of M'silah, some 10 km north of the town of Abu Saadah. In conjunction with the United Nations University and United Nations Development Programme, Algerian researchers prepared the site, identified local resources and materials, familiarized themselves with local problems and designed a village based on classical Arabic architecture for a population base of 2,000. The fully developed village relies almost exclusively on solar energy but also meets some of its energy requirements from geothermal and biochemical sources. The model solar village is part of a large project called 'the thousand village scheme', which involves development of solar villages on a vast scale and redistribution of the rural population of Algeria. The villages will be built in Warglah, Saidah, Tahart and M'silah provinces.

On the whole, the most interesting solar research is being carried out in capital-poor countries of the Middle East. Egypt, which already has two solar villages at Besisa and Mit Abul Qom, has a well developed and established solar research programme. At the Solar Energy Laboratory of the National Research Centre in Cairo, work is being done on photothermal power generation, solar cooling and drying, and desalination. The Ministry of Electricity and Energy is working on several major projects, including reverse osmosis and the generation of power using the Qattarah Depression. The latter project involves allowing water to fall from the Mediterranean into the depression, which has its deepest point 134 m below sea level, and then disposing of the water by natural solar evaporation. An estimated maximum of 8,000 MW could be generated using this technique from the Qattarah Depression.

In Jordan, the most important solar project is the multi-effect desalination plant being set up in al-Aqabah by the Royal Scientific Society. The Jordanian Telecommunication Corporation has developed a telephone system to serve small rural villages located in remote regions using solar cells as a source of power. Emergency photovoltaic telephones have also been installed along highways. The Faculty of Agriculture of the University of Amman is working on 'plastic agriculture', an integrated system which combines distillation and temperature control by solar energy techniques.

Turkey and Pakistan have lagged somewhat behind in solar research. However, work has now started in solar greenhouses in Turkey, and, in Pakistan, Pakistan Council for Scientific and Industrial Research (PCSIR) has started work on supplying solar power to remote villages.

Many of the solar energy projects in the Middle East have a strong high-technology bias and rely heavily on the transfer of technology from the West. In Saudi Arabia, Kuwait and Libya solar research amounts to little more than clearing the ground for the import of solar technology. Moreover, not one major solar energy project is free from Western control. The oil-rich countries have associated themselves with the solar programmes of the United States which concentrate on the needs of high technology and ignore the very simple needs of the Middle East societies. For example, considerable resources are being devoted to solar cooling for concrete buildings, while the traditional housing in most Arab countries not only optimizes the energy intake for human comfort but has one of the most sophisticated cooling systems. In the capital-poor states, solar energy research is dependent almost totally on outside help. For example, Egypt's programme, one of the most diversified, relies on funds from the United States and West Germany.

Unless the Middle East countries work to develop their own solar technologies, the Arab world will become saturated with solar energy systems manufactured in the West, which are often irrelevant to local needs and cannot be sustained with the available technological infrastructure in the region without foreign help. If the process continues, the Arab countries would then change from exporting oil to importing solar energy.

There are considerable resources – manpower, organizational, and financial – for indigenous solar energy research in the Middle East. But the major block towards this goal is the belief in the region's academic and scientific circles that research can be bought. Ali Kettani and M. A. S. Malik, in their solar energy survey for the Organization of Arab Petroleum Exporting Countries, identified four major hurdles towards genuine local research in solar technology:

1. Lack of proper allocation of finance and manpower for basic and applied research and lack of mechanisms for coordinating and promoting solar energy activities.
2. Weak relevance of projects undertaken to national plans and actual needs; most of the projects are being chosen under pressure from corporations and sometimes with their financial support; and from pressure of foreign consultants and advisers.
3. Lack of awareness of the capabilities of local industries and the needs of the potential users of solar technology and weak industry–university research linkage; also lack of awareness of production techniques and the necessity of continuous supply of technical know-how to industry.
4. Lack of insured financial stability with emphasis on contract research based on project planning, control and review.

While technology can be imported virtually overnight, the removal of such difficulties will take many years of dedicated effort. The choice is between permanent dependency on imported solar technology goods and generating local capability to harness one of the most abundant sources of power.

Apart from solar energy, research activity in other new and renewable sources of energy is virtually non-existent in the Middle East. There is some research being done on biomass and wind energy in Pakistan, Sudan, Tunisia and Algeria, but compared to the work being done in India, Brazil and China it is relatively insignificant. For example, the work on renewable energy resources in Pakistan is done by the Appropriate Technology Development Organization, Islamabad, and is limited to adaptation of a Chinese design of a biogas plant and testing multi-bladed windmills designed by the Intermediate Technology Development Group of London. In Turkey, work is being done on the extraction of heavy oil by reducing its viscosity with injections of carbon dioxide. The project, financed by the World Bank, would eventually enable Turkey to recover 5 to 10 per cent of its sizeable deposits of heavy oil. Biogas, biomass, wind and fuel wood do not have the high technology attraction of solar energy; neither do they have the aggressive backing of Western commercial interests, and it is therefore not surprising that they are ignored in the Middle East.

Table 1.5 Solar energy research and applications in the Middle East

Country	Solar furnace	Flat plate collectors	STC	Solar cooling	Water desalination	Water heating	Solar drying	Solar pumping	Storage	Solar greenhouse	Solar heating	Solar insulation	Photovoltaic conversion	Solar industry	Courses in solar energy
Algeria	×	×	×	×	×	×	×	×							
Bahrain		×	×	×	×	×									
Egypt		×	×	×	×	×	×	×				×	×		×
Iraq		×			×	×	×					×	×		×
Jordan		×	×	×	×	×	×					×	×	×	
Kuwait		×	×	×					×			×			
Lebanon						×	×								
Libya					×		×			×		×	×		
Morocco															
Oman															
Pakistan															
Qatar								×	×	×		×	×		
Saudi Arabia		×	×	×	×	×	×	×	×			×	×		
Sudan												×			
Syria												×			
Tunisia								×	×	×			×		
Turkey															
UAE															
North Yemen															
South Yemen															

Source: Kettani, M. A. and Malik, M. A. S., *Solar Energy in the Arab World: Policies and Programmes*, AOPEC, Kuwait 1979.

Microtechnology and Communications

Microtechnology in the Middle East has a strong commercial backing. The Middle East is a leading market for microtechnology, and computers, calculators, video cassette recorders and electronic games are found in abundance in the region. All the major producers of computers, such as ICL, IBM, Honeywell and Univac have spent considerable time and money in developing the Middle East market. Indeed, if the current drive in selling microtechnology to the region continues, within a decade every household in Saudi Arabia, Kuwait, Libya and the UAE will have some kind of IBM or Honeywell computer linked to a major European or North American network.

Almost all the major government agencies, universities and big businesses have now computerized their operations. In Saudi Arabia, for example, the National Computer Centre in Riyadh houses an IBM 370 135 computer, which is being used in the processing of data on the census of population and housing. The Ministry of Defence and Aviation has an IBM 360 20 computer and Saudia, the Saudi Arabian Airline, maintains an IBM 370 135 computer. The Data Processing Centre of the University of Petroleum and Minerals, one of the major data processing facilities in the Middle East, houses an IBM-370/158 computer, which services both internal university needs and on a fee basis is available to external governmental and industrial agencies. All the major Saudi universities also have computers, which are used both for administrative work and for research.

Where Saudi Arabia leads, Kuwait, Libya and Iraq follow. In these countries computerization will soon reach saturation point. The major trend-setter was undoubtedly pre-revolutionary Iran, which also provides a good example of the direction computerization in the region may eventually take.

Microelectronics is a conspicuous technology. It can induce a feeling of progress and modernization, and can generate needs that are not actually there. Under the Shah, an imaginary demand for sophisticated computers was created in Iran. Big plans were made to computerize almost every aspect of government administration and industry, and a similar feeling was introduced in business organizations. For example, Shojaeddin Sheikholeslamzadeh, Minister of Health and Welfare under the Shah, tried to implement a drive to have computer terminals in every village in the country, even the most remote, so that in the case of illness or accident the village could notify a central computer which, in its turn, would alert the authorities, who would send a helicopter to transfer the patient to the nearest hospital. Similar logic was followed in the Plan and Budget Organization, the Social Security Organization, Iran Air and other government and private organizations.

The result was an overabundance of computer hardware that the Iranians did not know how to handle, that cost astronomical sums of money, and which was too advanced and powerful for Iranian needs. The ITEL hardware purchased by the health ministry, for example, was enough to meet all the data-processing requirements of the government. Collectively the computer hardware available in Iran is capable of meeting the data-processing requirement of the entire Middle East.

There were also very serious problems with the software. The case of the Social Security Organization (SSO) is the most notable. SSO asked the US company Electronic Data Systems (EDS) to computerize its operations. EDS supplied a number of packages none of which met SSO's needs. EDS then obtained an extension of its contract from three to five years. However after four years, and an expenditure of $80 million, EDS had still not delivered the goods. Shortly after Iran had its revolution and the firm sued the Iranian government for breach of contract and the remainder of its money.

Developments in other Middle East countries have been less extreme but the pace at which computerization and automation are introduced in the region is increasing.

Besides over-ambitious computerization programmes, microelectronics is making its impact on the Middle East in three other forms. Firstly, Arab news agencies are rapidly developing networks of telephone-linked teleprinters and are increasingly relying on computerized photocomposition. Secondly, most Arab countries are in the process of completing their individual microwave communication networks which are linked across the borders – in the case of Tunisia, Algeria and Morocco, the linkage spans the Mediterranean to the European networks.

The final area is that of satellite communication. Most Arab countries – including Saudi Arabia, Kuwait, Egypt and Algeria – have ground stations in full operation, and work on establishing an Arab satellite is at an advanced stage. There is a strong desire to improve telecommunications in the region and to develop satellite technology for environmental monitoring and remote sensing. By the end of 1982, for example, Saudi Arabia will have a network consisting of seventeen new meteorological, environmental and marine stations, which will work in conjunction with six weather stations now in use. Existing stations rely on high-frequency communications for the transmission of information to regional centres. The new stations will rely on the European Meteorological Satellite (METEOSAT) to transmit information to a data processing centre planned for Jeddah. Another new ground station planned for Jeddah will receive information in the form of images from TIROS-N, the satellite orbiting the poles. These images cover an area extending from northern Europe to the Middle East and South Africa.

Remote sensing has also found a useful niche in the Middle East. The lead here is provided by Egypt. Its Remote Sensing Centre (RSC) has proved the value of remote sensing beyond doubt and has used the Landsat series of satellites for resource analysis at a very early stage and on a large scale. Started in 1971 as a cooperative venture between the then Egyptian Academy for Scientific Research, Oklahoma State University, and the United States National Science Foundation, the RSC has surveyed about 500,000 km^2 – plus 165,000 km^2 in southern Sudan, and developed highly accurate specialist maps from the information received.

However, despite the fact that Landsat ground receiving stations are relatively cheap, with the exception of Egypt no other country in the Middle East has plans to set up Landsat stations. Although Saudi Arabia and Kuwait have been approached, so far they have bought data second-hand from the Earth Resources Observation System (EROS) data centre in the United States. This is partly because of their lack of appropriately qualified manpower and the lengthy training necessary to produce such staff. But satellite imagery is an important technology for the Middle East. In areas suffering from desertification, for example, satellite monitoring can assess existing ecological and resource conditions, detect physical indicators of desertification and observe changes, either improvements or further deterioration. Some of these indicators, such as rainfall trends, grazing patterns in the vicinity of water holes, receding water levels in wells, changes in sediment load in streams, lakes and reservoirs and the transition of cultivated land areas into unsuitable dryland, can be observed on Landsat imagery; others, such as higher than normal temperatures and the frequency of dust storms, can be observed on the United States National Oceanographic and Atmospheric Administration's Synchronous Meteorological Satellite (SMS) satellite imagery. Still other indicators of desertification can be monitored on the ground by unattended data platforms, which transmit the data via satellite to receiving stations.

That Egypt can provide, and to some extent has provided, both expertise and manpower for the entire Arab world in this important technology is recognized by other countries in the area. Indeed, in 1976, CASTARAB adopted a recommendation to support RSC so that it could become a regional Arab centre. The Arab Fund for Economic Development in Kuwait and the Union for Arab Scientific Research Councils in Baghdad prepared feasibility studies for the implementation of the recommendation. However, the Arab boycott of Egypt after the Camp David accords and its subsequent suspension from the Arab League has prevented any further progress.

By the end of 1984, the Middle East is likely to have its own satellite – ARABSAT, an Arab-owned satellite communication system that will serve the countries of the Arab League covering the whole of North Africa and the Middle East. The Arab Satellite Communications Organization (ARABSAT) plans to develop three satellites: two to be launched in geostationary orbit 36,000 km above the equator, the first as a primary and the second as back-up, and the third to be stored for launching in case of emergency. The satellites, with a projected seven-year life span, will provide 8,000 telephone circuits, seven international circuits, and a community television broadcast channel. Ground stations are to be built in each of the twenty-one participating countries. The primary control station will be in Saudi Arabia, with a second to be set up in an as yet undecided Arab country. The aim of the ARABSAT system is substantially to improve, even to revolutionize, telephone, telex and data transmission in the Middle East. The community television broadcast service will require smaller ground stations of up to 3 m diameter, with simple receivers. The low cost of these ground stations means that they would be widely distributed throughout the Arab world. Thus, the entire ARABSAT system will comprise a complete regional satellite communications system of a kind that is likely to become widely in demand in the near future in other parts of the world.

The only country in the region with a programme for developing an indigenous capability in satellite technology is Pakistan. Since the launch of Pakistan's first rocket, Rehbar, in 1962, the country has launched some 150 experimental rockets. These rockets were launched with the aid of foreign space agencies; but now the Pakistan Space and Upper Atmosphere Research Commission (SUPARCO) has launched an ambitious programme designed to take Pakistan towards self-sufficiency in satellite technology. Initially a number of ground stations will be set up. Two laboratories, in Karachi and Islamabad, already have ground stations which are working on forecasting floods, collecting statistics on crop patterns, and predicting radio interference and other ionospheric problems. However, as Pakistan's satellite programme is in an embryonic stage, there is a long way to go before self-sufficiency can be claimed.

Information Science and International Centres

Microtechnology and satellites have also played a major role in building information centres in Saudi Arabia. The Saudi Arabian National Centre for Science and Technology (SANCST) has placed almost every American data base within easy reach of the Saudi researcher. The on-line information retrieval facilities at the SANCST office in Riyadh are linked by a satellite to the telecommunication networks in the United States and, hence, to computers and their stored data bases. SANCST has also developed on-line facilities to provide quick access to information about science and technology activities in Saudi Arabia. Universities in Saudi Arabia have well-developed and stocked libraries, fully automated or on their way to automation. Some Saudi libraries produce specialized information services. The International Airports Project Library, for example, located in Jeddah's King Abdul Aziz International Airport, produces the *International Airports Projects Index* and airports periodicals listings. Most Saudi research institutes publish their own journals: perhaps the most respected among these are the *Bulletin of the Institute of Applied Geology* of the King Abdul Aziz University and the *Arabian Journal of Science and Technology*, published quarterly by the University of Petroleum and Minerals.

Had the Iranian revolution not intervened, the Iran Documentation Centre (IRANDOC) at the Institute for Research and Planning in Science and Education, Tehran, would have followed developments very similar to those of the information unit at SANCST. It had started developing an information retrieval system and publishing an abstract journal of Iranian science and technology and union lists of periodicals in various libraries in Iran. However, the revolutionary government has stopped the budget of IRANDOC and most of the staff have now dispersed. The institution is at a standstill, and its future is uncertain. However, the Iranian Centre for Scientific and Industrial Research has announced its intention to restart documentation and publication activities.

The Iraqi Scientific Documentation Centre (ISDC) has not developed as rapidly as Saudi and Iranian efforts. Nevertheless, it has a modern scientific and technical library which does meet the needs of Iraqi scientists. Founded in 1972, ISDC has developed largely with the technical assistance of the United Nations Development Programme. It will undoubtedly be expanded and developed somewhat along the lines of SANCST's information service.

At the other end of the spectrum from SANCST, with a very meagre budget and virtually no computer facilities, is TURDOC which operates under the Scientific and Technical Research Council of Turkey. However, as an information organization, it is a highly efficient and organized, not to say productive, institution. TURDOC was established in 1966 and now has a staff of fifty who undertake literature searches, and prepare bibliographies and technical evaluative reports for scientists and technologists throughout Turkey. Much of the communication between TURDOC and its users is by correspondence; but telephones and personal visits are also used. The experience and expertise of TURDOC can be judged by the fact that it has developed an invisible college of experts throughout Turkey who are called upon regularly to answer enquiries from industry and specialist organizations. One of its major functions is to act as a switchboard, connecting users with documents, experts with experts, and industry with researchers. TURDOC supplies over 300,000 copies of documents annually and has published the union catalogues of scientific and technical periodicals in various libraries in Ankara and Istanbul. These catalogues are updated regularly. TURDOC's major publications are the *Current Titles in Turkish Science* and *International Meetings on Science and Technology*, both of which are published quarterly.

Egypt's National Information and Documentation Centre (NIDOC), located at the main laboratories of the National Research Centre in Cairo and established with the aid of UNESCO, has an extensive technical library. It carries out literature searches and prepares bibliographies, but, on the whole, it is a very passive and somewhat antiquated documentation centre. From 1955 to 1969 it published the *Documentation Bulletin* and in 1973, in association with ALECSO, the Association of Arab Universities and UNESCO, it began the publication of the much needed *Arab Science Abstracts*. However, its publication was suspended in 1975 since when the services of the NIDC to the Egyptian scientific community seem to have degenerated. Considering the scientific and technological infrastructure of Egypt, the output of Egyptian scientists, the number of local journals and the qualified information scientists and technical librarians in Egypt, the country could be expected to have a more professional and active national information centre and to provide a lead in information science to the region.

The Pakistan Scientific and Technological Information Centre (PASTIC), formerly PANSDOC, is suffering from similar inactivity and inefficiency. It too was established with the help of UNESCO in 1956; and since then has gone through a number of expansions and changes. Originally under the Pakistan Council for Scientific and Industrial Research, it is now under the Pakistan Science Foundation. It publishes *Pakistan Science Abstract* but provides very few services to the science community in Pakistan. At present it is temporarily located in a building in Islamabad, near the offices of the Pakistan Science Foundation. Under a new plan, it will be moved to the campus of Quaid-i-Azam University on the outskirts of Islamabad and its services will be expanded to include a National Science Reference Library and a Scientific and Technological Information Transfer Unit. It will also acquire a computer and should be able to provide on-line facilities. At present the Pakistan Science Foundation is debating whether to have a centralized National Science Reference Library or a decentralized network of cooperating technical libraries. The PASTIC improvements will take an estimated five years and are being carried out with the assistance of UNDP and Canada's International Development Research Centre.

The above examples notwithstanding, the state of affairs regarding the generation and utilization of specialized scientific and technical information in the Middle East is not a happy one. The observations made by Anees and Athar in this regard are pertinent:

1. Most national information services in the region are unaware of the real needs of their users and suffer from inadequate facilities for information processing.
2. National accession of scientific journals, books, monographs, conference proceedings and related materials from the Muslim world and Western countries involved long delay, which, in turn, have a great impact on the usefulness of information for the users.
3. High postal and tariff charges, foreign exchange muddles, stringent copyright regulations and poor postal services make the timely accession of primary and secondary scientific literature a nightmare for most of the countries in the region.
4. Scientific information services such as abstracting and indexing bibliographies, translations, state-of-the-art reviews and selective dissemination of information (SDI) are services which are not normally provided by national information centres in the Middle East; and where such services are provided they are usually of poor quality.

All this means that information science has a long way to go in the region. As scientific and technological activity increases, countries such as Algeria, Morocco, Tunisia, Syria, Iraq and Egypt will be forced to expand and improve their science information facilities. With the arrival of cheap microtechnology and the availability of satellite communications in the area, information and library facilities may develop quite rapidly. Certainly, this vital sector of scientific enterprise has been ignored far too long by the countries of the Middle East. The indigenous development of science and technology in the region cannot be conceived without the establishment of active and up-to-date national information centres in the area.

International centres of excellence, rather like information centres, have also been largely ignored in the Middle East until very recently. Thanks to the efforts of the Nobel-Laureate Abdus Salam there is now considerable interest in establishing such centres throughout the region. These institutions, it is argued, would maintain high research standards, be manned by an international cadre of research scientists, and tackle basic and applied problems common to the area.

A few such centres already exist in the Middle East. The Arab Centre for the Study of Arid Zones (ACAZ) located near Damascus, for example, was founded in 1971 and is run with the participation of fourteen countries. It undertakes a whole spectrum of arid zone research including investigations on water and pasture land, animal husbandry and desertification. There are also the Specialized Institute for Engineering Industries and the Regional Palm and Date Research Centre, both located in Baghdad; and the Regional Building Research Centre of the Royal Scientific Society of Jordan. But Salam wants such centres to proliferate as the Middle East has numerous problems – irrigation, schistosomiasis, marine pollution, to mention just three – which need the joint effort of scientists in the region.

When arguing for such centres of excellence, Salam often relates a story to show that the idea has deep roots in the history of Islamic science. He first recalled the story in his 1979 Nobel Lecture, and since then it has been published in a number of journals. Salam relates:

Seven hundred and sixty years ago, a young Scotsman left his native glens to travel south to Toledo in Spain. His name was Michael, his goal to live and work at the Arab Universities of Toledo and Cordova, where the greatest of mediaeval Jewish scholars, Musa bin Maimoun, had taught a generation before.

Michael reached Toledo in AD 1217. Once in Toledo, Michael formed the ambitious project of introducing Aristotle to Latin Europe, translating not from the original Greek, which he did not know, but from the Arabic translation then taught in Spain. From Toledo, Michael travelled to Sicily, to the Court of Emperor Frederick II.

Visiting the medical school at Salerno, which had been given a Royal Charter by Frederick of Sicily in 1231, Michael the Scot met the Danish physician, Henrik Harpestraeng – later to become Court Physician of King Eric IV Waldemarssön. Henrick the Physician had come to Salerno to compose his treatise on blood-letting and surgery. Henrik's sources were the medical canons of the great clinicians of Islam, Al-Razi and Avicenna, which only Michael the Scot could translate for him.

Toledo's and Salerno's schools, representing as they did the finest synthesis of Arabic, Greek, Latin and Hebrew scholarship, were some of the most memorable of international assays in scientific collaboration. To Toledo and Salerno came scholars not only from the rich countries of the East, like Syria, Egypt, Iran and Afghanistan, but also from developing lands of the West like Scotland and Scandinavia. Then, as now, there were obstacles to this international scientific concourse, with an economic and intellectual disparity between different parts of the world. Men like Michael the Scot or Henrik Harpestraeng the Dane, were singularities. They did not represent any flourishing schools of research in their own countries. With all the best will in the world their teachers at Toledo and Salerno doubted the wisdom and value of training them for advanced scientific research. At least one of his masters counselled young Michael the Scot to go back to clipping sheep and to the weaving of woollen cloths.

In respect of this cycle of scientific disparity, perhaps I can be more quantitative. George Sarton, in his monumental five-volume History of Science chose to divide his story of achievement in sciences into ages, each age lasting half a century. With each half century he associated one central figure. Thus 450–400 BC Sarton calls the Age of Plato; this is followed by half centuries of Aristotle, of Euclid, of Archimedes and so on. From AD 600 to 650 is the Chinese half century of Hsiian Tsang, from AD 650 to 700 that of I-Ching, and then from AD 750 to 1100 – 350 years continuously – it is the unbroken succession of the Ages of Jabir, Khwarizmi, Razi, Masudi, Wafa, Biruni and Avicenna, and then Omar Khayam – Arabs, Turks, Afghans and Persians – men belonging to the culture of Islam. After 1100 appear the first Western names; Gerard of Cremona, Roger Bacon, Jacob Anatoli – but the honours are still shared with the names of the Spanish Ibn-Rushd (Averroes), with Tusi and Ibn-Nafis – the man who anticipated Harvey's theory of circulation of blood. No Sarton has yet chronicled the history of scientific creativity among the pre-Spanish Incas, Mayas, and Aztecs, with their invention of the zero, of the calendars of the moon and Venus and of their diverse pharmacological discoveries, including quinine, but the outline of the story is the same – one of undoubted superiority to the Western contemporary correlates.

After 1350, however, the developing world loses out except for the occasional flash of scientific brilliance, like that at the Court of Ulugh Beg – the grandson of Timurlane, in Samarkand around AD 1400; or of Maharaja Jai Singh of Jaipur in 1720 – who corrected the serious errors of the then Western tables of eclipses of the sun and the moon by as much as six minutes of arc. As it was, Jai Singh's techniques were surpassed soon after with the development of the telescope in Europe. As a contemporary Indian chronicler wrote: 'With him on the funeral pyre, expired also all science in the East.' And this brings us to this century when the cycle begun by Michael the Scot turns full circle. . . .

Salam argues that places such as Toledo and Salerno, the first *Bait-ul-Hikmas* (Advanced Institutes for Sciences) 'where one can light a candle from a candle', are essential for a resurgence of science in the Muslim world. Most of the Third World is marginalized from science and technology because the scientists in the developing countries are isolated and do not have an adequate opportunity to expand their theoretical and experimental knowledge; the scientific communities to which they belong are sub-critical in size and as such they are not part of international science. Without internationalization, science in the Third World cannot flourish. Such centres guarantee keeping abreast of new ideas and transfer of science by the men who created it when they come to teach at these centres. Moreover, almost every developing country has a problem which needs international scientific expertise – and these centres would be the ideal institutional mould to tackle these problems.

The model for such centres of excellence is the International Centre for Theoretical Physics (ICTP) in Trieste, Italy, which Salam created himself in 1964. ICTP is a unique institution: it is located in a resort area, administered jointly by UNESCO and the International Atomic Energy Agency (IAEA); it deals with nearly all disciplines in contemporary theoretical physics; attempts in particular to aid physicists working in developing countries; and maintains continuing contact with a network representing a major portion of the world physics community. Every year some 1,200 physicists, half from ninety developing countries, participate in research workshops and extended research colleges held at the ICTP. The centre has pioneered an associateship scheme which guarantees that top physicists in developing countries can come to the centre for a period ranging from six weeks to three months, three times in six years, to work in a stimulating environment of their peers, and to return to their teaching and research positions. ICTP offers seventy such associateships, and has a network of fifty-two institutes of physics in developing countries federated with it. Indeed, ICTP is sustaining physics communities in such countries as Pakistan, Egypt and Jordan and without it physicists in these countries would lose touch with international developments in their disciplines.

Salam wants centres similar to ICTP for other disciplines throughout the Muslim world. Since 1979, he has been to almost every Muslim country with this message. And judging from the response to the first-ever meeting on 'Science Transfer and International Centres', held in Trieste in September 1981, he has achieved considerable success. A number of international centres are now planned for the Middle East; a few have already started functioning.

The largest of these centres will be the Saudi Energy Research Centre which will probably be located in Riyadh. This is planned as a 'Regional Centre of Excellence for Basic Energy Research', which will be a key component of the Saudi technological infrastructure, and as a major channel for 'creative technology transfer' it will provide a scientific base for high technology innovation industries in Saudi Arabia. The US$3 billion centre is expected to have a leading edge in machinery and instrumentation, which will include accelerators and reactors, and is planned to contain the following major facilities: a solar laboratory, a synchrotron laboratory, a heavy-ion acceleration laboratory, a radiopharmaceutical laboratory, a material science laboratory, a neutronless fusion laboratory, and a neutron source laboratory. While the major fraction of the scientists and staff of the centre will be Saudi, it is expected that there will be a strong representation from internationally known energy experts and that a large part of the resources will be devoted to scientists from developing countries.

In contrast, Pakistan plans to set up three centres of excellence of more modest size. A Centre for Basic Sciences was opened in April 1981. The centre promotes basic sciences in universities and provides links for national and international collaboration. It also disseminates research results through national and international forums. An International Centre for Science, Technology and Development is planned for Karachi. The first phase in the evolution of this centre will be based on a capital investment of US$2 million and an annual cost of about US$200,000, which will produce facilities for pure and theoretical research. The second phase envisages the establishment of a solid-state laboratory, including workshop facilities for an estimated cost of US$2 million. A third centre, the Research Centre on Earth Sciences, is at a very early stage of planning.

An Arab Centre for Systems Analysis and Research is planned by Jordan. The main objective of the centre is to identify the myriad problem areas in the Middle East and hence to formulate a research strategy for the region. The centre will also work on establishing an Arab scientific and technical information network.

Several other centres of excellence are in the making. A centre for the study of the problems related to the geographical and ecological situation of Bahrain (oil, water) is planned by Bahrain; an International Centre for Basic Research devoted to the study of desertification is planned by Sudan; Tunisia proposes to set up an International Centre for Ophthalmology; and OAPEC is promoting an Arab Solar Energy Centre. Most of these centres are in the early stages of planning, but they provide a good indication that science research centres run internationally, or nationally with a substantial component of international dimensions, in experimental and theoretical sciences, and are likely to mushroom in the Middle East in the near future.

Finally, there is the proposal for setting up an Arab Centre for the Transfer and Development of Technology. The proposal has been made by the United Nations Conference on Trade and Development (UNCTAD) in conjunction with the United Nations Economic Commission for Western Asia (ECWA). These organizations have noted that while certain dimensions of technological planning are taken care of by national research and development institutions or technical ministries, none of the Middle East countries possesses the institutional machinery for identifying technological needs or for drawing up technological policies. The proposed centre will not only identify technological needs of the region and help Middle East states formulate technology policies, but will also promote technological cooperation in the region, implement new norms and standards in implementing technology transactions, promote collective bargaining with foreign technology suppliers, and reduce duplication of research of development through greater specialization at regional level. The ECWA considers the main objectives of the centre to be to:

1. Assist countries of the region in strengthening their technological capability so that they are increasingly able to promote indigenous technological developments.
2. Improve the terms and conditions governing technology transfer.
3. Promote a greater exchange of technology with the region.
4. Assist the industrialization process of the region through advice on appropriate policies on the choice and development of technology.

5. Promote regional integration through the harmonization of technology policies in the region.
6. Facilitate access to information and technology.
7. Provide advice and technical assistance on policy issues.
8. Promote research and development on a collective basis and within individual countries.

ECWA has already initiated preparatory work on the establishment of the centre – it now remains for the Arab countries to take the proposal and turn it into a reality.

Regional Cooperation

The setting up of a number of international centres of excellence would provide a boost for scientific and technological cooperation among the countries of the Middle East. Up to now, countries in the region have tended to ignore their neighbours and to develop bilateral cooperation programmes with the United States, West Germany, France, the United Kingdom, and Sweden. However, with the emergence of regional organizations such as IFSTAD and CASTARAB, scientific cooperation between the countries of the region will increase considerably in the years ahead.

Towards the end of the 1970s, regional cooperation in the Middle East suffered two setbacks. The first was the disintegration of the tripartite alliance for Regional Cooperation for Development (RCD) between Pakistan, Turkey and Iran. The second was the expulsion of Egypt from the Arab League and the consequent move of ALECSO from Cairo to Tunis.

Established in 1964, RCD was the first significant alliance for regional cooperation between developing countries. The alliance grew out of the traditional relationship between Pakistan, Iran, and Turkey. While RCD did not fulfil all its early expectations, it did achieve moderate success in improving communications and technical cooperation between its members, and up to the beginning of 1980 it had some fifty joint industrial projects under development. It was responsible for developing the science information organization of the three countries – TURDOC, IRANDOC and PANSDOC (PASTIC), all developed under an RCD scheme – and for introducing and pursuing the ideas of appropriate technology. What was wrong with RCD was that it was short on funds and commitment from the political leaders of the member states, and, after the coming of the revolutionary government, Iran had the organization dissolved early in 1981, despite reluctance on the part of Pakistan and Turkey.

Until very recently, ALECSO was the major organization working to promote regional scientific cooperation in the Middle East. The Arab League's boycott of Egypt, following the Camp David accord, forced ALECSO to move its headquarters from Cairo to Tunis. The move hindered the work of the organization, with many projects being delayed for several years, and valuable documents being lost. Egypt's reaction to the expulsion was to freeze ALECSO's assets in Cairo and to withhold exit permits for Egyptian scientists, then constituting the bulk of ALECSO's manpower, who wanted to move with the organization to Tunis.

Since early 1980, when it moved to Tunis, ALECSO has been looking for new consultants and consolidating its regional programmes, such as the study on the environmental condition of the Palestinian refugee camps, monitoring desertification in North Africa and environmental considerations of industrial developments in the Middle East. Moreover, adjusting to Tunisia, a country where science and technology are minimal, after several years in the rich scientific environment of Egypt, has not been easy for ALECSO. It will be some years before ALECSO once again becomes a major instrument of regional cooperation in the Middle East.

However, ALECSO will soon receive strong backing from CASTARAB and IFSTAD. CASTARAB is already committed to setting up an Arab Fund for Scientific and Technological Research, with an initial capital of US$500 million, which would promote regional scientific and technological resources. IFSTAD, too, to a certain extent, would be a funding agency; but its main function would be to act as a catalyst for regional cooperation. IFSTAD's director, Ali Kettani, a noted Arab solar energy expert, is passionately committed to regional cooperation and one of his declared policy goals is to work towards producing a joint science policy for the member states of the Organization of Islamic Conferences. Also on IFSTAD's agenda is establishing a number of regional technical universities, although plans for this project have yet to be worked out in detail.

One regional university has already started functioning. The University of the Gulf in Abu Dhabi started functioning in 1980. The university is the brainchild of the Arab Bureau of Education for the Gulf States, which was formed in 1975 after the first Conference of the Ministers of Education of the Gulf States, held in Riyadh in October 1975. It has since then progressed through four conferences of education ministers and is now emerging as a leading regional organization. The Riyadh-based bureau is working to set up an Arab Centre for Education Research and to develop a unified curriculum for higher education in the Gulf states. Its prime objective is the renewal of a distinctly Arab and Islamic system of education, including Islamic models of curricula and methodology of education, which would best serve the region.

Scientific cooperation in the Middle East is also receiving considerable support from various Arab funds which have developed over the last ten years. The oldest and best-known of the Arab aid agencies is the Kuwait Fund for Arab Economic Development, which was established in 1961, on the last day of Kuwait's first year of independence. Since then seven other aid agencies have emerged: the Saudi Fund for Development, the Arab Fund for Economic and Social Development, the Arab Bank for Economic Development in Africa, the Islamic Development Bank, the OPEC Special Fund, and the Iraqi Fund for External Development. All back scientific and technological projects with the emphasis on development. However, it is the Arab Fund for Economic and Social Development which has been most active in promoting regional scientific and technological cooperation. It has been actively seeking projects and identifying key schemes. It therefore steers Arab scientific and technological developments to some extent, backing, in the process, a number of bold and imaginative ideas. These include plans to turn the Sudan into the 'bread basket' of the Middle East, studying the Arab brain drain and manpower, establishing pan-Arab computerized airline information, and developing an Arab data bank on natural resources using information from Landsat satellites. Indeed, it has already been acting as an Arab fund for science and technology, an argument that some Arab ministers responsible for science and technology have used against pushing ahead with the CASTARAB proposal for establishing an Arab Fund for Scientific and Technological Research. But there is no conflict of interests between the two funds: one is devoted to promoting development in the region and thus devotes some of its resources to promoting scientific cooperation, while the other is completely geared to backing scientific and technological research. Moreover, there are plenty of projects, particularly in capital poor states, that need urgent funding. The more diverse the source of funds the better chance science and technological projects in these countries have of being implemented.

The regional isolation of Egypt has led to schemes for scientific cooperation between Egypt and Israel. A small number of scientists in Egypt have been arguing that there are many advantages in undertaking joint projects as Israelis have certain expertise in research areas that are important to Egypt. One of the first collaboration projects is the proposal to build a 28 mV cyclotron at an estimated cost of US$4 million at the University of Cairo. The cyclotron, financed with the help of West Germany, will be used for the study of heavy ion interaction by both Egyptians and Israeli scientists. Similar projects on electronics, solid state physics and agriculture are being discussed. On the Israeli side, a US$100 million scheme to establish a desert research institute designed to benefit both Israel and Egypt is being proposed. Israel has also placed Haifa Technicon's research laboratories and testing facilities at the disposal of Egyptian post-graduate students.

In addition to these proposals, there are two other areas where Israel is seeking Egyptian cooperation. There is the long-standing proposal for co-operation in the Sinai peninsula. Since the 1967 war, the Israeli scientists have done extensive research on the peninsula, the results of which have now been handed over to the Egyptian scientists. From the time of President Eisenhower, a number of American presidents have suggested that joint Egyptian–Israeli power stations and desalination plants should be established in the Sinai. There is even a detailed scheme, prepared by the Oakridge National Laboratory, on how this project can be realized. The scheme envisages the installation of two reactors with a combined output of 1,000 MW to provide power for Egyptian and Israeli industries and producing enough desalinated water to irrigate 300,000 acres of Egyptian land and the Negev Desert.

Israel would like to take advantage of the Egyptian lead in remote sensing and has tried to persuade Egypt to develop a collaboration programme and turn its RSC into a regional centre with the collaboration of 'moderate' Arab states. The main force behind this proposal is the United States Agency for International Development (AID). AID argues that a regional centre in Cairo, established early in the normalization process between the two countries, would make a valuable contribution to the development of remote sensing in the region. AID has also tried to persuade Sudan and Tunisia, where the agency is developing remote sensing capabilities, to participate in the venture. But so far the proposal has not generated enough interest in Egypt, Sudan and Tunisia to be realized.

Egyptian–Israeli cooperation notwithstanding, scientific and technological collaboration between the Middle East states will certainly increase in the years ahead. Two of the most important regional organizations, CASTARAB and IFSTAD, taking several years to mature, have yet to make their impact on the region. Once CASTARAB and IFSTAD begin to realize their goals and a few of the planned regional centres of excellence materialize, regional cooperation in the Middle East will take on a new significance.

Scientific and Technological Assistance

Cooperation between capital-poor states of the Middle East and the industrialized countries takes the form of scientific and technological assistance. By far the biggest donors to the region are the United States and West Germany. Overall, French aid to the Third World is greater than West Germany, but the Middle East French aid is limited to former colonies – Morocco and Tunisia.

The bulk of American aid to the Middle East goes to Egypt and Israel. In 1981, Israel received US$810 million in aid from the United States. Some US$785 million of this was given as hard cash to assist Israel's economic stability. The remaining US$25 million was project-tied. In contrast, all of the US$717 million granted to Egypt in 1981 was project-tied. The aid figures for Jordan, Lebanon, Palestine, Morocco and Oman are virtually insignificant.

AID, the main arm of the American government for dispensing foreign assistance, administers two kinds of programmes – 'Development Assistance' and 'Security Supporting Assistance'. In cooperation with the Department of Agriculture, AID also implements Public Law 480 (commonly known as PL 480) funds, which relate to the sale of food on concessionary terms, the donation of agricultural commodities, and the provision of food under the Food for Development Programme. The Development Assistance Programme is focused on four critical areas: food, nutrition and rural development; population planning and health; education and human resources development; and technical assistance, energy, reconstruction and selected development programmes. Security Supporting Assistance is more politically oriented, and almost half of AID's budget is devoted to security supporting assistance.

In Egypt, AID's declared strategy is to support Egyptian efforts to 'achieve stable economic growth and improve the quality of life for its people'. To realize this goal, AID is building and expanding its infrastructure, industry (with special emphasis on the private sector) and agricultural production. In industry, AID is assisting Egypt to complete unfinished industrial projects, to expand its private sector through credit programmes and technical assistance, and to establish new industries which reduce imports or offer export potential. In agriculture, AID is attempting to increase production through land reclamation techniques, analysis of policy constraints, provision of irrigation and water drainage facilities and support of fertilizer production. There are over ninety AID projects in Egypt, ranging from the efforts to sort out the sewage of Alexandria and initiate family planning programmes, and the rehabilitation of the Mahalla textile plant and the Mahdi cement plant, to a complete overhaul of the scientific infrastructure of the country. Indeed, the scientific and technological infrastructure of Egypt is largely tied to AID assistance and would suffer considerably if that were withdrawn. For example, with the exception of a number of projects receiving aid from West Germany, almost all research projects at Cairo's National Research Centre, the largest research institution in the Middle East, are supported through PL 480.

Morever, most AID projects in Egypt are big, conspicuous technology projects which involve American companies transferring technology. For example, AID is financing the construction of a 900 MW thermal power generation plant in Shoubrah El-Kheima. The United States 'input' is major electrical equipment and services supplied by Overseas Bechtel, Inc. When the plant is fully operational, Bechtel will continue to hold a maintenance and services contract. There are similar projects for flat glass production, treatment of Cairo's sewage, poultry development, and irrigation management. There are, in addition, a number of planning projects that would further tie Egypt's development to the United States. The scheme for the development of complete physical infrastructures at the Cairo, Alexandria and Port Said Free Zones are good examples of this.

In 1982, Pakistan will join Egypt and Israel in receiving similar amounts of Security Supporting Assistance. Pakistan will receive US$3 billion in United States aid spread over five years: US$400 million a year in military sales credit and US$200 million a year in economic and technical assistance. Pakistan has had an aid relationship with the United States since 1952. Up to 1965, Pakistan was considered a model example of how American aid could lead to growth and development, but, between 1965 and 1978, United States aid to Pakistan was interrupted several times for political considerations. The present US$200 million economic and technological assistance is mostly project-tied, with projects ranging from water management and agricultural research to primary health care and population planning.

Besides AID, there are also a number of other government agencies that provide technical assistance to Middle East countries. The Board on Science and Technology for International Development (BOSTID), for example, has, over the past fifteen years, organized seminars and conferences in certain Middle East countries on issues of specific interest. There is also the National Science Foundation (NSF), which runs cooperative programmes, most of which are cooperative endeavours with the oil-rich states, such as the programmes under the Saudi–United States Economic Commission.

West German aid to the Middle East states is more equally distributed between Egypt, Tunisia, Sudan and the poorer nations of the Maghrib. Egypt's most recent acquisition from West Germany is the Theodor Bilharz Institute, built in the memory of the German scientist, Theodor Bilharz, who discovered the schistosoma worm in Egypt in 1852. The German Agency for Technical Cooperation (DSE) also makes regular awards to the National Research Centre at Cairo for such projects as solar powered desalination, solar cooling and flat plate power plants, and the production of protein from algae. Most of these awards are untied, cash grants.

DSE also spends considerable resources in promoting science education in the Middle East either directly or through conferences and seminars and training schemes. West Germans are particularly keen to check the over-emphasis placed on theory in the Middle East universities and are backing projects in Egypt, Tunisia, Turkey and Sudan, which emphasize experimentation and self-discovery in both universities and secondary schools.

All this does not mean that German aid is not concentrating on high technology. Desalination, solar energy and nuclear power are the main areas of West German technical assistance to the Middle East. Indeed, West Germany is the only country in Europe to have an Association for the Promotion of Seawater Desalination, a federation of twenty-two companies actively working on desalination research and development, which promotes joint ventures between West German industry and Middle Eastern governments. One of the association's major successes is the development of a number of membrane technologies – reverse osmosis, electrodialysis – for the production of fresh water from sea water, in cooperation with Egypt and Jordan. Dornier-System, an engineering firm based in Friedrichshafen, has developed a solar desalination system which has two main design elements, a solar collector and a distiller. The system derives from the solar drinking-water project initiated by the Royal Scientific Society of Jordan in conjunction with the German Ministry of Economic Cooperation. Many West German companies are working on similar desalination and solar technologies which are tied up via the German Ministry of Economic Cooperation as technical aid projects. West Germany is also providing nuclear technology to Egypt and Turkey.

German non-governmental organizations are promoting more enlightened projects in the Middle East. The Bremen Overseas Research and Development Association (BORDA), for example, runs several self-help projects in Tunisia and Sudan. In one project in Sudan, BORDA is helping to improve production in tanneries and preserve traditional craftsmanship. Previous attempts by other organizations to improve production in the industry through modernization of the tanneries in Khartoum, had resulted in an increase in price of locally produced leather goods and a sharp decline in traditional leather crafts. Moreover the newly modernized tanneries could not compete with imported leather and the local leather industry

Table 1.6 The use of transfer technology channels in the Middle East

Country	Public sector	Private sector	Research and development	Foreign consultants	Foreign aid	Patents	Movement of cadre	Information
Algeria	+	−		+			+	
Iraq	+	−	+	+	−	−	−	−
Jordan	−	+	−	+	+	−		−
Kuwait		+	−	+	−		+	−
Lebanon		+		−	−	−		−
Oman	+	+	−	+	+		+	
Pakistan		−		−	+	−	+	
Qatar	+	+	−	+	−		+	
Saudi Arabia	+	−			+	−	+	
Syria	+	−	−	+	+			
Turkey	+	−		+	+		+	
United Arab Emirates		+	−	+	−		+	
Yemen Arab Republic	−	−		+	+		+	

+ Important channel.

− Channel playing minor role.

Source: adapted from ECWA, 'The Status of Science and Technology in the Western Asia Region', in Zahlan, A. B. (ed.), *Technology Transfer and Change in the Arab World* (1978).

was almost destroyed. BORDA's approach is based on finding methods of increasing the production by the traditional craftsmen while preserving their craft. In another project near Khartoum, BORDA is working to upgrade traditional waterwheels and hydraulic rams so that they can operate lathes and saws and be put to better use in irrigation. The essential point is that BORDA is not promoting German technology. It is either developing widely-used traditional technology, or promoting in one Third World country a particular technology developed in another. Thus BORDA has introduced into Sudan, Tunisia and Mali biogas techniques and put these countries' scientists in touch with each other. Having set up a project BORDA leaves the local manpower to run the scheme.

Besides the United States and West Germany, the poor Middle East countries do not receive much scientific and technical aid from other industrialized countries. None of the countries in the region, for example, receives 10 per cent or more of its foreign assistance from Canada, one of the most favoured donor countries in the Third World. Before 1976, Pakistan was among the top five recipients of Canadian aid; however, after the withdrawal of Canada's support for the Karachi nuclear power plant, Canadian aid to Pakistan was terminated. Aid from Britain, Sweden and the Netherlands to the region is insignificant.

The region, however, does receive considerable assistance from various United Nations organizations. UNESCO, for example, has been implementing a number of regional projects in the Middle East. The Arab Chemical Research Project aims to establish an Arab network of chemical research to promote the development of regional and national infrastructures in chemical sciences and the Regional Exchange of Engineering Professors scheme promotes regional cooperation in the education and training of engineers. UNESCO, of course, has also played a major part in implementing the follow-up programme to the historic 1976 CASTARAB meeting and has been instrumental in starting the discussions on an 'Arab Scientific Plan of Action' and the formation of the Arab Fund for Scientific and Technological Research.

The European Economic Community (EEC) also has an initiative to provide scientific and technical assistance to the region. The so-called 'Euro-Arab Dialogue' is aimed at achieving understanding, and economic, scientific, and technological cooperation between the EEC and the Arab world. Under the umbrella of the dialogue, four projects have been under discussion for several years: the creation of a Euro–Arab centre for the transfer of technology, a feasibility study for an Arab institute on sea-water desalination, a feasibility study for a marine science infrastructure in the Red Sea and the Gulf of Aden, and a common Euro–Arab policy on the peaceful uses of atomic energy. However, because of the rift in the Arab world and the EEC, these projects are unlikely to materialize; indeed, the whole future of the forum itself is in doubt.

Future Trends

Both capital-rich and capital-poor countries of the Middle East will continue to rely on foreign assistance for decades to come. In some cases, as pointed out earlier, the technological infrastructure developed is so interlinked with foreign assistance that it would collapse without continuous aid. The oil-rich Arab states, who pay for their technological assistance with hard cash, are importing technology at a rate that is truly phenomenal. In less than a decade, vast programmes for urban development, construction of indus-trial complexes, transport and communication facilities have changed the physical environment of Saudi Arabia, Kuwait, Libya, Iraq and Algeria. And these transformations have brought with them the inevitable societal dislocations. The warnings of A. B. Zahlan is rather ominous: 'nations that import turnkey technologies may in time become turnkey states with turn-key cultures'.

It is certain that some technologies will continue to be imported on a mass scale. The advent of a computer terminal capable of generating the Arabic language with all of the 140 potential word shapes and 13 possible accents makes the computer more accessible to the region. It also means that imports of microelectronic goods and automatic systems will increase considerably and that distributed intelligence in terminals, computers, or the family television set, could be linked to European and American net-works, thus bringing the West much closer to Middle East society.

Besides microtechnology, the next big wave of imported technologies is likely to be irrigation technologies, pollution monitoring technologies and satellite technologies, and, of course, nuclear technology. By the end of the 1980s, Pakistan will become a major supplier of nuclear technology to the Middle East; it will also provide the only uranium enrichment facility in the region. Given the nuclear plans of Egypt, Iraq, Libya, Turkey, Syria and Saudi Arabia, and the conspicuous lack of anti-nuclear move-ments in these countries, nuclear proliferation is a strong possibility for the region.

Consequently, many of the Middle East environmental problems as well as social and cultural problems, which are a direct product of the pace of development and rate of change, will be aggravated. Problems such as the threat to traditional values, social tension and disruption, increase in mental illness, the alienation derived from a technology that does not integrate with the environment, and the accumulation of wealth and power in fewer and fewer hands will tend to solidify and multiply as technology transfer continues. It has been argued that these very problems were the root cause of the Iranian revolution; and that technology was transplanted into Iran with too little consideration for the cultural values of the country. Iran has also suffered unfavourable experiences in regard to Western multinational companies being established in the country or undertaking joint ventures with Iranian companies.

Other Middle East countries have taken heed of Iran's experiences and today bilateral contracts are signed only after thorough scrutiny; Saudi Arabia and Kuwait demand very strict adherence to the terms of agree-ments, with penalty clauses for delays and over-pricing. There is more awareness of the choice of technology, although appropriate technological choices are seen only in terms of physical and economic efficiency. But as environmental problems mount and cultural tensions come more and more to the fore, environmental and cultural factors will also become key determinants of technological choice. And technology assessment is being discovered by the science communities of the region.

In Pakistan, Egypt, Saudi Arabia and Kuwait a more subtle trend towards reducing the hazards of transfer of technology is emerging. These countries have set up programmes to keep pace with development in the industrialized countries. The aim of these programmes is to generate enough expertise to 'depackage' imported technologies, such as solar and nuclear technologies, in a manner that would allow them to produce locally as many components as possible and import only those parts which are beyond their industrial and technological capabilities. This way, it is hoped, they will be able to modify and adopt certain technologies to their conditions, reduce foreign exchange requirements, increase industrial and employment opportunities and overcome maintenance problems.

This trend indicates that the original goals of the transfer of technologies – to make available to local producers the necessary know-how to produce certain goods or to reduce production costs, in order to raise productivity and living standards – is slowly being extended to possession of, and not simply use of, advanced technology. This new extended goal will undoubtedly generate some conflict between the Middle East countries and the multinational companies.

Moreover, countries with reasonably developed scientific infrastructure, such as Pakistan, Egypt and Turkey, are becoming quite concerned about increasing their domestic capacity to generate technology indigenously. Egypt, for example, has had a historic bias towards basic science and towards internationally oriented state-of-the-art applied science. However, in the last few years, there has been a rapid growth in interest and activity in the areas of nationally oriented applied science and technology among the research establishment. Solar energy provides an interesting example. Despite a price environment which absolutely defeats most commercial applications of solar energy in Egypt in 1980, the scientific and technological community has had two notable shifts in this sector. First, energy scientists began to take interest in solar energy, disregarding the problem of commercial viability and the greater glamour of nuclear technology. While early interest centered on high-cost, high-technology applications, such as the power tower, more recent interest and scientific work has shifted to relatively basic field testing and developing low-cost, low-technology solar energy techniques which may compete with subsidized energy in terms of reliability as opposed to cost, especially in remote off-grid applications. The development of indigenous nuclear capability in Pakistan provides another example. When Canada withdrew its technical assistance and manpower from the KANUPP reactor, Pakistan had only two other choices: to let the reactor rot, or to develop a capability to run and manage it. That it chose the latter course is an indication of Pakistan's determination to develop indigenous technological capability.

Pakistan also provides a good example of a trend in foreign assistance that is likely to spread to countries with reasonably developed scientific communities. The practice of certain developed countries, to tie aid to projects, has considerably fragmented development in the region. It creates pressures to make a set of technological and development decisions which are neither integrated into a well articulated technology policy nor indicative of the recipients' development priorities. Pakistan's experience, spanning three decades, suggests that if local scientific communities have a research and development capability and can argue for and prove the relevance of certain projects, even tied aid can find its way to relevant programmes as shown by the successes that Pakistan secured in the 1960s with its foreign assistance programmes.

Biotechnology is one area where efforts are likely to be made to develop indigenous research and development capabilities. Most countries in the Middle East have reasonably adequate bases, in terms of institutions and manpower, for biological research. Biologists in the region are well aware that biotechnology is a nascent technology which is just beginning to find its investors and political masters. They are also aware that the early products of biotechnology, insulin, interferon and human growth hormones are unlikely to solve the Middle East's most pressing medical and agricultural problems. If the technology is to have a positive impact on the Middle East, the biologists in the region are coming to realize, it must develop its own biotechnology. Already there are indications that biotechnology will receive at least as much attention as solar technologies. But, unlike the case of solar technologies, the emphasis will be on developing indigenous capability rather than relying on imported technology. Jordan, Kuwait, Saudi Arabia, Iraq and Pakistan have already set up skeleton institutional frameworks for research in biotechnology. There are also moves to set up national and international research centres in such areas as fermentation and enzyme technology, molecular biology, genetics, immunology and toxoids, tissue culture and biological control of insect breeding and photosynthesis.

These positive trends could be turned into solid gains with the establishment of the proposed regional centres of excellence and if IFSTAD and CASTARAB work to promote genuine regional interests and cooperation. There is a vast scientific potential in the region which needs to be tapped and appropriately developed.

However, whether science and technology in the Middle East can flower indigenously in the next decades depends on whether or not it can take social and cultural roots, and that depends, to a considerable extent, on the outcome of efforts to Arabize the teaching of science and engineering, the debate on Islamic science, and a multitude of projects to internalize research and development activities in the Middle East. The indications of the last few years provide reasons for guarded optimism.

Bibliography

Abdullah, A. A., 'Problems of Arabisation in Science', *Impact of Science on Society*, **26**(3), 151–60 (1976).

Ahmad, M., 'The Organisation of Science: Occident and Orient', *Impact of Science on Society*, **26**(2/3) (1976).

Alsmeyer, D. and Atkins, A. G., *Guide to Science and Technology in the Asia/Pacific Area*, Francis Hodgson, London 1979.

Amin, M. A., 'Problems and Effects of Schistosomiasis in Irrigation in Sudan', in Worthington, E. B. (ed.) *Arid Land Irrigation in Developing Countries: Environmental Problems and Effects*, Pergamon Press, Oxford 1977.

Anawati, G., 'Moslem Science: A Theosophic–Historical View', *Impact of Science on Society*, **26**(2/3) (1976).

Anees, M. A. and Athar, A. N., 'Studies on Islamic Education', *The Islamic Quarterly*, **20–22**(4), 158–84 (1978).

—, —, 'Development of Higher Education and Scientific Research in the Arab World', *Journal of South Asian and Middle East Studies*, **2**(3), 93–100 (spring 1979).

—, —, 'Significance of Scientific, Technical and Social Information in the Muslim World', *Al-Ittihad*, **17**(1), 46–52 (1980).

ALECSO, *Informatics Development in the Arab Region*, Tunis 1978.

Ashoor, M. S., 'The Formation of Muslim Names', *International Library Review*, **9**, 491–500 (1977).

Baqai, F. U., 'Traditional Medicine in Pakistan', *Hamdard Medicus*, **20**(7-12), 3–14 (1977).

Barnett, A., *The Gezira Scheme – An Illusion in Development*, Frank Cass, London 1977.

Behbehani, K., Girgis, M. and Marzouk, M. S. (eds), *Proceedings of the Symposium on Science and Technology for Development in Kuwait*, Longman, London 1981.

Benyalia, M., 'Scientific Education and Research in Algeria', *Impact of Science on Society*, **26**(3), 177–80 (1976).

Blake, G. H. and Lawless, R. I. (eds), *The Changing Middle East City*, Croom Helm, London 1980.

Bortsch, R., *Economic Problems of Pest Control Examined for the Case of the Gezira*, Hurst and Co., London 1978.

Bucaille, M., *The Bible, The Qur'an and Science*, American Trust Publications, Plainfields 1978.

Carey, J. P. and Carey, A. G., 'Industrial Growth and Development Planning in Iran', *Middle East Journal*, **29**, 1–15 (1975).

Chen, P. I. and Borovansky, V. T., 'A Bibliographic System for Solar Energy Information in the Middle East', *Aslib Proceedings*, **32**(4), 187–98 (Apr. 1980).

Daghestani, F. A., Qasim, S. and Sakat, B. (eds), *Science and Technology for Development: Jordan's Science and Technology Policy Conference*, Royal Scientific Society, Amman 1981.

Dorozynski, A., 'Eden with Oil Wells', *Nature*, **257**, 78–80 (11 Sept. 1975).

—, 'Science, Technology and Education in the Arabian Peninsula', *Impact of Science on Society*, **26**(3), 193–98 (1976).

Earthscan, 'The Gulf: Pollution and Development', Briefing Document No. 24, London 1980.

ECWA, 'The Status of Science and Technology in the Western Asia Region', in Zahlan, A. B. (ed.), *Technology Transfer and Change in the Arab World* (1978).

Faksh, M. A., 'The Chimera of Education for Development in Egypt: The Socio-Economic Role of University of Graduates', *Middle East Studies*, **13**, 229–40 (1977).

—, 'The Consequences of the Introduction and Spread of Modern Education: Education and National Integration in Egypt', *Middle East Journal*, **16**, 42–55 (1980).

Al-Faruqi, I. R. and Naseef, A. O. (eds), *Social and Natural Sciences: The Islamic Perspective*, Hodder and Stoughton, London 1981.

Ford, J. G., 'A Framework for A New View of Islamic Science', *Adiyat Halab*, **4/5**, 68–74 (1978/79).

Galah, S., 'Current Trends of Scientific Activity in Arab and Islamic Countries', *Impact of Science on Society*, **26**(3), 169–76 (1976).

Georghiou, L. and Gord, G., 'Arab Silver for the Red Sea Mud', *New Scientist*, **89**, 470–72 (19 Feb. 1981).

Haider, S. J., 'Science-Technology Libraries in Pakistan', *Special Libraries*, **65**(10/11), 474–78 (1974).

Al-Hassan, A. Y., 'Science and the Islamic World', in Moraze, C. (ed.) *Science and the Factors of Inequality*, UNESCO, Paris 1979.

Husaini, S. W. A., *Islamic Environmental Systems Engineering*, Macmillan 1981.

ICARDA, *Report on Research Progress and Development at ICARDA, 1977–78*, Aleppo 1978.

—, *Introduction to Agriculture in West Asia and North Africa*, Aleppo 1979.

International Organization of Islamic Medicine, *Islamic Code of Medical Ethics*, Kuwait 1981.

Johnson, J. and associates, *A Review of United States Development Assistance to Pakistan 1952–1980*, Agency for International Development, Washington DC 1981.

Kadir, N. A., 'A Unified Research Council for Arab States', *Impact of Science on Society*, **26**(2/3), (1976).

Kettani, M. A., 'Solar Energy in the Arab World' in *New and Renewable Energy in the Arab World*, UN ECWA Report, Beirut 1981.

Kettani, M. A. and Malik, M. A. S., *Solar Energy in the Arab World: Policies and Programs*, AOPEC, Kuwait 1979.

Khan, M. A., *Nuclear Energy and International Cooperation: A Third World Perception of the Erosion of Confidence,* International Consultative Group on Nuclear Energy, Washington DC 1979.

—, 'Need for Developing Nuclear Energy in Muslim Countries', *Islamic Defense and Aviation Review*, **1**, 17-26 (1979).

El-Kholy, O. A., 'The 1976 CASTARAB Meeting – A Review', in Zahlan, A. B. (ed.), *Technology Transfer and Change in the Arab World*, Pergamon Press, Oxford 1978.

Khurshid, A., *Fact Sheets on Libraries in Islamic Countries*, Islamic Library Information Centre, University of Karachi, Karachi 1976.

Kuwait Institute for Scientific Research, *Regional Union List of Scientific and Technological Periodical in the Gulf Area*, Kuwait 1977.

Mallakh, R. and Kadhim, M., 'Arab Institutionalised Development Aid: An Evaluation', *Middle East Journal*, **30**, 471–84 (1976).

McMurdo, G., 'The IAP Library at King Abdulaziz International Airport', *Aslib Proceedings*, **33**(9), 363–67 (Sept. 1981).

Moustafa, S. M. A. and al-Hamoud, A., 'Solar Energy Programme at Institute of Scientific Research', *OPEC Review*, **5**(3), 98–111 (autumn 1981).

The Muslim Scientist, *Applied Science for Muslim World Development*, Plainfields 1981 (2 vols).

Naqvi, S. J., 'Importance of Nuclear Science and Technology to the Muslim World', *The Muslim Scientist*, **6**(1–2), 1–16 (June 1977).

Nasr, H. with the collaboration of **Chittick, W. C.** and **Zirnis, P.**, *An Annotated Bibliography of Islamic Science*, Tehran, vol. 1 (1975), vol. 2 (1979).

—, *Islamic Science: An Illustrated Study*, World of Islam Festival Publishing Co., London 1976.

Naseem, S. M., 'Some Economic and Social Implication of Brain Drain in Pakistan', in Zahlan, A. B. (ed.), *The Arab Brain Drain*, Ithaca Press, London 1981.

Nature, 'Development in the Muslim World', *Nature*, **272**, 195 (16 Mar. 1978).

—, 'Pakistan Needs Indigenous Medicine', *Nature*, **275**, 1 (7 Sept. 1978).

Newmark, P. 'Iranian Transplant', *Nature*, **261**, 358–59 (1976).

New Scientist, 'Pakistan Plans to Explode Nuclear Device in China', *New Scientist*, **91**, 203–04 (23 July 1981).

—, 'Reign of Terror Sweeps Iraq's Scientific Community', *New Scientist*, **90**, 3–4 (2 Apr. 1981).

Norman, C., 'Scientific Problems in the Middle East', *Science*, **215**, 639 (1982).

Pakistan Science Foundation, *Report of the years 1974–1979,* Islamabad 1980.
Parera, J., 'Nuclear Plants Take Root in the Desert', *New Scientist,* **83,** 577–80 (23 Aug. 1979).
—, 'Arabs Turn their Eyes to the Sun', *New Scientist,* **85,** 474–77 (14 Feb. 1980).
—, 'Was Iraq Really Developing A Bomb?' *New Scientist,* **90,** 688–90 (1981).
Pollard, N., 'The Gezira Scheme - A Study in Failure', *The Ecologist,* **11**(1), 21–31 (Jan.-Feb. 1978).
Oufriha, F.-Z., 'Aspects of Brain Drain in Algeria', in Zahlan, A. B. (ed.), *The Arab Brain Drain,* op. cit.
Oureshi, I. H., *Education in Pakistan,* Ma'aref, Karachi 1975.
Rasch, B., *Al-Hajj - Tent Cities,* IL 29, Institute of Lightweight Structures, University of Stuttgart, Stuttgart 1980.
Richard, A., 'Agricultural Technology and Rural Social Classes in Egypt 1920–1939', *Middle East Journal,* **16,** 56–83 (1980).
Roberts, Hugh, *An Urban Profile of the Middle East,* Croom Helm, London 1979.
Rana, M. H., 'Phosphate (and Contained Uranium) Resources of the Muslim World', *The Muslim Scientist,* **9**(3-4), 30–51 (Sept.-Dec. 1980).
Saber, Adel A., 'Science and Technology Policy and Planning in Arab Republic of Egypt', in Sharma, K. D. and Qureshi, M. A. (eds), *Science, Technology and Development,* Sterling Publishers, New Delhi 1978.
Sadar, M. H., 'An Islamic View of Science', *The Muslim Scientist,* **8**(2-3), 1–7 (June-Sept. 1979).
Salam, A., 'Across the Borders with Science', *Physics Bulletin,* **31**(7), 244–45 (Aug. 1980).
—, 'Gauge Unification of Fundamental Physics', *Reviews of Modern Physics,* **52**(3), 525–38 (July 1980).
Said, Hakim, 'Al-Tibb al-Islami', *Hamdard Medicus,* **19**(1-6) (Jan.-June 1976).
—, 'Eastern Medicine in National Science Policy', *Hamdard Medicus,* **19**(7-12), 3–44 (1976).
—, 'Influence of Islamic Medicine on the Principles of Modern Health and Hygiene', *Hamdard Medicus,* **20**(7-12), 15–22 (1977).
El-Sammani, A. Y., 'Sudan's Five-Year Plan for Research', *Impact of Science on Society,* **26**(3), 181–92 (1976).
Sardar, Z., 'The Function of Information in the Integration of the Muslim World', paper presented at the International Conference on Information and Communication in the Muslim World, Riyadh 1976.
—, *Science, Technology and Development in the Muslim World,* Croom Helm, London 1979; Humanities Press, New Jersey; Arabic etn, Amman 1981; Urdu etn, New Delhi 1981.
—, 'The Information Unit of the Hajj Research Centre', *Aslib Proceedings,* **30**(5), 158–64 (1978).
—, *A Bibliography of Hajj,* King Abdul Aziz University, Jeddah 1978.
—, 'Saudis Warm up to Solar Energy', *Nature,* **273,** 700–01 (1978).
—, 'Saudi Arabia: Indigenous Sources of Information', *Aslib Proceedings,* **31**(5), 237–44 (May 1979).
—, 'AH 1400: Science - the Key to the Future', *8 Days* (24 Nov. 1979).
—, 'The Middle East', in Greenberg, D. (ed.), *Science and Government Report International Almanac 1978–1979,* Science and Government Report Inc., Washington DC 1979.
—, *Islam: Outline of a Classification Scheme,* Clive Bingley, London 1979.
—, 'Islamic Scientists Prepare for UNCSTD', *Nature,* **278,** 679–80 (1979).
—, 'A Revival for Islam, A Boost for Science?', *Nature,* **282,** 354–57 (1979).
—, 'Scientific Thinking Behind Khomeini', *Nature,* **282,** 439–41 (1979).
—, 'Science in Turkey: Choosing the Wrong Priorities', *Nature,* **282,** 668–70 (1979).
—, 'Incalculating an Appropriate Sense of Confidence', *Nature,* **280,** 530–31 (1979).
—, 'Middle East Brain Drain Switches Back from the West', *Nature,* **283,** 327–28 (1980).
—, 'The State of Arab Science', *Nature,* **288,** 30–31 (1980).
—, 'Israel and Egypt: Can Their Scientists Cooperate?', *New Scientist,* **88,** 488–90 (1980).
—, 'Can Science Come Back to Islam?', *New Scientist,* **88,** 212–16 (1980).

—, 'Meaningful Gestures', *New Scientist*, **87**, 724–25 (1980).

—, 'Ayatollah's Dilemma', *New Scientist*, **85**, 51–52 (1980).

—, 'Shake-up in Syrian Science Imminent', *New Scientist*, **86**, 5 (1980).

—, 'Cooperation for Development', *New Scientist*, **86**, 2 (1980).

—, 'Micros and Society: The Troubled Interface', *8 Days*, 10–13 (26 Apr. 1980).

—, 'US Foreign Aid: Changes in Style But Not in Nature', *Impact International*, **10**, 7–8 (25 Apr.–8 May 1980).

—, 'UNCSTD: Heads I Win, Tails You Lose', *Impact International*, **10**, 12–14 (28 Dec. 1979–10 Jan. 1980).

—, 'UNCSTD Update: You Can Take the Horse to Water . . .', *Impact International*, **10**, 14 (28 Mar.–10 Apr. 1980).

—, 'Agriculture: A New Way for the Fertile Crescent', *8 Days*, 20–22 (15 Mar. 1980).

—, 'Salam: Man of Islamic Science', *8 Days*, 20–22 (29 Mar. 1980).

—, 'Cairo's Scientific Think Tank', *8 Days*, 53 (19 July 1980).

—, 'Iran Assaults Pollution Problems', *Ambio*, **9**(6), 320–21 (1980).

—, *Science and Technology in Islam and the West: A Synthesis*, International Federation for the Institutes of Advance Study, Solna (Sweden) 1981.

—, 'Between GIN and TWIN: Meeting the Information Needs of the Third World', *Aslib Proceedings*, **33**(2), 53–61 (1981).

—, 'Egyptian Calamities', *New Scientist*, **89**, 297 (1981).

—, 'Why the Third World Needs Nuclear Power', *New Scientist*, **89**, 402–04 (1981).

—, 'Red Sea States Unite Against Pollution', *New Scientist*, **89**, 472 (1981).

—, 'Germany: Third World Benefactor', *New Scientist*, **89**, 538–39 (1981).

—, 'Islamic Science Foundation Launches its First Projects', *New Scientist*, **89**, 791 (1981).

—, 'The Day the Saudis Discovered Technology', *New Scientist*, **90**, 481–84 (1981).

—, 'Iranian Research Gets an Islamic Flavour', *New Scientist*, **91**, 9 (1981).

—, 'How Good is Arab Aid for the Third World?', *New Scientist*, **91**, 233–35 (1981).

—, 'Does Technology Change the Nature of Man?', *Impact International*, **11**, 11–12 (29 Sept.–12 Oct. 1981).

—, 'Science For the People of Islam', *New Scientist*, **93**, 244–45 (1982).

—, 'Why Islam Needs Islamic Science', *New Scientist*, **94**, 25–28 (1982).

Sardar, Z. and Rosser-Owen, D. G., 'Science Policy and Developing Countries', in Spiegal-Rosing, I., and Price, D. de Solla (eds), *Science Technology and Society: An Interdisciplinary Perspective*, Sage Publications, Beverley Hills and London 1977.

Sardar, Z. and Badawi, M. Z. (eds), *Hajj Studies: Vol 1*, Croom Helm, London 1978.

Sayigh, Y. A., *The Economies of the Arab World*, Croom Helm, London 1978.

—, *The Determinents of Arab Economic Development*, Croom Helm, London 1978.

Shihata, I. F. I., 'The OPEC Fund for International Development – the First Five Years', *The OPEC Review*, **5**(3), 1–8 (autumn 1981).

Sinion, Jan, *Middle East Health*, World Health Organization Regional Office for the Eastern Mediterranean, Alexandria 1980.

Technical University of Istanbul, *Proceedings of the First International Congress on the History of Turkish–Islamic Science and Technology*, Istanbul 1981 (4 vols).

El Tom, M. E. A., 'Sudan: The Role of the Educational System of Higher Level Manpower', in Zahlan, A. B. (ed.), *The Arab Brain Drain*, op. cit.

TUBITAK, *Annual Report 1979*, Ankara 1980.

Turner, S., 'The Gezira Scheme: Restructuring the Future', *Sudanow* (Mar. 1980).

Turkcon, E., 'The Limits of Science Policy in a Developing Country: The Turkish Case – A Study Based on the Experience of the Scientific and Technical Research Council of Turkey', *Research Policy*, **2**, 336–63 (1974).

UNCSTD, L'Algérie: National Paper, A/CONF.81/NP.46, Vienna 1979.

—, Bahrain: National Paper, A/CONF.81/NP.107, Vienna 1979.

—, Kuwait: National Paper, A/CONF.81/NP.72, Vienna 1979.

—, Libya: National Paper, A/CONF.81/NP.117, Vienna 1979.

—, Le Moroc: National Paper, A/CONF.81/NP.102, Vienna 1979.

—, Palestine: National Paper, A/CONF.81/NP.129, Vienna 1979.
—, Pakistan: National Paper, A/CONF.81/NP.12, Vienna 1979.
—, Saudi Arabia: National Paper, A/CONF.81/NP.17, Vienna 1979.
—, Sudan: National Paper, A/CONF.81/NP.74, Vienna 1979.
—, Syria: National Paper, A/CONF.81/NP.17, Vienna 1979.
—, La Tunisie: National Paper, A/CONF.81/NP.118, Vienna 1979.
—, Turkey: National Paper, A/CONF.81/NP.55, Vienna 1979.
—, United Arab Emirates: National Paper, A/CONF.81/NP.120, Vienna 1979.
—, Yemen: National Paper, A/CONF.81/NP.108, Vienna 1979.
—, 'Science and Technology in the Muslim World – Background Paper Presented by the Organisation of Islamic Conference', A/CONF.81/BP/IGO/14, Vienna 1979.
—, 'Science and Technology Policy Priorities for Joint Arab Scientific Programmes – A Background Paper Presented by the Union of Arab Scientific Research Councils, Baghdad, June 1979', A/CONF.81/BP/IGO/3, Vienna 1979.
UNESCO, 'Science and Technology in the Development of Arab States', Science Policy Studies Document No. 41, Paris 1977.
UNESCO Regional Office for Science and Technology in the Arab States, 'A Case Study of Some UNESCO Projects Related to the Brain Drain', in Zahlan, A. B. (ed.), The Arab Brain Drain, op. cit.
UNEP, 'Final Act of the Kuwait Regional Conference of Plenipotentiaries on the Protection and Development of the Marine Environment and the Coast Areas', Kuwait 1978.
UNERG, Algeria: National Report, A/CONF.100/NR/30, Nairobi 1981.
—, Iraq: National Report, A/CONF.100/NR/13, Nairobi 1981.
—, Pakistan: National Report, A/CONF.100/NR/1, Nairobi 1981.
—, Tunisia: National Report, A/CONF.100/NR/12, Nairobi 1981.
—, Sudan: National Report, A/CONF.100/NR/11, Nairobi 1981.
University of Aleppo, The Second International Symposium for the History of Arabic Science (abstracts only), Aleppo 1979; Supplement, 1980.
University of Riyadh, Islamic Solidarity Conference in Science and Technology (abstracts only), Riyadh 1976.
Wei, Julie, 'Aswan and After: The Taming and Transformation of the River Nile', The Research News: University of Michigan, 31(7), 1–32 (July 1980).
Wheeler, S. E. L. and Shah, K. T., Greece, Turkey and the Arab States, Guide to World Sciences Series, Vol. 12, Francis Hodgson, London 1976.
El-Yacoub, H., 'Sudan's Five-Year Plan for Research/Development', Impact of Science on Society, 26(2/3) (1976).
Yanchinski, S., 'US Aid at the Crossroads', New Scientist, 85, 167–69 (1980).
Zahlan, A. B., 'Manpower Planning: The Problem', in Kazimi, M. S. and Makhoul, J. I. (eds), Perspective on Technological Development in the Arab World, The Association of Arab University Graduates, 1977.
—, (ed.), Technology Transfer and Change in the Arab World, Pergamon, London 1978.
—, 'An Arab Solution', Mazingira, No. 3, 78–83 (1979).
—, 'Arab Universities and Technology', Middle East Yearbook 1980, 179–82, International Communications Ltd, London 1980.
—, Science and Science Policy in the Arab World, Croom Helm, London 1980.
—, (ed.), The Arab Brain Drain, op. cit.
Zain, M. G., 'The Brain Drain in the Context of Social Change in Democratic Yemen and Problems in High Level Manpower Training at Aden University', in Zahlan, A. B. (ed.), The Arab Brain Drain, op. cit.
Zureik, E. T., 'Values, Social Organisation and Technology Change in the Arab World', in Zahlan, A. B. (ed.), The Arab Brain Drain, op. cit.

PART II

REGIONAL ORGANIZATIONS

Arab Bureau of Education for the Gulf States – ABEGS

Origins

The Arab Bureau of Education for the Gulf States (ABEGS) was formed on the initiative of the First Conference of the Ministers of Education of the Gulf States convened in Riyadh on 20 October 1975. Resolution No. 2 of the conference called for the establishment of what was then called the Regional Office of Education (ROE). ROE was given a number of responsibilities, most important of which were:

1. To propose the establishment of joint centres for the development of higher education in the Gulf.
2. To oversee all participating units and centres to be set up in the states concerned.
3. To coordinate the activities of Arab educational, cultural and scientific organizations and UNESCO.

The First Education Conference also formed an executive council and established an administrative secretariat and a temporary head office for ROE at the Ministry of Education of Saudi Arabia.

The Second Conference of the Ministers of Education of the Gulf States, attended by Bahrain, Kuwait, Iran, Oman, Qatar, Saudi Arabia and the UAE and held in Riyadh on 9–11 May 1977, changed the name from the Regional Office of Education to the Arab Bureau for the Education of the Gulf States. It also established a permanent head office for the bureau in Riyadh in a purpose-built building and asked the bureau to prepare the ground work for the establishment of an Arab Centre for Educational Research.

The Third Conference of the Ministers of Education for the Gulf States was held in Abu Dhabi on 18–20 April 1978. The conference accepted the draft Charter for the Arab Centre for Educational Research and prepared the guidelines for the unification of the curricula of education for the Gulf States. The conference also asked the bureau to prepare a medium-term development plan of its projects.

The Fourth Conference of the Ministers of Education for the Gulf States, held in Bahrain on 3–4 May 1979, adopted a resolution to establish the University of the Gulf in Bahrain.

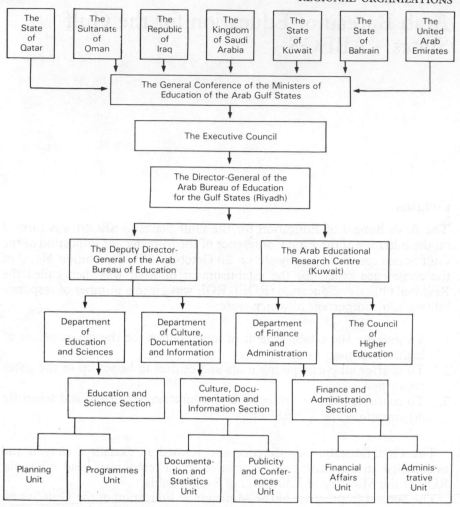

Source: adapted from ABEGS *Bulletin*, Vol. 1, No. 1 (1975).

Fig. 2.1 The organization chart for the Arab Bureau of Education for the Gulf States

Projects and Programmes

ABEGS has two major projects: to set up the Arab Educational Research Centre for the Gulf States (AERCGS) in Kuwait and to establish the University of the Gulf in Bahrain.

Although AERCGS will be one of the organizations of the Bureau, it has a separate legal identity, and when fully functional, it will have an independent budget. According to AERCGS's charter, it will undertake the following duties:

1. To make complete research studies which will define the reality of the educational systems in the member states and at the same time evaluate their effectiveness in light of the goals which have been set for them.
2. To experiment with recent educational innovations in an attempt to benefit from them.
3. To make necessary studies for educational projects having a regional character and application to the Gulf States and to suggest plans for implementing them.
4. To provide information about and the results of educational experiments made in the Gulf States, then to analyse and publish them.
5. To make contacts with both Arab and international educational research centres in order to exchange experience with them as well as to become acquainted with new theories, trends and techniques in this field.
6. In the proficient performance of its duties, the centre will utilize scientific and national educational organizations, colleges of education, appropriate planning and technical affairs units of the ministries and special organizations in the member states.
7. To share in the development of a technical cadre in educational fields in the member states.
8. To work on the development of teacher training during research and field studies and to benefit from the latest trends and practices in this field.
9. Upon request, to present advisory services to the member states in the development of teacher training during research and field studies and to benefit from the latest trends and practices in this field.
10. To provide planners responsible for educational programmes and curricula, school books, educational aids, teachers, persons responsible for educational evaluations and testing in experimental field research.

The University of the Gulf will be a regional university with faculties for medicine, education and science on a unified campus in Bahrain. ABEGS has already prepared the charter of the university and a site has also been selected. The university is expected to start some of its courses by 1985.

In addition to these two projects, the education and sciences section of ABEGS is working on a detailed evaluation of the goals of science curricula in educational institutions of the Gulf, a survey of laboratory facilities in secondary schools in the Gulf, and an assessment of educational planning in the Gulf states. The culture, documentation and information section of ABEGS is setting up a regional technical library and publishes statistical summaries of all stages of education in the Gulf states.

Documents

Charter of ABEGS

In the name of Allah, the Merciful, the Compassionate . . .

PREFACE

The states participating in this bureau share one area, one language and the Islamic faith. They have a common economic base and the same social and cultural conditions. They share common historical glories.

Therefore it is in the continued interest of all to unify the goals of education. This includes a uniformity of curriculum and an integrated effort aimed at the growth and development of education. For it is in this way that future generations will be formed: by emphasizing the Islamic Arab character of the region; by providing for its cultural requirements and it's spiritual needs; by strengthening the unity of its people and constructing a system of education on a scientific basis whose goals and objectives are clear; and protecting future generations from deviation and assuring the Islamic character of the area which is the source from which we draw the bases of our distinctive existence and our humanistic civilization.

This bureau has been founded to realize these aims and it will function according to the attached charter.

CHAPTER ONE

Article 1: *Terminology*

Except in cases where they are contrary to the meaning of the text, the terminology used in this charter will have limited meanings as follows:

Charter: The Charter of the Arab Bureau of Education for the Gulf States.

Bureau: The Arab Bureau of Education for the Gulf States.

Member States: They are:

1. The United Arab Emirates.
2. The State of Bahrain.
3. The Republic of Iraq.
4. The Sultanate of Oman.
5. The State of Qatar.
6. The State of Kuwait.
7. The Kingdom of Saudi Arabia.

Conference: The General Conference of the Ministers of Education of the Member States.

Council: The Executive Council for the Arab Bureau of Education for the Gulf States.

Administration: The General Administrative Body of the Arab Bureau of Education for the Gulf States.

Article 2: *The functions of the administration*

In order that the bureau may accomplish the goals for which it was established, the administration will have the following functions:

1. To take the necessary measures to guarantee that the decisions of the Ministers of Education of the member states will be executed and followed up; to coordinate and complete activities involving the growth and

development of education; to make the Arab Islamic personality of the area well known; to support the unity of its people; and guarantee that education is based on clear scientific goals and information.

2. To establish educational organizations and centres in the member states.
3. To work toward and encourage active cultural cooperation and contacts as well as the exchange of experts as per the following:

    (a) Cooperation with educational and cultural organizations and centres established in the member states;
    (b) To organize the exchange of visits by educational specialists and to arrange for educational, scientific and cultural seminars and meetings as well as participation in conferences and trips between the member states;
    (c) To organize educational scholarships for the youth of the member states;
    (d) To keep in contact with Arab and international organizations and to represent the bureau at their conferences;
    (e) To ensure that contact is kept with Arab cultural, educational and scientific organizations and to ensure representation by the bureau as observers in their meetings and conferences.

4. To work toward the realization of coordination and integration in the field of university and higher education as well as with research centres in the member states in order to facilitate the mutual exchange of experience and experiments and to unify educational degrees and their evaluations.
5. To cultivate Arab Islamic culture and give attention to affairs concerning contemporary Arab Islamic thought with a view toward its dissemination; to work towards the spread of the Arab language and to facilitate its study in foreign countries, especially in Islamic countries, and to propose effective means for realizing this goal at the conference.
6. The bureau will assume the responsibility of issuing the invitations for both ordinary and extraordinary meetings of the ministers of education as well as invitations to hold conferences and seminars on all levels.

CHAPTER TWO

Article 3: *The structure of the bureau*

The Arab Bureau of Education for the Gulf States is composed of the following:

1. The Executive Council.
2. The General Administration.
3. Other centres or branches which may be instituted in the future.

[. . .]

Article 14: *Formation of the general administration of the bureau*

[. . .]

3. The specialized departments which are:

    (a) Educational and scientific programmes;

(b) Cultural, documentation and information programmes;

(c) Financial and Administrative Department;

(d) Any other department which the conference may see fit to create.

A. The Department of Educational and Scientific Programmes will be charged as follows:

1. To work toward the unification of goals, systems of education, basic curricula, teaching aids and textbooks, and the raising of educational standards in the states of the region.

2. To exchange experience and information in various educational fields, emphasizing the preparation of and increase in teachers, school libraries, testing, evaluations and educational planning.

3. To encourage the exchange of visits among specialists in education, to organize regional educational and cultural seminars, and to organize scholarship programmes between member states.

4. To organize joint programmes and projects such as: anti-illiteracy and adult education; vocational and technical education; education for the handicapped and special education; education evaluation methods; and in-service teachers training.

5. To coordinate foreign aid to sister Arab states and other friendly countries and make it effective.

6. To coordinate the efforts of the member states in the field of science.

7. To assist in the exchange of experience during the conferences and seminars, to publish appropriate scientific information and technological experience as well as the results of practical and applied research.

8. To support scientific research and applied technology in the member states.

9. To cooperate with other organizations in the Arab states and with international organizations which are concerned with educational affairs and scientific and technological matters by way of seminars, conferences and the exchange of information and experience in order to achieve the highest possible level of educational and scientific advancement generally and especially as regards the available natural resources of the region.

B. The Cultural, Documentation and Information Department will be charged as follows:

1. To be concerned with all areas of cultural thought in the participating countries and especially that which concerns Islamic culture; cultural history; the sciences, arts and literature of the Arabs; and Arab Islamic culture and civilization.

2. To advance the Arabic language and facilitate the study of its grammar; facilitating printing and methods of teaching; exerting efforts towards disseminating it abroad by way of establishing schools and cultural centres and encouraging translations into Arabic; working toward the unification of technical terms in the region with the cooperation of other Arab countries and taking scientific and linguistic academies into consideration.

3. To work toward the exchange of information, experience and

the results of research in the participating countries; to offer technical and cultural assistance to hold conferences and seminars; and to cooperate with international bodies and organizations in realizing these aims.

4. To strengthen and support cultural cooperation in the information media and to organize cultural festivals and visits.

5. To offer assistance in making teachers, books, equipment and scholarships available to the participating states.

6. To strengthen relations with foreign institutes which are involved with Arab and Islamic studies and to develop a mutual exchange of relations with Islamic states and societies as well as with cultural and scientific groups, organizations and conferences.

7. To maintain cooperation with the Arab Organization for Education, Culture and Sciences as well as with UNESCO; to work toward the advancement of all branches of human knowledge by keeping abreast of the latest international developments; to do research and acquire the results of successful study projects which can advantageously be utilized in cultural, social and economic development.

8. To collect documents which are specially concerned with the region (books, publications, periodicals, etc.), prepare a bibliography of them, and facilitate access to them by participating states upon request.

9. To help supply research needs in the other specialized departments and to produce bibliographical studies on subjects with which they are concerned.

10. To supply educational, cultural and scientific circles in the member states with newspapers, booklets and special publications such as statistical, informational or bibliographical publications.

11. To publish educational, cultural and scientific magazines in cooperation with the other departments and units.

12. To take responsibility for the technical production of publications, photographs and data records and to keep all the documentation.

13. To make available to the Arab Bureau of Education for the Gulf States all necessary office services and to look after all matters which are not included in the functions of the other departments or which are delegated to it by the director-general.

[. . .]

Source: The Educational Documentary Bulletin for the Arab Gulf States, Issue No. 1, Riyadh 1979.

Arab League Educational, Cultural and Scientific Organization – ALECSO

Origins

The Arab League Educational, Cultural and Scientific Organization (ALECSO) was created by the League of Arab States on 25 July 1970. At its first general conference, the membership of ALECSO was limited to Jordan, Algeria, Sudan, Syria, Iraq, Kuwait, Egypt, and the Democratic Peoples' Republic of Yemen. After its Fourth General Conference, held in December 1975 in Cairo, the UAE, Bahrain, Tunisia, Saudi Arabia, Somalia, Oman, Palestine, Qatar, Libya, Morocco, Mauritania and the Arab Republic of Yemen also joined the organization.

The constitution of ALECSO, which had its head office in Cairo, defined its aim to be 'the attainment of unity of thought between the Arab countries through education, culture and science and through raising of cultural standards in these countries so that they may follow world progress and participate positively in it'. Within this framework, the organization set itself the following targets:

1. To assist in the formation of Arab education systems, and cultural and scientific organizations, and to strengthen coordination and integration, paying special attention to the elimination of illiteracy through the integrated approach and through programmes of life-long education.
2. To explore new areas of Arab cooperation in the fields of education, culture and science, and to mobilize Arab energies and resources in these fields to serve progress and development in the Arab world and so raise the efficiency of Arab participation at the international level.
3. To care for Arab heritage and to seek the continuity and development of the Arabic language in accordance with the requirements of present-day trends.
4. To develop exchange of information and communicate between Arab countries in the field of education, culture and science with all that that entails in the provision of data through modern methods in information systems.
5. To give special attention to the problems of the people of Palestine and to the preservation of their national and cultural identity.

In 1979, Egypt was expelled from ALECSO because of the Egyptian-

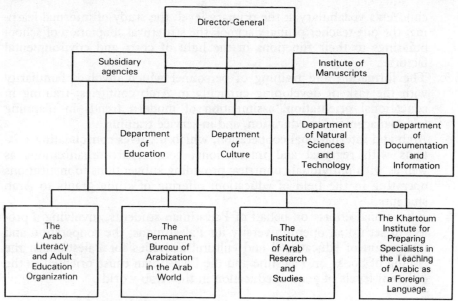

Fig. 2.2 Organization of ALECSO

Israeli peace treaty, and the headquarters of the organization was moved, in 1980, from Cairo to Tunis.

Projects and Programmes

ALECSO has four departments: education, culture, natural sciences and technology, and documentation and information; and an Institute of Manuscripts. It also has four subsidiary agencies: the Arab Literacy and Adult Education Organization, the Permanent Bureau of Coordination of Arabization in the Arab World, the Institute of Arab Research and Studies, and the Khartoum Institute for Preparing Specialists in the Teaching of Arabic as a Foreign Language. With the exception of the Department of Culture, the Arab Literacy and Adult Education Organization and the Khartoum Institute, all department and subsidiary agencies do some work in the field of science and technology.

The Department of Education works on:

1. The planning and application of education, involving the study of continuing education and the definition of the nature of this within the framework of Arab heritage and modern trends; the funding of educational projects through the proper use of joint Arab capital investments; the study of demographic aspects and their relation to both manpower and education; the provision of equal opportunity for education to the under-privileged.
2. Educational curricula, their means and their methods, involving the study of methods of teaching children to read; the study of school-

children's vocabulary at the primary level; the study of informal learning; the one-teacher primary school; the structural adaptation of school
buildings to their functions in the light of costs and environmental
factors.
3. The formation and training of personnel which involves familiarity
with the task of developing curricula in Arab countries; training in
educational orientation; assimilation of modern trends in planning
and management in education, and in-service training.
4. Arab and international cooperation, which involves consolidating relations with regional and international counterpart organizations as
well as with individual countries; providing subventions to institutions
operating in the field of education; offering of study grants to Arab
students.
5. Educational efforts on behalf of Palestinian students, involving a project to set up an open university for Palestinians; the cooperation and
integration of educational and cultural activities for Palestinians; the
issuing of books on Palestine and the Palestinian cause oriented to the
different levels of general education in the Arab world.

The Department of Natural Sciences and Technology has sections for
scientific publications, environmental and natural resources, popularization of science, and instrumentation and promotion of scientific research.

The scientific publication section has published a number of monographs of particular relevance to the Middle East, such as underground
water, water resources, phosphate ores, medicinal herbs, animal husbandry
and oil research. The section also publishes a quarterly journal of Arab
abstracts in Arabic, English and French editions.

The environment and natural resources section is working on a major
programme for environmental studies on the Red Sea and the Gulf of
Aden which includes developing a network of pollution-monitoring stations
and research institutes around the Red Sea and has set up an Arab Council for Marine Environment to coordinate the activities and studies on the
Red Sea and Persian Gulf marine environments. It is responsible for setting
up the Convention on the Protection of Marine Environment of the Red
Sea and the Gulf of Aden (see pp. 93–96). It will also become increasingly
involved in the implementation of the Kuwait Action Plan to clean up the
Gulf (see pp. 96–101). The section is also working, in cooperation with the
United Nations Environmental Programme (UNEP), on arresting desertification in North African Arab states: the 'green belt' scheme involves research on a selection of plants, training of personnel and social studies on
arid zones. Other environmental programmes include a study on the environmental condition of the Palestinian refugees, a regional survey of
water resources, a study of closed basins shared by the Arab states, and a
project on environmental considerations for establishing industrial complexes. The section is also working on an Arab Plan of Action for harnessing renewable sources of energy, and it provides courses for technicians in
solar energy applications.

The popularization of science section publishes popular books and organizes exhibitions. It specializes in science publications for children and has an ongoing study on communicating scientific ideas and concepts to children.

The instrumentation section is working to establish a Regional Centre for Scientific Apparatus, which will be located in Amman, Jordan. It runs a number of training schemes in glass technology, electronics and mechanical instruments.

The section for the promotion of scientific research is particularly concerned with informatics and is promoting research on informatics and related disciplines in the region. Its Arabization of Informatics programme aims at unifying the syllabuses and methods of training in computer and information sciences. It also holds seminars and symposia on research topics of relevance to the Arab world.

The Documentation and Information Department of ALECSO is working on the alterations to the Dewey Decimal Classification Scheme to fit the needs of Arab libraries and compiling an Arabic subject-heading list. The section also prepares analytical and comparative studies on reports and statistics submitted to ALECSO by member states on the conditions and innovations in education and science and technology.

The Institute of Manuscripts works on the location, duplication and indexing, in all disciplines, of Arab manuscripts found, authentication and republication of rare and valuable books, and compiling and publishing of indices of reproduced manuscripts available at the institute.

The Permanent Bureau of Coordination of Arabization in the Arab World is based in Rabat and works on the coordination of efforts to further the use of Arabic in scientific and technical education at all levels, developing the Arabic language by 'Arabizing' scientific and technical terms and monitors the Arabization movement throughout the region. The bureau also publishes technical glossaries and dictionaries and organizes seminars and conferences on specific issues of Arabization.

The Institute of Arab Research and Studies is concerned with ecological and demographic studies on the Arab world, examination of the problems of transport and communication, and the preparation of monographs on member states of ALECSO.

Documents

1. The Convention on the Protection of the Marine Environment of the Red Sea and the Gulf of Aden and its Protocols

Ethiopia;
The Hashemite Kingdom of Jordan;
The Kingdom of Saudi Arabia;
The Democratic Republic of Sudan;
The Democratic Republic of Somali;
The Arab Republic of Egypt;
The Yemen Arab Republic; and
The People's Democratic Republic of Yemen.

Being the states bordering the Red Sea and the Gulf of Aden;

Realizing the economic cultural and social significance of the marine environment of the Red Sea and the Gulf of Aden;

Recognizing their responsibility to protect the marine environment of the Red Sea and the Gulf of Aden for the benefit of the successive generations;

Mindful of the need for regional cooperation to protect the marine environment of the Red Sea and the Gulf of Aden against pollution from all sources;

Have agreed as follows:

Article 1: *Definitions*

For the purposes of this convention and its protocols.

1. 'The Red Sea and the Gulf of Aden' means the water mass of the Red Sea and the Gulf of Aden within the frame of integrated ecosystems.
2. 'Pollution' means introduction by man directly or indirectly, of substances or energy into the marine environment resulting in such deleterious effects as harm to living resources, hazards to human health, hinderance to marine activities including fishing, impairment of quality for use of sea water, and reduction of amenities.
3. 'Ships and aircraft' means waterborne or airborne or amphibious craft of any type whatsoever, including hydrofoil boats, air-cushion vehicles, submersibles, floating craft whether self-propelled or not, and fixed or floating platforms and any other structure.
4. 'Oil' means petroleum in any form including crude oil, fuel oil, sludge, oil refuse and refined products, whose introduction might impair the marine environment.
5. 'Harmful substance' means all substances whose introduction or presence causes a danger threatening or impairing the environment.
6. 'The board' means the Board for the Protection of the Marine Environment of the Red Sea and the Gulf of Aden established under Article 8 of this convention.
7. 'The general secretariat' means the General Secretariat of the Board for the Protection of the Marine Environment of the Red Sea and the Gulf of Aden established under Article 10 of this convention.

Article 2: *Basic obligations*

1. The contracting parties shall individually and in common take all appropriate legal, administrative or other relevant measures in accordance with the provisions of this convention and the protocols thereto to prevent and abate pollution of the marine environment of the Red Sea and the Gulf of Aden.
2. The contracting parties convenant to implement this convention and the protocols thereto in such a manner as to avoid the pollution of sea areas outside the Red Sea and the Gulf of Aden.

Article 3: *Measures for prevention and abatement of the different types of pollution*

1. The contracting parties pledge themselves to take all appropriate meas-

ures to prevent and abate pollution of the marine environment of the Red Sea and the Gulf of Aden caused by:

(a) Discharges from rivers, coastal establishments or outfalls, or originating from any other sources within their territories;
(b) The exploration and the exploitation of the seabed and its subsoil;
(c) Ships;
(d) Dumping from ships and aircraft;
(e) Other possible sources.

2. To this end they shall cooperate in the formulation and adoption of protocols to this convention, prescribing agreed measures, procedures and standards.

Article 4: *Liability and compensation*

The contracting parties shall cooperate in the formulation and adoption of a protocol to this convention establishing appropriate procedures for the determination of responsibility and the remedies for damage resulting from acts or omissions in violation of the convention and the protocols thereto.

Article 5: *Pollution emergencies*

1. Whenever there is an imminent danger to the marine environment, the coast or related interests of one or more contracting parties due to the presence of massive quantities of oil resulting from an accident or any other accidental cause or the accumulation of quantities of oil or the presence of any other substance harmful to the environment:

(a) The contracting parties shall endeavour to cooperate and coordinate their efforts in combating this danger immediately and in a way that would confine the spreading of its damaging effects, avoiding means and methods use thereof [which] would cause harm to the marine environment;
(b) Any of the contracting parties who comes to his knowledge the presence of a danger mentioned in this article, shall undertake to inform, utilizing the quickest and most reliable communication, other party or parties who are nearest to the danger, at the same time informing the general secretariat who, in turn, shall send immediate notification utilizing the quickest and most reliable communication to all contracting parties and the concerned international organization;
(c) In the cases of item 6 of this article the general secretariat shall ascertain the nature and size of danger and inform all parties affected or which may be affected by the danger.

2. Each contracting party shall nominate and notify the general secretary with the name and address of the competent national organization responsible for combating, prevention and abatement of pollution, to receive reports and notifications of pollution emergencies, to issue permits mentioned in the second protocol to this convention; and which is responsible for other matters dealing with combating, prevention and abatement of pollution.

Article 6: *Monitoring*

The contracting parties agree to establish, in collaboration with the appropriate international bodies, a pollution monitoring system for the Red Sea and the Gulf of Aden.

[. . .]

Source: ALECSO, *Programme for Environmental Studies, Red Sea and Gulf of Aden,* Cairo 1976.

2. Action Plan for the Protection and Development of the Marine Environment and the Coastal Areas of Bahrain, Iran, Iraq, Kuwait, Oman, Qatar, Saudi Arabia and the United Arab Emirates (the Kuwait Action Plan)

INTRODUCTION

1. The Region has been recognized by the Governments concerned and by the Governing Council of the United Nations Environment Programme (UNEP) as a 'concentration area' in which UNEP, in close collaboration with the relevant components of the United Nations system, will attempt to fulfil its catalytic role in assisting States of the Region to develop and implement, in a consistent manner, an Action Plan commonly agreed upon.
2. The protection and development of the marine environment and the coastal areas of the Region for the benefit of present and future generations will be the central objective of the Action Plan. This Action Plan sets forth a framework for an environmentally sound and comprehensive approach to coastal area development, particularly appropriate for this rapidly developing Region.
3. Recognizing the complexity of the problem and the numerous ongoing activities, the Action Plan has been based upon:
   3.1 Findings of an inter-agency mission organized by UNEP in cooperation with UN/ESA which visited Bahrain, Iran, Iraq, Kuwait, Oman, Qatar, Saudi Arabia and the United Arab Emirates from 15 March to 25 May 1976;
   3.2 Consultative Meeting on Marine Sciences in the Region convened by UNESCO in Paris, 11–14 November 1975;
   3.3 Recommendations for a marine science project endorsed by the Conference of Arab Ministers of States Responsible for the Application of Science and Technology to Development, CASTARAB, convened by UNESCO in Rabat, 16–25 August 1976;
   3.4 Meeting of a Group of Experts on Coastal Area Development convened by UN/ESA in New York, November 1974;
   3.5 Recommendations of the Kuwait Technical Meeting on Coastal Area Development and Protection of the Marine Environment co-sponsored by UNEP and UN/ESA in Kuwait, 6–9 December 1976;
   3.6 A feasibility study for a coordinated applied marine science and

basic marine science programme conducted by UNEP and
UNESCO in cooperation with the Intergovernmental Oceanographic Commission (IOC) and FAO;

3.7 Regional Meeting of Legal Experts on the Protection of the Marine
Environment held by UNEP in Bahrain, 24–28 January 1977;

3.8 Experts Meeting on the Protection of the Marine Environment,
Nairobi, 13–18 June 1977;

3.9 Additional suggestions and proposals received from the United
Nations system.

4. The Action Plan aims to achieve the following:

4.1 Assessment of the state of the environment including socio-
economic development activities related to environmental quality
and of the needs of the Region in order to assist Governments to
cope properly with environmental problems, particularly those concerning the marine environment;

4.2 Development of guidelines for the management of those activities
which have an impact on environmental quality or on the protection and use of renewable marine resources on a sustainable
basis;

4.3 Development of legal instruments providing the legal basis for cooperative efforts to protect and develop the Region on a sustainable
basis;

4.4 Supporting measures including national and regional institutional
mechanisms and structure needed for the successful implementation of the Action Plan.

5. For this document, it is assumed that the Region includes the marine
area bounded in the south by the following rhumb-lines:

From Ras Dharbat Ali
    Lat. 16°39′N   Long. 53°3′30″E; then
to a position in:
    Lat. 16°00′N   Long. 53°25′E; then
to a position in:
    Lat. 17°00′N   Long. 56°30′E; then
to a position in:
    Lat. 20°30′N   Long. 60°00′E; then
to Ras Al-Fasteh in:
    Lat. 25°04′N   Long. 61°25′E.

The coastal area to be considered as part of the Region will be identified by the relevant Governments of the Region on an *ad hoc* basis
depending on the type of activities to be carried out within the framework of the Action Plan. Nevertheless, coastal areas not included in the
Region as defined above, should not be a source of marine pollution.

6. All components of the Action Plan are interdependent and provide a
framework for comprehensive action to contribute to both the protection
and the continued development of the ecoregion. No component will
be an end in itself. Each activity is intended to assist the Governments
of the Region to improve the quality of the information on which environmental management policies are based.

7. The protection of the marine environment is considered as the first priority of the Action Plan, and it is intended that measures for marine and coastal environmental protection and development should lead to the promotion of human health and well-being as the ultimate goal of the Action Plan.

8. The Action Plan is intended to meet the environmental needs and enhance the environmental capabilities of the Region and is aimed primarily toward implementation by way of coordinated national and regional activities. To achieve this goal, an intensive training programme should be formulated in the early phases of the implementation of the Action Plan.

9. A general description of the various components of the Action Plan is given in the following paragraphs.

I. ENVIRONMENTAL ASSESSMENT

10. Environmental assessment is one of the basic activities which will underlie and facilitate the implementation of the other components of the Action Plan.

11. The identification of the present quality of the marine environment and the factors currently influencing its quality and having an impact on human health will be given priority together with an assessment of future trends.

12. Due to the lack or inadequacy of available basic data on the marine environment, a coordinated basic and applied regional marine science programme and marine meteorological programme will be formulated as a basis for the protection of the marine environment of the Region. In formulating the operational details of these programmes, planned and ongoing national and regional programmes will be taken into account.

13. The following programmes are recognized as components of the coordinated regional environmental assessment programme:

13.1 Survey of national capabilities of the Region in the field of marine sciences including marine meteorology covering:

(a) Scientific and administrative institutions;
(b) Information centres and data sources;
(c) Research facilities and equipment;
(d) Manpower;
(e) Existing environmental laws and regulations;
(f) Ongoing and planned activities;
(g) Publications.

13.2 Assessment of the origin and magnitude of oil pollution in the Region comprising:

(a) Baseline studies on the sources, transport and distribution of oil and petroleum hydrocarbon pollution in the Region;
(b) Physical, chemical and biological oceanography of the Region

relevant to the transport, distribution and fate of oil as a pollutant;

(c) Marine meteorology relevant to the transport and distribution of oil as a pollutant.

13.3 Assessment of the magnitude of pollutants affecting human health and marine ecosystems of the Region consisting of:

(a) Survey of land-based sources of industrial and municipal wastes discharged directly or indirectly into the sea or reaching it through the atmosphere;

(b) Studies on the impact of industrial and municipal waste, including microbiological agents, on human health;

(c) Research on effects of pollutants and other human activities, such as dredging and land reclamation on important marine species, communities and ecosystems;

(d) Baseline studies and monitoring of the levels of selected pollutants, in particular heavy metals, in marine organisms.

13.4 Assessment of factors relevant to the ecology of the Region and to the exploitation of its living resources including:

(a) Biology of commercially important species of crustaceans, molluscs and fish in the Region, including their stock assessment;

(b) Plankton productivity and distribution in the Region;

(c) Ecological studies of important natural habitats in the intertidal and subtidal zones, including creeks (khores) in the Region.

13.5 Assessment of geological processes such as sedimentation contributing to, or modifying, the fate of pollutants in the Region, and their impact on human health, marine ecosystems and human activities, as well as effects of coastal engineering and mining.

14. The programmes listed in paragraph 13 are interdisciplinary and interrelated in nature. Therefore, while preparing the operational details of each programme, due attention should be paid to their close coordination in order to avoid duplication.

15. The priorities to be assigned to the activities listed in paragraph 13 will be determined by the Governments of the Region taking into account the present level of development in the Region and the pressing need to provide reliable and comparable data on which sound management decisions can rest.

16. The agreed programme will be executed primarily through existing national institutions within the framework of regional cooperation keeping in mind that for some projects a training programme should be formulated and that the assistance of experts from outside the Region might be required in the initial phase of some projects.

17. Operational details of each programme will be developed primarily by experts nominated by the Governments of the Region. The documents describing the operational details of the approved programme as well as the national institutions participating in the programmes will be approved by the Governments before the implementation of the programmes.

II. ENVIRONMENTAL MANAGEMENT

18. The countries of the Region have experienced unprecedented rates of growth during recent years, particularly in areas such as urbanization, industrialization, agriculture, transport, trade, and exploration and exploitation of the Region's resources. Continuous socio-economic development can be achieved on a sustainable basis if environmental considerations are taken into account.

19. To achieve the objectives of the development and environmental management component of the Action Plan the following preparatory activities should be undertaken:

    19.1 Preparation and up-dating of a directory of Government-designated institutions available in the Region and active in fields related to the environmental management components of the Action Plan;

    19.2 Assessment of present and future development activities and their major environmental impact in order to evaluate the degree of their influence on the environment and to find appropriate measures to either eliminate or reduce any damaging effects which they may have;

    19.3 Identification of the most relevant ongoing national, regional or internationally supported development projects which have beneficial environmental effects such as the various fisheries projects of FAO, the environmental sanitation activities of WHO, and the assistance in industrial waste treatment provided through the United Nations Industrial Development Organization. The most significant of these projects should be strengthened and expanded to serve as demonstrations and training sites on a regional basis.

20. Furthermore, in view of the priorities and needs of the Region, the following cooperative programmes relevant to the management of regional environmental problems stemming from national development activities will be undertaken:

    20.1 Formulation of regional contingency plans for accidents involving oil exploration, expoitation and transport, and strengthening the meteorological services contributing to the development of contingency plans and to their execution in coordination with existing or future marine regional meteorological programmes;

    20.2 Assistance in development of national capabilities in engineering knowledge needed for regional environmental protection;

    20.3 Strengthening the national public health services and their coordination whenever transboundary interests require it;

    20.4 Rational exploitation and management of marine living resources, including aquaculture, on a sustainable basis, and the establishment of protected aquatic and terrestrial areas, such as marine parks, wetlands and others;

    20.5 Coordination of marine and land transport activities and the creation of a regional transport coordinated programme with special emphasis on port-generated pollution;

    20.6 Development of principles and guidelines for coastal area development and management through workshops;

    20.7 Coordination of national water management policies including community water supply and water quality control, whenever they may have impact on the marine environment of the Region;

20.8 Upkeep of records of oil pollution incidents in the Region with relevant information on the impact of such pollution on the marine environment.

21. As part of the activities and regional cooperative programmes mentioned in paragraphs 19 and 20 a vast training programme should be developed for personnel from the Region. Such a programme may be executed through training at existing national, regional or international institutions ready to offer their facilities.

22. Marine and coastal area environmental protection and enhancement cannot be achieved without the full support and cooperation of all those concerned. Therefore, adequate resources should be devoted to systematic and regular campaigns for public awareness of environmental issues in the Region.

[   ]

Source: Final Act of the Kuwait Regional Conference of Plenipotentiaries on the Protection and Development of the Marine Environment and the Coastal Areas, United Nations Environmental Programme, Kuwait 1976.

The Conference of Arab Ministers Responsible for the Application of Science and Technology to Development – CASTARAB

Origins

The first meeting of CASTARAB was held, at the initiative of UNESCO, in Rabat in August 1976. The preparatory work for the conference was extensive and involved a comprehensive review of the status of science and technology in the Arab world, including studies on training and brain drain. ALECSO also participated in the preparatory work of the conference. A preliminary meeting of Arab scientists in Kuwait defined the outlines of the conference.

CASTARAB was the fourth of a series of conferences on the application of science and technology to development (CAST) organized by UNESCO in various regions of the world. Previous conferences, held at the rate of one every two years, focused on Latin America (CASTALA), Asia (CASTASIS) and Africa (CASTAFRICA).

The CASTARAB recommendations have been described as 'the first coherent Arab scientific plan'. The main outcome of the CASTARAB I includes:

1. The adoption of the Rabat Declaration and the resolution on an Arab Scientific Plan of Action (comprising some thirty-eight decisions and recommendations).
2. The decision to set up, at ministerial level, a CASTARAB Standing Conference to meet at three-year intervals.
3. The decision to create a CASTARAB Continuing Committee composed of four ministers, elected by the Standing Conference, and meeting every six months.
4. The recommendation to set up an Arab Fund for Scientific and Technological Research with a capital of US$500 million and entrusting to The Ministerial Continuing Committee the preparation of the feasibility study and draft articles of the agreement for submission to Arab governments and the Arab development funds.

Projects and Programmes

CASTARAB's main concern is to follow up, in conjunction with UNESCO and ALESCO, the main recommendations of the conference,

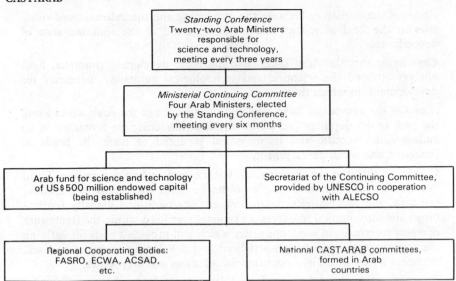

Source: UNESCO Regional Office for Science and Technology in the Arab States, 'A Case Study of Some UNESCO Projects Related to the Brain Drain', in Zahlan, A. B. (ed.), *The Arab Brain Drain*, Ithaca Press, London 1981.

Fig. 2.3 CASTARAB organs and links

promote regional cooperation on a number of specified fields, and to set up the Arab Fund for Scientific and Technological Research. A feasibility study and draft articles of the agreement to set up the fund have already been completed. A number of national CASTARAB Committees have also been set up.

Documents

1. The Rabat Declaration

The Conference of Ministers of Arab States Responsible for the Application of Science and Technology to Development (CASTARAB), convened in Rabat from 16 to 25 August 1976 by the United Nations Educational, Scientific and Cultural Organization (UNESCO), with the cooperation of the Arab Educational, Cultural and Scientific Organization (ALECSO) and the United Nations Economic Commission for Western Asia (ECWA),

Bearing in mind the resolutions and recommendations of the Conference of Arab Ministers Responsible for Scientific Research and Heads of National Research Councils in the Arab States, held in Baghdad in 1974,

Fully aware of the present situation of science and technology in the Arab world and of its immediate and more distant future needs in scientific fields, in both the medium and long term,

Convinced of the vital role of science and technology in economic, social and cultural development and in the fulfilment and liberation of man,

Aware of the disparities between the developing and the industrialized countries in the field of science and technology and of the resulting state of dependence,

Considering that the Arab states, like the other developing countries, have not yet attained the scientific and technological autonomy, necessary for development, to which they aspire,

Aware of the causes that have hindered the advance of the Arab world along the path to development and of the obstacles hindering the formation of an endogenous scientific and technological potential to meet the needs of economic and social development,

Convinced that the development of science and technology in the Third World will continue to encounter obstacles until the means of acquiring scientific and technological know-how are equitably and globally redistributed and until natural resources are rationally utilized within the framework of a new international economic order which will provide a basis for defining the relationships between industrialized and developing countries and will represent a new phase of civilization for all states and all peoples,

Convinced of the need to promote and develop the Arabic language in order to make it a tool of authentic scientific and cultural development,

Reaffirming the right of all Arab citizens to have access to an adequate scientific and technological culture and to enjoy its socio-economic benefits,

Noting with great satisfaction the keen desire of the participants to develop and strengthen collective inter-Arab action in the fields of science and technology at the international and regional levels and also bilaterally.

Declares

1. That the Arab nation is resolved to apply science and technology to economic, social and cultural development in order to improve the quality of life and to reduce inequalities between countries and between peoples.

2. That scientific and technological development is vitally necessary for the purpose of reducing the inequalities in economic and political power which at present characterize relationships between states and constitute a potential danger to world peace.

3. That the Arab nation, at a decisive turning point in its history, has the capacities, the human potential and the material means of meeting the challenge of implanting science and technology in order to emerge from underdevelopment, to eliminate poverty and ignorance and ensure the well-being of its population.

4. That the exploitation of science and technology in order to improve the human condition requires enormous efforts and a number of concrete actions, in particular;

   (a) The reconsideration of problems bearing on science and technology in a global and intersectoral context with a view to their integration in the long-term national development policies and plans of every Arab country and of Arab society, in keeping with its historic civilization;

   (b) The creation of national bodies responsible for science and technology policies and of research and development institutions, the strengthening of existing institutions, increasing the resources available to them and ensuring continuous training;

(c) The establishment of closer links between educational, scientific and technological policies, in order to promote the teaching of science and technology and to ensure endogenous scientific and technological development suited to economic and social situations and needs;

(d) The attainment of a proper balance between the endogenous development of local technology and the importation of knowhow in accordance with a clear strategy reconciling the execution of priority projects with the formation of the scientific and technological potential of tomorrow, to which end the technological strategy should be spread over a number of stages of greater or lesser urgency in order to respect the objectives of the Arab states, both individually and collectively, in the field of civilization and culture;

(e) Recognition of the great value of scientific information, of the need to use modern technical procedures which give access to it, and also of the necessity of creating national documentation and information centres or of strengthening those already in existence;

(f) The improvement of the administrative, legal and social status of scientific research workers and technologists, and promotion of the establishment of scientific institutions and bodies that could create an environment conducive to scientific progress in general and to putting an end to the outflow of talent from which the Arab world suffers in particular;

(g) Elaboration of integrated policies on natural resources covering the study, prospection and rational exploitation of such resources and the protection of the environment in accordance with national overall long-term objectives;

(h) Setting up schemes for inter-Arab cooperation harmonizing and coordinating national and overall Arab strategies within the framework of existing organizations and institutions before envisaging the creation of new structures;

(i) Dissemination of scientific culture and promotion of wider public awareness of the importance and necessity of science from the economic, social and cultural points of view, thereby guaranteeing the necessary backing and support for the endogenous development of science and technology and for the improvement of the human condition.

5. *Calls on* governments of Arab states and on competent regional and international organizations to endeavour to apply the recommendations of this conference which together constitute *an Arab scientific plan of action* indicating the prospects and options available to the Arab world at a decisive stage in its history.

6. *Emphasizes* the importance of the recommendation adopted with regard to the creation of an Arab Fund for Scientific and Technological Research, which reflects the determination of the Arab world to act effectively to eliminate one of the obstacles impeding scientific development and cultural progress.

7. *Emphasizes* the importance of establishing a CASTARAB Continuing Committee to follow up the implementation of the recommendations of

the conference, to make preparations for CASTARAB II and to harmonize the position of the Arab states at the second United Nations Conference on Science and Technology for Development (1979).

2. Arab Fund for Scientific and Technological Research

The conference *recommends*:

1. That there be established an Arab Fund for Scientific and Technological Research in the Arab world.
2. That the CASTARAB Continuing Committee establish, by such means as it shall consider appropriate and drawing on the experience of the competent authorities, a Technical Study to define the tasks and organs of the Fund, and adopt the technical and administrative rules that will govern its activities.
3. That this study should take into account the existence of such Arab funds as the Arab Fund for Economic Development, and of other funds which could furnish, either wholly or in part, the resources of the proposed Arab Fund for Scientific and Technological Research.
4. That the CASTARAB Continuing Committee should be responsible for communicating with governments and competent Arab bodies, including the Arab Fund for Economic and Social Development, to encourage them to participate in the financing of the technical feasibility study to be carried out concerning the proposed Arab Fund for Scientific and Technological Research.
5. That the Technical Study should be completed within one year and its conclusions submitted to the Arab governments with a view to determining the objectives and administrative and technical status of the proposed Arab Fund for Scientific and Technological Research.
6. That it would be desirable to set the initial amount of the fund at a minimum of US$500 million.

Source: UNESCO, *Science and Technology in the Development of Arab States,* Document SC-76/CASTARAB/3, 1976.

The Islamic Foundation for Science and Technology for Development – IFSTAD

Origins

The proposal for the establishment of IFSTAD, a supranational body that will promote and coordinate science and technology activities throughout the Muslim world was first made at the Fifth Islamic Conference of Foreign Ministers, held at Kuala Lumpur in June 1974. Following the conference, several studies on IFSTAD were prepared and a Group of Experts from amongst the members of the Organization of Islamic Conferences (OIC) met frequently until the beginning of 1979, to draw up plans for launching IFSTAD and finalize the US$50 million first phase of its expansion. The charter of the foundation was finally approved by the Tenth Islamic Foreign Ministers Conference which met in Fez, Morocco, in May 1979. A fifteen-member Advisory Science Council, which determines the foundation's policy, was set up in 1981.

Projects and Programmes

IFSTAD's projects are carried out within a general framework developed by the First Islamic Science Conference, held in Jeddah, Saudi Arabia, in March 1979. The conference prepared the report of the OIC for UNCSTD held in August 1979 in Vienna. The Tenth Islamic Conference of Foreign Ministers approved this report for presentation to UNCSTD as a common position paper of the member states of OIC. In January 1980, the Fifth Session of the Islamic Commission for Economic, Cultural and Social Affairs approved two priority programmes to be undertaken by IFSTAD: development of a plan of action to set up programmes and institutions for research on Islamic values and ethics on science and technology for development and the establishment of an inter-governmental committee to study brain drain, selective migration and better utilization of indigenous talents (see documents).

In addition to these two priority programmes, IFSTAD plans to develop a common science policy for the member states of the OIC and set up mechanisms which will act as catalysts in implementing this policy. Preparatory work is also being carried out on the establishment of much-needed scientific and technological institutions in the Muslim countries, particularly technical universities in Africa and South-East Asia. IFSTAD will also work to improve the status of scientists and technicians in Muslim countries and special attention is to be given to Muslim scientists working in the West. IFSTAD will also be undertaking an advisory role in science planning and policy-making and will provide particular assistance to countries which do not have national science bodies.

Documents

1. Charter of IFSTAD

PREAMBLE

Keeping in view the objectives of the OIC which seek to promote Islamic solidarity among member states and to strengthen cooperation between them in the economic, social, cultural, scientific and other vital fields;

Conscious of the fact that the promotion of science and technology is essential for the purpose of achieving rapid, coordinated and wide-ranging socio-economic development of the Muslim peoples;

Conscious also of the rich historical experience of the Muslim world in the fields of science and technology, and of the need to foster the distinctive Islamic culture which combines the universal spiritual and moral values of Islam with the world view of science;

And in implementation of the Resolutions adopted by the 6th, 7th, 8th and 9th Islamic Conferences of Foreign Ministers, in this respect;

The member states of the OIC have decided to set up a subsidiary organ for science, technology and development, in terms of Article V (paragraph 5) of the Charter of the Islamic Conference and in accordance with the following provisions:

Article I: *Name*

The name of the organization shall be:

THE ISLAMIC FOUNDATION FOR SCIENCE, TECHNOLOGY
AND DEVELOPMENT (IFSTAD)

hereinafter referred to as 'The Foundation'.

Article II: *Headquarters*

The Headquarters of the foundation shall be in Jeddah.

Article III: *Objectives*

The objectives of the foundation shall be as follows:

1. To promote and encourage research activities in the fields of science and technology within an Islamic framework to help solve some of the current problems of the Muslim World and of mankind in general.

2. To promote cooperation and coordination in the fields of science and technology within the Islamic world in order to strengthen the bonds of Islamic solidarity.
3. To ensure that all member countries of the OIC, both individually and collectively, make the greatest possible use of science and technology (including the social sciences) in the formulation and implementation of their socio-economic plans, keeping in view the need to consolidate the unique Islamic personality and character.

Article IV: *Functions*

To achieve the objectives outlined in Article III, the foundation shall have the following functions:

1. To render advice to the member states and to the secretary-general on matters connected with science and technology and carry out studies required by the Conference of Foreign Ministers or by the secretary-general.
2. To formulate a strategy for the establishment of an Islamic strategy for development, coordination and cooperation in the fields of science and technology.
3. To invite and assist member countries which do not have national organizations responsible for science policy-making and planning to establish such bodies which should be affiliated to the highest authority in the country and to assist these national bodies in effectively carrying out their functions.
4. To work out appropriate models for science policy and assist the member countries to adopt them.
5. To survey and evaluate the available scientific and technological potentials of the member countries.
6. To prepare plans for the training of scientific manpower capable of disseminating Islamic scientific culture.
7. To support existing research institutions in the member countries and assist research activities by Muslim scientists in conformity with the objectives of the OIC.
8. To promote the establishment, where needed, of scientific and technological institutions in member countries, particularly technical universities in Africa and South-East Asia.
9. To determine the financial resources needed to ensure the effectiveness of scientific activities in the member countries, and suggest means for raising these funds and advise on their utilization.
10. To undertake continuous evaluation of efforts in the fields of science and technology in the member countries and follow up the execution of scientific plans with a view to ensure permanent progress.
11. To promote scientific cooperation with advanced research centres in other countries and with international and regional organizations.
12. To introduce and promote modern scientific disciplines, such as nuclear sciences, and research will be given priority to enhance the creation of distinctive technologies indigenous to the Islamic world.
13. To undertake, promote and or support joint programmes of research in scientific and technological fields such as:

(a) Geological surveys and resources maps.
(b) Energy resources, e.g. solar, geothermal and nuclear energy.
(c) Petroleum, its derivatives and petrochemicals.
(d) Water resources and water desalination.
(e) Electronics and engineering industries.
(f) Medical research and pharmaceuticals.
(g) Oceanography and exploitation of marine resources.
(h) Space research.
(i) Defence technology and defence science.
(j) Ecology.
(k) Food and agriculture.
(l) Irrigation.
(m) Education.
(n) Housing.
(o) Any other specific fields in science and technology as may be required.

14. To conduct studies on the impact of utilization of science and technology in socio-economic plans on Islamic culture and heritage.
15. To establish Islamic centres for scientific documentation and information and to support the existing centres.
16. To give special care to Muslims living in non-Muslim countries and particularly those in the industrialized countries. It is proposed to set up one or more Islamic universities for science and technology in these countries.
17. To study and suggest means for improving the status of scientists and their assistants in the member countries of the OIC. In this respect special care should be given to the problem of brain drain, including measures to encourage scientists who have gone abroad to return to their countries.
18. To conduct studies on mineral resources, particularly petroleum and their optimum utilization.
19. To promote cooperation between Islamic countries in the field of scientific equipment repair, design and manufacture.
20. To promote the teaching of Arabic language in non-Arabic Islamic countries and publish scientific and technical books, periodicals and reviews in Arabic.
21. To hold Islamic scientific conferences, seminars and study groups.
22. To publish Islamic scientific journals.
23. Any other function assigned to the council.

[. . .]

Article VI: *Functions of the Advisory Science Council*

The council shall, in accordance with the Charter and the Regulations of the Islamic Science Conference:

1. Determine the foundation policy in scientific and technical matters.
2. Approve detailed schemes of research, development and scientific education and decide on any supplementary programme of activities of the foundation.
3. Adopt the budget and determine the financial arrangements of the

foundation in accordance with the provision made by the Islamic Conference.

4. Form permanent and/or *ad hoc* committees to undertake any specific studies.
5. Make the regulations for its own meetings and draw up the rules and regulations of the foundation.
6. Have such other functions as may be assigned to it.

[. . .]

Source: OIC Document ICFM/10–79/CS/D.7 Annex.

2. Priority Programmes of IFSTAD

(a) *Plan of Action to Establish Programmes or Institutions for Studies, Research and Publications on Islamic Ethics and Values in Science and Technology for Development*

IFSTAD will support the establishment of programmes for studies, research, and publications on Islamic Ethics and Values in Science and Technology (Islamic-EVIST). It will also try to guide member states and their educational and other institutions to take full advantage of the United Nations bodies in setting up Islamic-EVIST programmes in accordance with the UNCSTD Recommendation 90(c).

The fundamental issues and problems in Islamic-EVIST concern Islamic epistemology; Islamic philosophy and sociology of education, science and technology; Islamic social sciences; history of Muslim and non-Muslim science and technology; etc., in their relation to issues of values and ethics regarding: 1. the genesis, growth, development, and assimilation of science and technology; and 2. the identification and removal of the *internal* obstacles in the behavioural Muslim culture, and their educational, economic, political, and other institutions.

These broad concerns could be more specifically defined in terms of the 'subject categories of science and technology policy' in the UNESCO project, 'World Survey of Research Projects, Studies and Courses in Science and Technology' (UNESCO/NS/ROU/459/EC, Paris, June 1979). Some of these subject areas particularly relevant to our interests are: the Islamic theory, philosophy, and systematization of science and technology; history of Muslim science and technology (including the medieval and modern interaction between the Muslim and other legacies in science and technology); Islamic sociology and ethics of science and technology, and of science and society; creativity and psycho-sociology of scientific research (historical and contemporary); Islamic economics of science and technology; Islamic analysis and assessment of scientific and technological potential (personnel, institutions, funds, facilities, etc.); Islamic theory, and Muslim practices, of science and technology policy-making and legislation at the global, regional, and national levels; Islamic scope for and constraints on the transfer, diffusion and implementation of science and technology, especially of contemporary non-Muslim origins; Islamic organization and management of scientific and technological activities of the levels of the performers and institutions; pan-Islamic, regional, and international cooperation, policy and legislation in science and technology; Islamic societal analysis and assessment of the content and results of scientific and technological plans and projects, etc.

An even more specific identification of the programme subjects can be made in terms of the publication, *EVIST Resource Directory: A Directory of Programmes and Courses in the Field of Ethics and Values in Science and Technology* (American Association for the Advancement of Science, 1776 Massachusetts Ave, N.W., Washington DC 20036. USA, AAS Pub. 78–6, 1978). This *EVIST Resource Directory* gives detailed information on EVIST programmes with Western orientation in 117 United States universities concerning 'science, technology and human values', and 'bio-medical concerns'. Some of the possible 'programme subjects' and subject areas amenable to the application of Islamic ideology, ethics and values are:

1. Islamic philosophy and sociology of science and technology.
2. History of Muslim science, technology, and learning (and their correlation with the history of Islamic ideas, institutions, and Muslim cultures).
3. Science and Islamic public policy (e.g., population, food, and science; issues in biology and genetics, such as evolution and heredity; politics of science; professional ethics of scientists and public interest; social and government regulation of scientific research and manpower planning).
4. Technology and Islamic public policy (e.g., appropriate technology; alternative technology and development; ethics and values in technology assessment; impact on technology of socio-economic value judgements; technology and social change; law, ethics and industrial regulations).
5. Environmental studies and Islam (e.g., conservation and management of natural resources, and Islamic concepts of welfare); Islamic ideological, value, and ethical aspects of ecology (e.g., wildlife preservation), of environmental chemistry (e.g., use of herbicides and pesticides), of energy (e.g., nuclear power development, design of houses), of environmental policy-making (e.g., air pollution control vs. industrialization; forests conservation vs. agricultural development); Islamic ethics, economic efficiency, and technology; Islamic impact assessment of engineering-economic projects.
6. Medicine, health care, and Islam (e.g., Islamic ethics in health care for rural and poor communities; law and politics of health care; ethical response to disease, grief, ageing, dying and death; experimentation with dead and alive human beings and animals; drug use and control, transplantation of organs; euthanasia).

Criteria for Selection of Programme Subjects
In order to set up an Islamic–EVIST programme or institution, an educational or research institution of a member state would need to select a specific 'programme subject' or 'subject category' in relation to the fundamental issues and problems in Islamic–EVIST. It is obvious that all these subjects or categories need Islamic treatment. Importance and urgency of a problem, its relevance to overall and technological development, existing or available capabilities of scholars, institutional and individual interests, etc., will be factors in the selection of priorities while setting up a programme. The more fundamental issues and practical problems should be tackled instead

of launching programmes dealing with remote, unusual, uncommon, and highly abstract issues and concerns. Islamic–EVIST programmes are programmes for the *application* of Islamic ethics and values in science and technology to solve problems of hunger, disease, education, housing, transportation, etc. For example, the programme in history, philosophy and sociology of science and technology should not lead to more philosophizing and moralizing, or historical romanticism concerning the achievements of medieval Muslims. Such programmes should lead to reforms in curricula, science and technology policy, research and development policies, manpower development policies, economic development strategies, etc.

IFSTAD would probably give priority to publication of manuscripts of brochures or books which have remained unpublished for lack of funds, and support for the author to finalize his manuscript.

Preference might be given to setting up a programme with an existing institution. Thus the 'programme' or 'institution' would have the organizational form of an 'institute', 'centre', 'programme', 'department', etc., within a university, research institute (private or governmental), government agency or ministry, etc. The programme could take the form of a new set up or merely involve the re-organization and re-orientation of existing resources, human and institutional, to serve the goals and objectives of Islamic–EVIST.

Programme of Action

The member states are requested to identify an individual and an agency as a 'focal point' for liaison in implementation of this 'plan of action'. The focal point might be an official in the highest national science, technology and educational body responsible for policy-making and coordination.

The member states, educational and research institutions, and Islamic non-governmental organizations are urged to publicize this plan of action, and to suggest the names of specialists in Islamic-EVIST. They might form a group of experts and advisers who could be called upon to advise and assist IFSTAD in preparing the detailed plans and in implementing them by establishing Islamic–EVIST programmes in interested countries and institutions . . .

The IFSTAD requests the educational and research institutions and the Islamic non-governmental organizations of the member and non-member states to send their formal proposals to establish Islamic–EVIST programmes or institutions.

(b) *Proposal for formation of Intergovernmental Committee on Reverse Brain Drain, Selective Migration and Better Utilization of Indigenous Talents: A Unified System Approach to Manpower Planning*

The Problem

The talents and skills of specialists and creative individuals in science, technology and the inter-disciplinary fields are a principal national asset. Such a stock of human resources is, perhaps, the most important and scarce, and the worst utilized resource among all the factors of production. These talented persons are the Muslim and non-Muslim citizens of member states as well as the Muslims of the minority Muslim communities in Non-Member developing countries.

The loss of such talented and creative persons occurs in various forms. Their migration from the less advanced countries to the Western countries is well known as 'brain drain'. Second, the migration to, or prolonged settlement in, a 'gainer' or 'recipient' capital-rich developing country is also a loss to the backward 'loser' or 'donor' country. Such transfer of talents among developing countries tends to be looked upon favourably as a net increase in the global Muslim welfare. However, this might aggravate the problems of the developing loser country. Third, the inefficient utilization, misuse, or mis-allocation of such talents within a member state or minority Muslim community, is also a loss of brain trust. A distinction might be made here between the 'external' (first category) and the 'internal' brain drain (third category). This internal brain drain is presently, perhaps, the most serious loss among the three categories. A unified and comprehensive approach needs to be adopted to preserve, develop and utilize the skilled manpower and the creative persons within a member state and those potentially available from the industrially advanced countries. Efforts made so far in successfully reversing the brain drain have shown that, by and large, either such a success has proven to be short-lived or the persons concerned could not achieve much in their recipient countries. The conditions and attitudes which prevent the full utilization of indigenous talents, their growth and development, also provide 'the push-factors' that make local talents leave their home country.

It becomes a matter of paramount importance, therefore, that the unified approach focuses on the causes and solutions for the deficiencies and inefficiencies of the whole system in a backward country. The unified approach must also be a systems approach that identifies at the operational level the deficiencies and inefficiencies in each sub-system such as the ethical, the motivational, the legal, the political, the economic, the social, the organizational, etc. The unified systems approach must offer specific recommendations for action at the level of each sub-system. This also requires a boldness for self-critique, a self-educational and purificationist campaign, and a will for action through the strategies of both gradualism and radical transformations. The successful implementation of such a unified systems approach is essential to provide a 'big push' towards the development of science and technology and, consequently, comprehensive socio-economic development.

Programme of Action
IFSTAD will form an 'Inter-Governmental Committee on Reverse Brain Drain, Selective Migration, and Better Utilization of Indigenous Talents'.

The committee would want to create, first, a taskforce to make a thorough study of the problem and the solutions that have been tried or proposed. The report of the taskforce should be prepared in a given period of time. The taskforce will collect, for example, published studies and data, the laws and regulations enacted and implemented, the measures taken at an operational level by specific industrial or academic or governmental institutions, and the recommendations made in conferences as well as internal memoranda. The taskforce will also commission special studies, for example, on the brain drain talents in Western Europe, North America, and Australia, conduct surveys and collect data on talented persons from the poorer developing countries working in the capital-rich developing countries, conduct surveys of opinions and attitudes of talented persons as to the conditions to induce them to return to their countries of origin or another developing 'Third' country, etc. The taskforce will give special emphasis to the problems of indigenous talents whose skills are, or are perceived to be, not efficiently and fully developed and utilized. The solution of the problem of the indigenous talents provide the best 'pull-factors' in attracting, retaining and the optimum utilization of potential brain drain talents.

The taskforce would consist of specialists drawn from the academic institutions, the government agencies, the industry, the non-governmental organizations, and individuals selected on the basis of their expertise. The Intergovernmental Committee will consist of persons nominated by the governments of the member states of a level high enough to suggest and implement policy recommendations in the areas of proposed model legislation, socio-economic measures, institutional action, etc.

The report of the taskforce will be published in the interests of dissemination of information and encouragement of discussion. The recommendations of the committee will be presented for approval by the Islamic Conference of Foreign Ministers which may wish to create a higher-level and a more prestigious Intergovernmental Committee to function as a follow-up committee in order to encourage implementations in the member states.

Source: OIC Document IS/3–81/CS/D.2.

Union of Arab National Research Councils – UANRC

Origins

UANRC was formed in May 1975 in Baghdad on the initiative of Iraq's Foundation for Scientific Research. It operated with temporary staff until July 1977 when a full-time executive secretary was appointed. Algeria, Egypt, Iraq, Jordan, Kuwait, Palestine, Sudan and Tunisia are affiliated with the union.

Projects and Programmes

Since its formation the union has concentrated on following selected recommendations of CASTARAB, including the proposed Arab Fund for Scientific and Technological Research. It plans to establish a network of Arab seismological stations and to carry out a field study of agricultural stations in the Arab world. The union has also floated the idea of setting up two Arab centres, one in Jordan and one in Sudan, to coordinate projects on desertification in the region. The union has also taken an active part in establishing the proposed Arab Centre for the Transfer and Development of Technology in Baghdad; and has negotiated, under the auspices of the Euro–Arab Dialogue, with Denmark and Ireland, to set up a pilot centre under its administration. The union also has plans to publish a bulletin on forthcoming Arab conferences.

PART III

COUNTRY PROFILES

Afghanistan

Demographic and Economic Background

Afghanistan is a land-locked country with two major boundaries – with the Soviet Union to the north, and with Pakistan to the south and east. Mainly at an altitude of 1,200 m, it covers about 650,000 km with high and irregular mountain ranges, and there is always risk of earthquakes. In 1979, Afghanistan had an estimated population of 15.5 million. Apart from the capital Kabul, there are only four cities with over 100,000 inhabitants. Over 85 per cent of the total population live in rural areas, 70 per cent of whom are inhabitants of remote and scattered villages or nomads.

Afghanistan's economy is almost entirely based on agriculture. Main agricultural products are cotton, fresh and dried fruits, wheat, rice, barley and millet. Though self-sufficient in wheat production, Afghanistan depends on imports in times of natural catastrophes and during years of low yield. Cotton is grown in northern provinces, but cultivation has now also started in the Helmand Velley and Herat. Two of Afghanistan's principal foreign-exchange earners are karakul pelts and hand-woven carpets. Sheep, excluding karakul, are the main source of meat for the country and produce enough wool for export.

Industry contributes less than 10 per cent of the country's GDP. Some of the local demand for textiles, edible oils, sugar, footwear, fertilizer and cement are met indigenously. A major industrial estate, some 8 km from Kabul, is being set up with Soviet help. The estate contains seventy plants, including textile mills, heavy vehicles repair workshops, ice-manufacturing plants, fruit processing plants, shoe factories and factories for producing soap, washing powder, nails, car batteries and lubricants. The estate is to be completed by 1983.

Afghanistan has considerable reserves of coal, natural gas, salt and lapis lazuli. Iron ore has also been discovered recently. Exploratory oil drilling, with Soviet help, has located oil in northern provinces and the search for oil has now been extended to southern parts of the country. The natural gas reserves are located near Mazar-i-Sharif from where gas is exported directly to the Soviet Union. Lapis lazuli, a semi-precious stone, has been mined in Afghanistan since 2500 BC. The only major mine in the world of this distinctive stone is located in the north-eastern province of Badakhshan.

With Soviet assistance, Afghanistan's government is planning to expand the industrial sector extensively. A plan is being developed to use natural gas for the conversion of iron ore into steel. Industrial capacities of local textiles, edible oils, sugar, footwear, fertilizer and cement industries will be improved and new processing and handling industries will be set up to promote leather and animal casings exports and exports of fruits, vegetables and meat.

Government Science and Research

The Afghanistan Academy of Sciences, established in 1979, is responsible for science policy and planning and the administration of research in the country. In February 1981, the academy signed a wide-ranging agreement for cooperation and assistance with the Soviet Academy of Sciences. The agreement calls for training Afghan scientists and engineers and setting up a National Sciences Centre of the Afghanistan Academy of Sciences.

The academy has three institutes: the Institute of Natural Sciences, the Institute of Social Sciences and the Institute of Languages and Literature. The Institute of Natural Sciences has departments for botany, zoology, geology, chemistry and seismology. Research is largely concerned with geological and seismological surveys and flora and fauna of Afghanistan. The institute also maintains a plants museum and a botanical garden.

Some research is also carried out at the Afghan Cartographic and Cadastral Surveys Institute in Kabul and the Departments of Mines and Geology of the Ministry of Mines and Industry. The Department of Mines and Industry carries out geological and mineralogical research and exploitation and is preparing extensive geological maps of Afghanistan. It publishes the *Bulletin of Geology of Afghanistan*.

The Institute of Public Health in Kabul conducts research into public health and studies of indigenous diseases. It is also responsible for the compilation, publication and analysis of statistical data and is a government reference laboratory. It publishes the *Afghan Journal of Public Health*.

The Ministry of Agriculture has a Research and Extension Department where research on improving the local breeds of cattle is being conducted.

Academic Science and Research

Afghanistan has two universities: Kabul University and the University of Nangrahar. Kabul University was founded in 1932 and has eleven faculties, including faculties for medicine, pharmacy, veterinary medicine, science, agriculture, engineering and a Polytechnic Institute. The university has an extensive collaboration programme with the Soviet Academy of Sciences, which is promoting research at all the science-oriented faculties. Research with the faculties is coordinated through the University Research Centre, which is governed by an academic board. The Faculty of Science has a nuclear physics laboratory and houses the Atomic Energy Commission.

The university maintains a Science Museum, a Museum of Pathology, and publishes the *Afghan Medical Journal*.

The University of Nangrahar was founded in 1972 from the Medical Faculty of Kabul University. It has faculties for medicine, agriculture, engineering, education and training. Research at the university is focused on medicine, particularly internal medicine, forensic medicine, paediatrics, neuropsychiatry and pathology.

Algeria

Demographic and Economic Background

Algeria is in North Africa; the Mediterranean Sea forms its northern boundary, Mali and Niger lie to the south, Tunisia and Libya to the east, and Morocco, the Sahara and Mauritania to the west. Geographically the country is divided into two zones. The north is mountainous and relatively humid and virtually all of the country's cultivable land is there, the mountain sides being green and thickly forested. The south of the country is part of the great Sahara Desert. The total area of the country is 2,382,000 km², and in 1979 the population was estimated to be 18.2 million, with an average annual growth rate of 3.3 per cent. About 55 per cent of the population is less than twenty years of age, and as a consequence, a large proportion of the Algerian population is inactive economically, since effective working age is at least fifteen years.

Algeria is mainly an agricultural country, but it is rich in natural resources such as oil, natural gas, phosphorus and iron ore. The country is following an industrial expansion programme based on these resources.

All the agricultural activity in the country is carried out on the northern coastal strip. Emphasis is on farming cooperatives, 'socialist villages' and encouraging the nomads to settle and cultivate land. Wheat and barley are among the most important crops, but grapes for wine, olives for olive oil and tobacco are also grown. Massive irrigation schemes have been introduced in the north. Similar schemes are now being introduced in the southern arid regions; one such scheme is the 'green dam' project, which involves a massive 20-km wide strip of forest to be planted in the south of the country, from the Moroccan to the Tunisian borders. It consists of Aleppo pine and cypress and includes fruit and olive trees and water is provided from wells drilled in a line.

Algeria has an expanding industrial sector. There are some 300 industrial plants in the country producing products ranging from steel and fertilizers to heavy machinery. But petroleum is the main product sector and provides the revenues for industrial development of the country. Gas is also becoming increasingly important and there are plans to build pipelines to Europe.

The present five year development plan (1980–84) is aiming for significant improvements in agriculture with vast plans for efficient use of water supplies, irrigated farming, and the construction of some hundred dams, mostly in the previously neglected high plateau region, in the next few years. Major projects include the agro-industrial complex at Tebessa, land reclamation near Batna, and other irrigation programmes in the Sidi Bel Abbes region.

Massive exploration programmes in the Hogger region have revealed large uranium deposits. It is estimated that Algeria could be producing 1,000 tonnes of uranium concentrate per year by 1985. Other minerals in the region include gold and tungsten. An experimental dry extraction plant for gold has been set up at Tiririne. There are plans to set up further plants for extraction of gold and to bring new mines into production. Algeria already mines phosphate and iron ore, and in lesser quantities, sulphur, zinc, tungsten, antimony, mercury, copper, manganese, and salt.

Science Policy and Organization

Algeria has an aggressive science policy which emphasizes applied research and indigenous adaptation of imported technology. The responsibility for science policy and planning is shared between the *Ministère de l'Enseignement Supérieur et de la Recherche Scientifique* (MESRS) (Ministry of Higher Education and Scientific Research), the *Conseil National de la Recherche Scientifique* (CNRS) (National Council for Scientific Research) and the *Organisme National de la Recherche Scientifique* (ONRS) (National Organization for Scientific Research). A national research plan, originally prepared in 1973, outlines three areas of research: energy, with strong emphasis on solar energy, hydrocarbons and nuclear energy; agriculture, with emphasis on agronomy, arid zones, soils, geology and seismology, oceanography and hydraulics; and habitat, with emphasis on rural and urban housing, built environment and traditional architecture. All research institutes and centres in Algeria reflect the emphasis of this research plan.

Scientific research and development activities at all levels are supported by the government. MESRS, which is one of the two constituent ministries of the *Ministère de l'Éducation Nationale* (Ministry of National Education), finances research institutes and teaching at university level. Some of the *grandes écoles* are also under the control of this ministry. However, some agricultural research is supported by the Ministry of Agriculture and the Ministry of Industry and state-owned industries such as SONATRACH, the Algerian petroleum and minerals company, support industrial research and development.

The National Council for Scientific Research was established in 1973. The council's functions include elaboration of national science policy, providing guidelines for research and overseeing the administrative, economic and financial aspects of research and development activities in Algeria.

The National Organization for Scientific Research is the principal research organization in Algeria. It was established in 1973 at the same time as CNRS and is responsible for executing the government's science policy directives. ONRS has fourteen institutes and centres and conducts research in close collaboration with industries and universities in Algeria.

The research centres under the ONRS are:

1. *Centre de Recherches Anthropologiques, Préhistoriques et Ethnographiques* (Anthropological, Prehistoric and Ethnographic Research Centre), which was established in 1957 and is based in Algiers.

2. *Centre National de Recherches sur les Zones Arides* (Arid Zones Research Centre), which is located in Beni-Abbes, Belcher, and has an extensive programme on passive solar cooling and heating, greenhouses, irrigation, and desertification.

3. *Centre de Recherches Océanographiques et des Pêches* (Oceanographic and Fisheries Research Centre), which is attached to the University of Algiers.

4. *Centre de Recherches sur les Ressources Biologiques Terrestres* (Biological Terrestrial Resources Research Centre).

5. *Centre des Sciences et de la Technologie Nucléaires* (Nuclear Science and Technology Centre), which is attached to the University of Algiers. The centre was founded in 1958 to conduct research in nuclear physics, solid-state physics, and electronics. The centre also has a solar energy programme concerned with photovoltaic power conversion, solar housing, solar water heating and water distillation. It has two Van de Graaf linear accelerators, one of 3 mV and one of 2 mV, for low-energy scattering experiments. There is an isotope separator of the Saclay type, which came into operation in 1966, and a 600 kV Sames accelerator.

6. *Centre National de Recherches et d'Application des Géosciences* (National Geosciences Research and Application Centre).

7. *Centre Universitaire de Recherches, d'Études et de Réalisations* (University Research, Study and Realization Centre), which is attached to the University of Constantine.

8. *Centre d'Informations Scientifiques et Techniques et de Transferts Technologiques* (Scientific and Technical Information and Technological Transfer Centre), which is based in Algiers and provides science and technology information services to the Algerian scientific community.

9. *Centre de Recherches en Économie Appliquées* (Economic Applied Research Centre).

10. *Centre de Recherches en Architecture et Urbanisme* (Architecture and Town Planning Research Centre), which is based in Algiers and conducts research in traditional architecture, urban development, and solar housing.

11. *Centre National d'Études et de Recherches pour l'Aménagement du Territoire* (Land Management Study and Research Centre).

12. *Centre d'Études et de Recherches Agronomiques* (Agronomic Study and Research Centre).

13. *Centre de Coordination des Études et des Recherches sur les Infrastructures, les Equipements du Ministère de l'Enseignement Supérieur et de la Recherche Scientifique* (Centre for the Coordination of Study and Research on the Infrastructure and Resources of the Ministry of Higher Education and Scientific Research).

14. The *Station d'Énergie Solaire* (Solar Energy Station) is based at Abu

Zarriah and was built by the French in the 1950s before Algerian independence. It has a thermal furnace and is used for experiments of solar collectors.

With the exception of the Nuclear Science and Technology Centre, the Anthropological, Prehistoric and Ethnographic Research Centre, and the Solar Energy Station, most of the other ONRS research centres have been established in the last five years. The ONRS also maintains an observatory in Bouzareah, Algiers.

Academic Science and Research

Of the seven universities in Algeria, the *Université d'Alger* (University of Algiers) is the oldest, having been founded in 1879 and reorganized in 1909. It gained full university status at the time of reorganization. The university is headed by the rector, who is responsible to the Ministry of Higher Education and Scientific Research. The scientific faculties are those of sciences, medicine and pharmacy. The following institutes and centres are attached to the university:

1. *Institut de Recherches Sahariennes* (Sahara Research Institute), which conducts research on all aspects of the desert, including problems concerning the agriculture of arid zones, and geological surveys.
2. *Institut de Géographie* (Geography Institute).
3. *Institut d'Urbanisme* (Town Planning Institute).
4. Nuclear Science and Technology Centre.
5. *Centre Anti-Cancéreux 'Pierre et Marie Curie'* (Pierre and Marie Curie Anti-Cancer Centre).
6. *Institut d'Odonto-Stomatologie* (Dentistry and Stomatology Institute).
7. *Institut du Trachôme et d'Ophtalmologie Tropicale* (Trachoma and Tropical Ophthalmology Institute).
8. *Institut d'Hygiène et de Médecine d'Outre-Mer* (Overseas Institute of Health and Medicine).
9. *Institut de Biochemie Générale et de Biochemie de la Nutrition* (General and Nutritional Biochemistry Institute).
10. *Institut National Agronomique* (National Institute of Agronomy), which has departments for general agronomy and phytotechnology, botony, zoology, rural economy, animal husbandry, agricultural technology, soil sciences, agricultural engineering, and forestry and silviculture.
11. *Institut des Sciences de Terre* (Earth Sciences Institute).
12. *Institut de Météorologie et Physique du Globe* (Meteorology and Global Physics Institute).
13. *Centre de Recherches Océanographiques et des Pêches* (Oceanographic and Fisheries Research Centre), which is concerned with research in marine productivity, photosynthesis, biology of small crustaceans in plankton, nearshore molluscs, eggs and larvae of fishes, calcareous flagellates, and the study of the Atlantic currents off Algeria.
14. The *Université d'Oran* (University of Oran), which was established in

1965, has a faculty of medicine and pharmacy, and the *Université de Constantine* (University of Constantine), which was established in 1970, has institutes for medicine, science, and biological sciences. These universities have the same structural organization as the University of Algiers and are also under the jurisdiction of the Ministry of Higher Education and Scientific Research.

Two science and technology universities were established in 1974 and 1975. The *Université des Sciences et de la Technologie d'Alger* (Science and Technology University of Algiers) has institutes for biology, chemistry, mathematics, physics, earth sciences and electronics; and the *Université des Sciences et de la Technologie d'Oran* (Science and Technology University of Oran) has teaching and research facilities for the same disciplines. Two general universities, the *Université d'Annabah* (University of Annabah) and *Université de Sétif* (Setif University), were established in 1976 and 1978, respectively. Both universities have facilities for teaching pure sciences.

The *École Nationale Polytechnique* (National Polytechnic) also comes under the Ministry of Higher Education and Scientific Research. It is closely connected with the University of Algiers. The chief task of the polytechnic is the training of skilled personnel necessary for the increased industrialization of the country. Courses are given in chemical, civil, electrical, and mechanical engineering; telecommunications, petrochemistry, and applied mathematics.

Agricultural Science and Research

Besides various research centres of the ONRS and the University of Algiers, agricultural research is conducted at the *Centre National de Recherche et d'Expérimentation Forestières* (National Centre for Forestry Research and Experiment) and the *Institut de Recherches Agronomiques Tropicales et des Cultures Vivières* (Tropical Agriculture and Food Crops Research Institute), both of which are under the Ministry of Agriculture.

The National Centre for Forestry Research and Experiment is situated in el-Mouradia. The centre was founded in 1959 to conduct research in forestry and to devise methods of developing new forests in the semi-arid zone of southern Algeria. The centre is actively engaged in establishing regional forestry research stations throughout the country. Since 1975, six regional stations have been created. The first of these was in the region of Sidi-bel-Abbes in the north of the country, which is concerned with the harvesting and conservation of seeds, and problems connected with Aleppo pines and with substitution of species; this station has semi-arid, arid and desert conditions in which to work. A second station in the region of Djelfa in the south of the country studies pines and the problems of esparto steppes under arid conditions; and a third station at Annaba in the east of the country studies species with rapid growth characteristics in humid conditions. Three other stations have been set up at Batna, Setif and Djidelli. The centre trains its own workers and special courses are given in pedology, ecology, biogeography, dendrometry, forestry management, silviculture, and reafforestation; special attention is paid to the complex problems of the preservation of the natural environment. Research projects include the study of indigenous pine trees; techniques of reafforestation; and choice of species for the widely differing bioclimatic conditions. The centre maintains contact and enjoys a certain amount of collaboration with the FAO. The centre publishes two journals: *Les Annales du CNREF*, and *Notes Techniques Forestières*; it also maintains a library of relevant literature.

The Tropical Agriculture and Food Crops Research Institute has an experimental station at el-Khemis Miliana, which conducts research on cultivation of grapes, citrus fruits, olives, figs and dates, tobacco, wheat, barley and oats.

The Ministry of Agriculture also maintains an *Institut de Téchnologie d'Horticulture* (Horticultural Technology Institute).

Other Research Institutes

The Ministry of Industry maintains the *Institut Algérien des Pétrôles* (Petroleum Institute of Algeria), which is conducting research on hydrocarbons, petrochemicals, and development of petroleum products.

In the field of medicine and biology, the *Institut Pasteur d'Algérie* (Pasteur Institute of Algeria), which was founded in 1910, conducts research in microbiology and parasitology. It also prepares vaccines and sera and cooperates with the health services of Algeria. The institute has an extensive library.

The *Service Géologique d'Algérie* (Geological Service of Algeria) was established in the late nineteenth century; it conducts geological surveys and publishes charts and maps.

Egypt

Demographic and Economic Background

The Arab Republic of Egypt occupies the north-east corner of Africa: it is surrounded by the Mediterranean Sea, which forms the northern boundary and the Red Sea, which forms the eastern boundary. Egypt also has frontiers with Israel to the east, the Sudan to the south and Libya to the west. In mid-1979 the World Bank estimated Egypt's population to be 38.9 million, with an annual growth rate of 2 per cent. By the year 2000, Egypt will have an estimated population of 60 million. Of the total area of 1,001,000 km², a major part is desert. Some 45 per cent of the population lives in urban centres, much of it concentrated in Cairo and Alexandria. The rural population is concentrated around the River Nile. The settled land is only 3.5 per cent of the total area of the country.

Egyptian agriculture is suffering from decades of under-investment and mis-investment. At present, it employs 50 per cent of the labour force, provides 30 per cent of the GDP and accounts for 80 per cent of Egypt's exports. Past policies emphasizing land reclamation and pricing are not noted for their success. However, the latest development plan (1980–84) places considerable emphasis on agricultural development and is designed to make Egypt self-sufficient in foodstuffs. Egypt's major crops are wheat, cotton and rice. Vegetables and animal feed are also grown extensively. In 1979, Egypt's main export was cotton, with vegetables and cereals also being exported in large quantities. Future plans call for improving productivity by improving drainage facilities, complete mechanization of agriculture by 1990, and increasing usage of fertilizers.

Egyptian industry employs some 20 per cent of the population. It is dominated by foodstuffs and textiles, which account for 50 per cent of the output. In recent years it has shown an average growth rate of 7.8 per cent. The country has a number of heavy industries; the iron and steel complex at Helwan will have an output of 2 million tons in 1982; the aluminium plant at Nag Hamadi has an output of 100,000 tons; and plans are underway for the development of a phosphate fertilizer complex to utilize the phosphate deposits found at Abu Tarter. Another fertilizer plant is being planned using the gasfields of Abu Madi. Under the new development plan, Egypt's industrial infrastructure will be developed further; there are numerous plans to set up plants for the production of trucks, cars, engines, refrigerators, etc., and a wide-ranging programme to expand the petroleum sector.

Among the Arab states, Egypt is considered to be the most scientifically and technologically advanced country. Egyptian universities and colleges produce more graduates than the economy can absorb. Consequently, Egypt exports skilled manpower to all oil-rich Arab states. There is a tradition of research and development work and the country has some of the most established and respected laboratories and scientific institutions in the Arab world.

Science Policy and Planning

Egyptian science policy and planning is linked to development planning. A science and technology action plan has been prepared to run in parallel with the five-year development plan. Egypt's National Paper to UNCSTD identified deficiency in science and technology executive systems, weak links between research institutions and industry, weak science information systems, inadequate national expenditure on research and development, and imbalanced scientific manpower as the major obstacles in better utilization of science and technology in Egypt. The National Paper enumerates the following measures which Egypt would take to eliminate these obstacles:

1. Delineation of the long-term areas of vital importance to socio-economic development where science and technology could play an effective role.
2. Adoption of modern methodologies for forecasting and planning of science and technology activities to assure the optimal mobilization of available resources and favourable conditions necessary for the full participation of the research and development community in the national development.
3. Design of concentrated research and development programmes which effectively contribute to advancement of science and technology in a manner which integrates with the overall national developmental planning and assures coordination between all sectors.
4. Reinforcement and consolidation of the existing science and technology infrastructure, while providing adequate balance at both the horizontal and vertical levels.
5. Reinforcement of the national science and technology policy system through the appropriate legislations which provide stability, centralization of research and development planning, and contractual implementation of the projects.
6. Coordination of all technology importation and adaptation activities through the central science and technology system under a definite legislative arrangement.
7. Technological self-reliance should be a national target, particularly the technologies related to rural development and handicraft industries,

and those of national importance, e.g. cotton, food, drug, power, metal, tool, building, transport, and capital goods industries.

8. Efficient training of science and technology personnel of all categories, with special emphasis on those involved in the applied sectors, as well as the youthful and female elements.

9. Realistic treatment of the problem of brain drain, through institution of new systems for employment and reward, and social and health care, in order to create a favourable balance between the pull and push forces.

10. Paying special attention to the science and technology services, such as information and documentation, maintenance of equipment, invention and innovation promotion, data banks, standardization and meteorology, and product quality control.

11. Bilateral cooperation with other countries should be so designed that optimal utilization be made of the opportunities available and created through the open-door economy policy, and of the technical aid programmes provided by regional and international groups or organizations.

12. Appropriate schemes should be developed for the coordination of science and technology activities at the African and Arab world levels to maximize the benefits reaped by all parties involved.

13. Egypt should collaborate with developing countries in the implementation of a number of research and development projects – in which the developed countries could participate – such as the utilization of marine resources, production of non-conventional energy, horizontal agricultural expansion, and exploitation of arid and semi-arid zones.

14. International development agencies, established by the developed countries, should increase their technical and financial assistance and loans with fair terms and without imposing political conditions.

15. Regional and sub-regional organizations (governmental or otherwise) should be alert of the rapid progress in science and technology, and consequently be aware of their responsibilities at present and in the future.

The science and technology action plan, prepared by the Academy of Scientific Research and Technology, is based on the following approaches for integrating science and technology in social and economic development:

1. Realistic research activities aimed at practical targets which benefit the Egyptian community at large.

2. To divert energy from over-emphasis in publication-oriented research, contract research will be promoted and legislation will be passed to ensure that satisfying remuneration for researchers does not take academic accomplishment exclusively into consideration.

3. Linkage between research and industry will be strengthened by creating intermediate bodies such as the Engineering and Industrial Design and Development Centre and the Invention and Innovation Development Service.

4. Strengthening the extension services rendered by the research and development community through 'adaptive' research, which involves the provision of information on foreign techniques and know-how, after they have been adopted to local conditions, and to local industry.
5. Concentrating on applied research without neglecting basic research: and optimum mix of 80:20 per cent is expected to be attained.

Organizations of Science and Research

Academy of Scientific Research and Technology

The main body responsible for science and technology in Egypt is the Academy of Scientific Research and Technology established by the Presidential Decree No. 2405 in 1975. The organization of the academy, which has its head office in Cairo, includes the academy council, its bureau and technical secretariat, advisory board, technical staff of the office of the president of the academy, specialized research councils, principal committees and national committees. The academy also has units for research and development, coordination and integration and inventions and innovations. The following institutions, which are described below, are affiliated to the president of the academy:

1. The National Research Centre.
2. Theodor Bilharz Research Institute.
3. Central Metallurgical Research and Development Institute.
4. Institute of Oceanography and Fisheries.
5. Institute of Astronomy and Geophysics.
6. National Institute of Standards.
7. Petroleum Research Institute.
8. Remote Sensing Centre.

The academy is also responsible for the National Information and Documentation Centre, the Scientific Instrumentation Centre, the Patent Office and the Science Museum.

The National Information and Documentation Centre (NIDOC), established with the aid of UNESCO in 1955, has 50,000 reference books and 5,000 periodicals. It was established to include the National Reference Library for Science and Technology and to encourage the establishment of other central scientific libraries. It is located at the National Research Centre's main complex in Dokki, Cairo, and has an annex at the University of Cairo.

The Scientific Instrumentation Centre (SIC) has departments for electronics, optics, glass-blowing and mechanical engineering. It is a service centre providing technical assistance, maintaining instruments, and designing, developing and manufacturing specially requested devices for Egypt's research institutes and universities.

The Patent Office registers Egyptian and foreign patents and has more than 1.5 million patents from the United States, the United Kingdom, France, West Germany and the Soviet Union.

Table 3.1

Major research projects at the NRC 1979–80: most of these projects are backed by the US under its PL 480 programme, other studies are supported by the International Development Research Centre of Canada, the West German Organization of Technical Cooperation, and Sweden's International Foundation of Science.

1. Water quality studies on the River Nile and Lake Nasser
2. Micro- and macro-organisms of disease and fouling, and corrosion and protective measures
3. Corrosion and corrosion cracking of materials used in petroleum and chemical industries
4. Mechanisms of degradation of cotton and effects of mercerization-stretching upon the course of these mechanisms
5. Utilization of cane sugar bagasses
6. Aflatoxin residues in Egyptian food and feed derived from plant and animal sources
7. Distribution and inactivation of parasitic and bacterial pathogens in edible fish
8. Poisonous plants contaminating edible ones and toxic substances in plant foods
9. Metabolic reactions in fungi
10. Biological pest control in Egypt
11. Synthesis of nitromethanes and related substances of broad spectrum antimicrobial, molluscicidal and larvicidal activities
12. Microwave physics and dielectrics
13. Biochemical and physiological studies of certain tick vectors of disease agents
14. Solar energy projects
15. Micronutrients and plant nutrition problems in Egypt
16. Production of proteins from algae
17. A chemosystematic study of some Trigonella and Medicago species
18. Investigation of selected wild Egyptian plants for their coumarin constituents
19. Establishment of an economic process for the production of solasodine and progesterone under Egyptian conditions

National Research Centre – NRC

Located in Dokki-Giza, a suburb of Cairo, where it has its own campus complete with laboratories, administrative offices, pilot plant and support facilities, the NRC is the biggest scientific institution in the Middle East. It is managed by a director who works within the general policy guidelines laid down by the governing board. The NCR has forty-six laboratories organized into the following fourteen divisions: textile industries, metallurgy, food industries and nutrition, pharmaceutical industries, chemical industries, engineering, agriculture, animal health, medical sciences, applied organic chemistry, applied inorganic chemistry, physics, fundamental sciences, and environment.

At present, NRC has a research staff of 1,250, of which at least 40 per cent have a postgraduate qualification. Much of the research at the centre is financed by the United States Agency for International Development through its PL 480 programme. The NRC also has a number of collaborative agreements with international research organizations. Within Egypt, it has established joint scientific boards with various industrial and agricultural organizations. These include boards covering the following areas: petrochemicals, ceramics, metallurgy, textiles, food industries, plant production, bilharzia, pharmaceutical industries, and environmental protection.

Since 1975, research and development activities of the centre have been organized under the following five areas:

1. *Technology transfer:* concentration of research and development activities connected with both vertical and horizontal transfer of technology in the industrial sector, in particular the textiles, pharmaceuticals, metallurgy, chemical, food and electronics, industries.
2. *Food and agriculture:* integrated research on plant and animal production, food and agricultural by-products and unconventional methods of food production.
3. *Health and environment:* focus on environmental pollution, endemic diseases (with special emphasis on schistosomiasis), ophthalmological diseases and the manufacture of drugs from local natural products.
4. *Energy:* studies on the possible use and the development of unconventional sources of energy, with particular emphasis on solar energy.
5. *Natural resources:* concerned with search for various ores and minerals in the land and seas of Egypt.

NRC also provides consultancy services and training programmes for Egyptian graduates. The centre has special teams of consultants for industry and agriculture and has provided consultancy services to Saudi Arabia, Kuwait and ALECSO. It has a number of masters and doctoral research programmes which are run in conjunction with local universities.

Theodor Bilharz Institute – TBI

The TBI operates under the umbrella of the NRC. Although the foundation of the institute was laid in 1962, the institute began its function in 1978. The hospital activities of the institute were started in early 1980. Set up with the assistance of West Germany, the TBI has a research staff of 105 working on a general plan of research on bilharzia developed by the Ministry of Health and the Academy of Scientific Research and Technology. The institute, located at Imhala, Giza, is organized into three sections: control, environmental health and chemical sections. Research is pursued in the zoological, pathological, physiological and epidemiological aspects of the disease. Emphasis is also given to immunology and efforts are being made to establish a method of vaccination which may protect against infection or prevent severe complications.

Central Metallurgical Research and Development Institute

The institute has been set up particularly to develop strong links between research and industry. It conducts research into various aspects of metallurgy, such as ore microscopy, ore dressing, extractive ferrous and non-ferrous metallurgy, and foundry techniques. It was set up by the Industrial Executive Organization and operates under the umbrella of the NRC.

Institute of Oceanography and Fisheries – IOF

The IOF is one of the oldest scientific institutions in Egypt. It has four branches: Mediterranean, located at Alexandria; Red Sea, located at al-Ghardaqa; inland waters; and shore protection. Its research programme includes surveys of fishing areas and detection of new ones, expansion of fish culture, development of fishing areas and studies on the ecological conditions of Egyptian waters.

Institute of Astronomy and Geophysics – IAG

The IAG has its headquarters in Cairo and carries out research in astronomy, geophysics, meteorology, geomagnetic and seismic phenomena. It has four observatories including the noted Helwan Observatory.

National Institute of Standards – NIS

The NIS comprises the National Physical Laboratory for Metrology and the Central Laboratory for Metrology and Materials Testing. The former laboratory acts as the research body and is concerned with the maintenance of national standards; the central laboratory is concerned with the calibration of measuring instruments and materials testing.

Petroleum Research Institute – PRI

The PRI is one of the newest specialized research centres set up by the Academy of Scientific Research and Technology. It has been set up with the cooperation of the General Petroleum Authority and the French Petroleum Institute. It has sections for exploration, production, crude oil evaluation, refining, petrochemicals, product application and design and development. The PRI's research programme is focused on the evaluation of crude oil found in Egypt, production of protein from gases, Lub-oil additives, and upgrading of petroleum and petrochemical products.

Remote Sensing Centre – RSC

The RSC, Cairo, was started in 1971 as a cooperative venture between the then Egyptian Academy of Scientific Research and the United States, represented by Oklahoma State University and the United States National Science Foundation. It now has a research staff of sixty-five specializing in such disciplines as geology, mineral and energy resources, hydrogeology, agriculture, soils, geophysics, photogrammetry and data processing. The centre has accumulated a large inventory of Computer Compatible Tapes, digital data from Landsat satellites and ERTS and Landsat satellite images for almost all the territories of the Arab world. It has some of the most advanced equipment for aerial data collection and multi-spectral data analysis and well equipped interpretation and photographic laboratories.

The RSC was one of the few centres in the world which applied Landsat imagery interpretation both visual and digital at a very early stage and on a large scale. The centre therefore has unique experience in this field. Already about 500,000 km², representing some 50 per cent of the territories of Egypt, and 165,000 km² in southern Sudan have been covered by accurate and highly standardized regional geological, structural lineation and drainage maps, and in parts by soil, vegetation, groundwater potential and petroleum, mineral and construction materials maps. The RSC has also used Landsat imagery interpretation for prospecting for specific minerals, especially iron ores leading to the discovery of a new locality in the western desert, and for large-scale irrigation, power generation and land reclamation projects.

Apart from Landsat, the RSC has also used aircraft remote-sensing techniques, such as multi-spectral photography, thermal infrared imagery, magnetometry, and gamma radiometry in several important development projects in Egypt. These projects include sub-surface investigations of the Suez Canal Zone, mineral prospecting for iron ores over large areas of the western desert of Egypt, uranium and evaporites, and construction sites in the vicinity of Cairo and Alexandria. Apart from the applied nature of this aircraft work, RSC has demonstrated various technological problems related to the testing of these techniques on land and shallow waters under arid and semi-arid conditions.

In cooperation with UNESCO, the RSC has formulated a programme under the UNEP project for the implementation of the World Plan of Action to Combat Desertification. The RSC project deals with the management of major regional aquifers in north-east Africa, including territories in Egypt and Sudan. A major part of this project deals with the use of remote-sensing techniques in surveying regional aquifer and in delineating geologic, structural, drainage and geomorphologic features which are significant for determining potentials of groundwater and directions of flow in this major regional aquifer.

The RSC acts as the African Regional Training and User Assistance Centre and is considered to be a strong candidate to become the African Regional Centre for Remote Sensing. Attempts have also been made to turn the RSC into a regional centre for the Middle East.

Other Research Centres

The Geological Survey and Mining Authority is under the Ministry of Petroleum and Mineral Wealth and is concerned with the prospecting for, evaluation of, and exploitation of mineral deposits. The survey also undertakes regional geological cartography and prepares reports on the technical and economic aspects of its work.

The Building Research Institute is supported by the Ministry of Housing and Reconstruction and carries out basic and applied research on building materials and means of construction.

The General Organization for Housing, Building and Planning Research is attached to the Ministry of Housing and Reconstruction and carries out pure and applied research on architectural and structural designs for housing, public buildings and building elements, building materials from natural sources and from industrial and agricultural wastes and the traditional methods of construction and industrialized methods suitable for local conditions. It prepares codes of practice for design and construction, helps in preparing standard specifications for building materials, and acts as a consultant to the different authorities concerned with building and construction.

Academic Science and Research

The nine universities in Egypt are: Ain Shams University, University of Alexandria, al-Azhar University, American University in Cairo, University of Assiut, University of Cairo, Mansoura University, Tanta University and Zagazig University. Research and development work is carried out largely at the Ain Shams University, the University of Alexandria and the University of Cairo.

Ain Shams University was established in 1950 and was originally called Ibrahim Pasha University; in 1954 its name was changed to Ain Shams University since it was located close to the ancient city of Ain Shams, which had been the centre of science and knowledge of its time. The university is located in the Zaafran Palace, Abbassiah, Cairo.

The University of Ain Shams is administered by the president, who is appointed by presidential decree at the recommendation of the Minister of Higher Education; three vice-presidents, similarly appointed; and the university council, which is composed of the president and vice-presidents, the deans of the faculties, and a maximum of four other members with experience in education and public affairs.

The Faculty of Science was established in 1950, its basis being the scientific section of the Teachers' Higher Training Institute. Research and teaching is carried out in departments for pure and applied mathematics, physics, chemistry, biochemistry, botany, zoology, entomology, and geology.

The Faculty of Medicine was also founded in 1950 from the existing Abbassiah Faculty of Medicine which had been affiliated to Cairo University. The children's hospital, which belonged to the Egyptian Society for Child Welfare was annexed to the teaching hospital and a new hospital, called Ain Shams Hospital, has been established. The faculty has departments for physiology, biochemistry, pharmacology, anatomy and histology, pathology, bacteriology and parasitology, surgery, anaesthesiology, special medicine, medicine, special surgery, paediatrics, obstetrics and gynaecology, ophthalmology, radiology, forensic medicine, and for public hygiene, preventive medicine and industrial medicine. New clinical sections have been established in order to keep treatment up to date; these include sections for chest and cardiac diseases, endemic diseases, allergies, endocrines, diabetes, hypertension, gastro-intestinal diseases, and sterility cases. There is also a radioactive isotopes treatment centre, which was the first department of its kind to be introduced into the university hospitals of Egypt; professors from the faculty and researchers from the Atomic Energy Institute carry out research and the treatment of patients. The nucleus for a new Faculty of Medicine has been established in Zagazig, in Sharkia Province, which is under the supervision of the University of Ain Shams.

The Faculty of Engineering has a long history, since its forerunners were established as long ago as 1839; its immediate predecessor was the Higher Institute of Engineering, which was established in 1940. The present faculty carries out teaching and research in mathematical and physical sciences, architectural engineering, structural engineering, irrigation and hydraulics, public works, electrical engineering, and mechanical engineering.

The present Faculty of Agriculture had its origins in the Higher Institute of Agriculture at Shibin-el-Kom, which had been set up in 1924. New buildings and facilities for the faculty were completed at Shoubra in 1964. The faculty carries out teaching and research in agricultural economics, soil sciences, plant protection, animal production, food sciences, plant pathology, genetics, horticulture, field crops, and agricultural microbiology. There is a Faculty of Agriculture at Zagazig, which has departments for plant production and protection, agricultural economics, food sciences, animal production, agricultural botany, and soil sciences. Also at Zagazig is a Faculty of Veterinary Medicine, which carries out teaching and research in animal histology and anatomy, animal physiology, animal health, animal pathology, animal surgery and gynaecology, and in internal diseases.

Attached to the University of Ain Shams is the Middle East Research Centre, which was established in December 1967. The centre is a scientific organization whose aims are:

1. Carrying out, encouraging and publishing research concerning the Middle East, especially research concerned with current problems.
2. Collecting documents, prints, maps, statistics and periodicals concerned with the Middle East, and making them available to serious researchers, whether Arabs or foreigners.
3. Exchanging research results and promoting cooperation among those concerned with Middle East studies in Egypt and with other organizations working in the same field throughout the world.
4. Encouraging the interpretation of scientific research dealing with specific problems of the Middle East.
5. Issuing scientific journals to serve the above-mentioned purposes, in which research results are to be published in Arabic and foreign languages.

At present the centre is composed of three branches, the Natural Resources Branch, the Political and Economic Studies Branch, and the Humanities Branch. The Natural Resources Branch supervises research concerned with natural resources in all countries in the Middle East. Of current importance are soil research, water resources, wood, mineral wealth, and especially petroleum wealth. The branch aims at finding the best ways of developing and exploiting these resources.

The University of Alexandria was founded in 1942 as a state university, incorporating former branches of the faculties of Fouad I (Cairo) University, known as the Farouk I University until 1953. The university senate is the governing body. It has faculties of arts, law, commerce, agriculture, engineering, medicine, pharmacy, dentistry, education and sciences. The university also has institutes for public health, medical research, and nursing, and centres for sanitary engineering research and a computer science centre. The Institute of Public Health is attached to the Faculty of Medicine and research projects are undertaken in nutrition, epidemiology, bacteriology, parasitology, occupational health, public health engineering and biostatics. The Faculty of Agriculture has a very strong research programme focusing on irrigation (particularly the drip method of irrigation), drainage, soil salinity, and techniques of increasing agricultural productivity. Its *Alexandria Journal of Agricultural Research* is a respected journal.

Attached to the University of Alexandria is the University of Alexandria Research Centre (UNARC). UNARC was established in 1972 as a UNESCO/UNDP project to assist Egypt in strengthening research capabilities in physics and biological sciences with the ultimate aim of establishing a 'centre for excellence' in these fields in Egypt and, at a later stage, for the Middle East.

When UNARC was first opened in 1972, the first phase of research activity concentrated primarily on physical sciences utilizing UNESCO experts and the university faculty and students. In the second phase, which was initiated in 1975, research on molecular biology was introduced. The centre now has a third research division – applied sciences – where research is concentrated largely on environmental sciences.

The physical sciences division has research groups working on material research, thin films and surfaces, electrochemistry and corrosion, polymer and colloids, photo-energy transduction, computer sciences, mathematics and statistics, and laser studies. The biological sciences division has research groups working on biochemical and molecular genetics, cell biology, membrane biology, molecular and biomolecular studies and photobiology. The applied science section has investigation teams looking into aquatic pollution around Alexandria and the Mediterranean; emphasis is given to the study of effects of oil spills and industrial pollutants on marine communities and ecosystems. The applied science section is also working on developing mechanisms of coordination between research and industry.

The centre is administered by a director who is chosen by the thirty-five Egyptian professors who constitute the permanent staff of UNARC for a period of three to five years. The main policy-making body of the centre is the research council, which consists of representatives of the various research groups. The centre also has a high level advisory board consisting of noted national and international scientists.

The University of Cairo was founded in 1908 as a national university and became a state university in 1925; it was known as Fouad I University until 1952. It has faculties for arts, law, medicine, dentistry, pharmacy, engineering, agriculture, veterinary medicine, commerce, and economics and politics. Attached to the various faculties are: the Institute of Statistical Study and Research, the Institute of Cancer Research, the Institute of Meteorological Studies, and the Institute of Mass Communication. Attached to the University and the National Research Centre is the Plant Pathology Research Institute, which is carrying out research on the control of plant

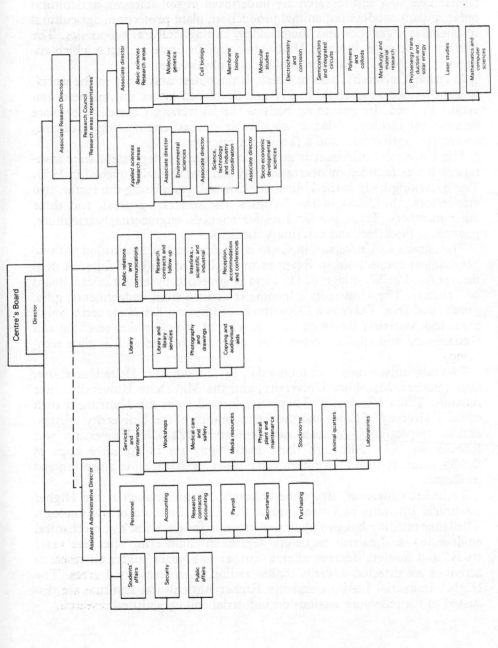

Fig. 3.1 Administrative structure of the University of Alexandria Research Centre (UNARC)

diseases and publishes the *Agricultural Research Review, Egyptian Phyto-pathology* and the *Journal of Applied Microbiology*.

The Faculty of Agriculture has extensive laboratories and experimental farms. Teaching and research are undertaken in soil sciences, agricultural botany, plant production, animal production, plant protection, agricultural biochemistry, genetics and bacteriology, and agricultural economics. The Faculty of Science directs a Hydrobiological Institute at Ataqa which engages in research in plankton ecology and physiology.

Al-Azhar University, also in Cairo, is the oldest university in the world. It was founded as a school in 970 and developed into a full, modern university in 1965. Its governing body is the University Council. There are faculties for theology, Islamic law, Arabic studies, engineering, medicine, commerce, agriculture, and a faculty for sciences.

The University of Assiut is an administratively independent state institution. It was founded by decree in 1949 and was formally opened in 1957. The governing body is the University Council, comprising the rector, two vice-rectors, the deans of the faculties, the secretary-general, and three other members. There are faculties for sciences, engineering, agriculture, pharmacy, medicine, and veterinary medicine.

The American University in Cairo is an independent institution with no government connections in Egypt or in the United States of America. It is incorporated in Washington, DC, and is governed by an American Board of Trustees. The University's income is derived from endowments, gifts, grants, and fees. There is a Department of Physical Sciences, and a Solid-State and Materials Research Centre. The latter undertakes teaching and fundamental and applied research in solid state studies and in glass technology.

Two new universities were founded in 1972: the East of Delta University, later renamed Mansoura University, and the Mid-Delta University, later renamed Tanta University. They were formed from the Mansura branch of the University of Cairo and the Tanta branch of the University of Alexandria, respectively. Another new university, Zagazig University, was founded in 1974. Although these institutions are in an early stage of development, faculties have been established for sciences, engineering and medicine.

Technical education, and some research, are undertaken at the Higher Technical Institute, in Cairo, and at the Cairo Institute of Technology. The latter institute has two main departments for electrical and mechanical engineering, and awards bachelors degrees in engineering after five years study, and masters degrees after a further two years study; all research activities are directed towards topics leading to the masters degrees. The Higher Industrial Institute and the Higher Agricultural Institute are discussed in the following sections on industrial and agricultural research.

Agricultural Science and Research

Research in agricultural sciences is conducted at the faculties of the universities, various technological institutes, and in other specialized agricultural organizations.

The Egyptian Agricultural Organization, in Cairo, was founded in 1898 and is the main body for the production of certified seeds, and for importing and propagating seeds of vegetable and horticultural crops. Particular emphasis is placed on cotton research, since Egypt is the world's principal producer of long staple cotton. The organization maintains a stud farm at Zahra, which specializes in the breeding of pure-bred horses and which enjoys worldwide renown.

The Desert Institute, at Mataria, Cairo, was founded in 1950 for the study and development of desert areas. The institute is responsible for research into aspects of geology, geophysics, soil conservation, groundwater sources, ecology, animal production, and meteorology. Facilities include a library and a museum, and many laboratories. The institute issues its own bulletin twice annually.

There are Higher Agricultural Institutes at Edfina, Kafr-al-Sheikh, Mansura, Minya, Tokh, Shibin el-Kom, and Zagazig.

Medical Science

Research in public health, medicine, pharmacy and dentistry is carried out at the Universities of Cairo, Ain Shams and Alexandria, as well as in specialized institutes of research.

Attached to the NRC is the Medical Research Executive Organization which controls and coordinates the work of six institutes:

1. The Medical Research Institute, in Alexandria, carries out basic and clinical medical research work. Facilities available include a hospital and an extensive laboratory network. Research groups are working on biochemistry, pathology, histochemistry, cytochemistry, pharmacology, physiology, parasitology, radiodiagnostics, oncology, radioisotopes, biophysics and experimental surgery.
2. The Theodor Bilharz Research Institute.
3. The Industrial Health Research Institute.
4. The Drug Research Institute.
5. The Nutrition Research Institute.
6. The Ophthalmology Research Institute.

The Public Health Laboratories, in Cairo, which are under the control of the Ministry of Health, were founded in the nineteenth century. They carry out studies in the administration of public health services, provide a testing and control service in the field of drugs, produce sera and vaccines, maintain a public diagnostic service, and carry out research in virology and epidemiology and similar public health-related fields.

The Research Institute and Hospital for Tropical Diseases, in Cairo, is divided into sections for tropical medicine, helminthology, entomology, biochemistry, haematology, virology, bacteriology, protozoology, animal breeding, and clinical medicine. The institute has four field research stations in Khanka, el-Haram, Fayed, and Rosetta.

The Memorial Institute for Ophthalmic Research, in Cairo, carries out research and preventive medicine in all fields of ophthalmology.

Industrial Research and Development

There are a number of industrial research organizations, of which the Petroleum Research Institute and the Central Metallurgical Research and Development Institute have been described above.

The Engineering and Industrial Design Development Centre is a governmental centre established in 1968 jointly with UNIDO to carry out product design and develop prototypes for manufacture by local firms, particularly in the engineering sector. Located in Cairo, the centre has expanded into industrial design, engineering process design, and capital equipment design. It is now an autonomous unit attached to the Ministry of Industry, and incorporates the former Small Scale Industry Institute.

The Hydrological Research Station, at the Kenater-al-Khaiyria Barrages, in Cairo, was founded in 1902, and conducts research in hydrology using scale models.

The Textile Research Centre, in Alexandria, conducts fundamental and applied research into dyeing and textile finishing, physical and mechanical textile testing, dyestuffs and fibres, and bleaching and preparation.

There are Higher Industrial Institutes in Aswan, Mansura, Minya, Port Said and Suez and a Higher Industrial Institute of Electronics at Munf.

Nuclear Science and Research

The Atomic Energy Establishment (AEE), at Dokki, Cairo, was set up in 1955. It has a 2 MW research reactor, which is used for experiments on nuclear and reactor physics, fast and thermal neutrons, scattering and heat transfer and transport phenomena. At Inchass there are laboratories for engineering and nuclear instrumentation, geological and raw materials, isotope production, nuclear chemistry and nuclear physics. The AEE has a radioisotope centre which was established in 1957 in Alexandria.

The Middle East Regional Isotope Centre for Arab States was founded in 1963, having been developed from a regional centre, with the cooperation of the International Atomic Energy Agency. The centre has eleven laboratories for research and development in the application of radioisotopes in the scientific, medical, agricultural and industrial fields. The centre also undertakes the training of specialists. Research in hydrology, tropical and subtropical diseases, fertilizers, and entomology is given special attention. Promotion of the use of radioisotopes in all Arab countries is one of the primary functions of the centre.

Scientific and Technical Information Services

The National Information and Documentation Centre (NIDOC) operates under the Academy of Scientific Research and Technology and is located at the National Research Centre complex in Dokki, Cairo, and has an annex at the University of Cairo. It has six departments: libraries, bibliography, translations, reprography, editing, and publishing and printing. It publishes eighteen scientific journals.

Scientific Societies and Associations

The Egyptian Society of Dairy Science in Cairo was established in 1972 and publishes the *Egyptian Journal of Dairy Science.*

The Alexandria Medical Association was established in 1921 and publishes the *Alexandria Medical Journal.*

The Egyptian Medical Association is located in Cairo. It was established in 1919 and publishes a monthly journal.

The Egyptian Society of Medicine and Tropical Hygiene was founded in 1927 in Alexandria.

The Ophthalmological Society of Egypt is the professional body in Egypt. It was founded in 1902 in Cairo and publishes mimeographs and an *Annual Bulletin.*

The *Société Entomologique d'Égypte* was founded in Cairo in 1907.

The Zoological Society of Egypt was established in 1927 and is located at the Giza Zoo, Giza, Cairo.

The Egyptian Society of Engineers is based in Cairo, where it has been operating since 1920.

The Gulf States

The Gulf States are Bahrain, Oman, Qatar and the United Arab Emirates (UAE). These sheikhdoms all have economies based exclusively on oil.

Bahrain is an archipelago which is close to Qatar on the west coast of the Persian Gulf. The total area of the islands is approximately 370 km². The island of Bahrain is the largest of the islands and is about 50 km long and 15 km wide. The total population is approximately 350,000.

Oman is in the south-east of the Arabian peninsula, with the UAE in the north, Saudi Arabia to the north and west, and the People's Democratic Republic of the Yemen in the west. Until 1970 it was officially known as Muscat and Oman. The coast of Oman extends for over 1,600 km. The total area of the country may be in the region of 260,000 km², but since the boundary with Saudi Arabia is not well defined, this is difficult to establish. Total population is under 1 million.

Qatar is a peninsula on the western coast of the Persian Gulf, and has a total area of approximately 10,000 km². Total population is in the region of 250,000.

The UAE was formerly known as the Trucial States, or Trucial Oman. The individual emirates are Abu Dhabi, Dubai, Sharjah, Ras al-Khaimah, Umm al-Quwain, Ajman, and Fujairah. The total area of the UAE is approximately 85,000 km²; there is a 1,100-km² coastline along the Persian Gulf which stretches from Oman to the Qatar peninsula, and Saudi Arabia lies in the hinterland. The population, which is estimated to be in the order of 550,000, is now mainly concentrated in the oil-rich areas of Abu Dhabi and Dubai.

The total area of the Gulf States is 234,922 km². The total population is under 2 million and all the countries have very high population growth rates – Bahrain 3.3 per cent and Qatar 7.6 per cent.

The Gulf States do not have a developed educational and research infrastructure. The University of the Gulf will be established in Bahrain by ABEGS. Bahrain also has a technical college – the Gulf Technical College – situated at Isa Town, which was founded in 1968.

The University of Abu Dhabi was established in 1980 and has not yet developed into a fully-fledged institution. Abu Dhabi also has a Centre for Documentation and Research, which was founded in 1968 and which is attached to the Ministry of Cabinet Affairs. It carries out research on subjects related to the area and publishes a review entitled *Arabian Gulf Research Review*.

The UAE has a Building Research Centre and a Central Laboratory, used mainly for training. The Emirates also has an Arid Lands Research Centre and a university at al-Ain, which was opened in 1977.

Iran

Demographic and Economic Background

Iran shares its borders with Afghanistan and Pakistan to the east, the Persian Gulf and the Gulf of Oman to the south, Iraq and Turkey to the west, and to the north are the Caspian Sea and the territories of the Soviet Union. It is a country of 1,684,000 km² and a population estimated at 37 million. More than half the land is regarded as uncultivable; some 11 per cent of it is devoted to agriculture, which employs 40 per cent of the total labour force. A further 11 per cent is under forest or woodland, although forestry as a scientific subject is a comparatively recent development.

Agriculture accounts for less than 30 per cent of the national income and 20 per cent (principally in the form of raw cotton, wool, leather and fruit) of total exports, excluding oil. Iran is the second largest oil-producing member of OPEC.

After the 1979 Islamic revolution, the country adopted an Islamic constitution, which gives legislative and administrative powers to a National Consultative Assembly and executive powers to a president and a council of ministers. Since the revolution, Iran's economy, educational institutions and scientific and technological establishments have been undergoing reform.

Science Policy and Planning

While the revolutionary government of Iran does not have a specific science policy, most of the post-revolution planning has shown a strong bias towards rural development, indigenous industrial research and conservation and environmental concerns. The Ministry of Science and Higher Education, the Institute for Research and Planning in Science and Education and its two subsidiaries – the Centre for Scientific and Education Planning and the Centre for Scientific and Research Policy – and the Budget and Planning Organization, all based in Tehran, are involved in formulating new science, technology and educational policies.

Research in Iran is conducted in ministries and universities. Almost all ministries have their own research institutes and centres, although at present it is difficult to describe the specific nature of their work.

Academic Science and Research

The entire higher educational system of Iran is undergoing reform. The new system is being developed under the *Jihad-e-Daneshgahi* (University of Jihad) programme, which is administered by a seven-member council that has mobilized some 3,000 academics to translate and write 2,000 books for the new courses. The emphasis of the new curricula is on pragmatic education within the framework of Islam, practical research, and developing indigenous skills. The *Jihad-e-Daneshgahi* has given priority to universities with strong technical and medical bias. The names of most of the universities have been changed and some of the smaller universities have been combined to form larger regional institutions.

The University of Tehran is the largest and probably the best-equipped university in Iran. It is an autonomous institution, responsible to the Ministry of Education, but governed by a university council which has representatives from the teaching staff, students and workers. Its facilities include those for agriculture, dentistry, medicine, pharmacy, science, engineering, veterinary medicine, forestry, and public health, and natural resources. The faculties of science and of veterinary medicine each maintains a library.

The Faculty of Agriculture includes the departments described below. The Department of Agricultural Economics studies the application of economics in agriculture, and maintains a library. The Department of Agricultural Industries covers fermentation industries, food chemistry, food industries, food microbiology, food preservation, milk industries, sugar industries, tea, flour, and starch technology, and tea industries; it has laboratories for food analysis and control, and microbiology. The Department of Agronomy covers the production and breeding of field crops, it has laboratories for analysis of chemical materials, cytology, field crops technology, and genetics; it also maintains a library. The Department of Horticulture covers floriculture, landscaping, sub-tropical plants, tree plantation, and vegetables; it has laboratories for botany, floriculture, tree plantation, and vegetables, and it maintains a library. The Department of Mechanics and Agricultural Machinery covers the fields of agricultural mechanization, and utilization of combustion motors and electro-motors in agricultural units; it has laboratories for agricultural machines, combustion motors, and electro-technics. The Department of Plant Pathology investigates plant protection against pests and diseases; it has laboratories for entomology, plant diseases, plant pests, and therapeutics; it also has a zoology museum and maintains a library. The Department of Soil Science researches the erosion and protection of soil and typology of soils; it maintains a laboratory for soil science and a library. The Department of Animal Breeding and Nutrition conducts research on the feeding and wool of sheep; it has laboratories for animal food analysis, artificial insemination, equality testing, and wool technology. The Department of Animal Husbandry covers animal breeding and feeding, it has laboratories for animal breeding, animal husbandry, animal nutrition, and wool technology. The Department of Irrigation and Reclamation investigates rural development; it has laboratories for geology, hydraulics, irrigation and drainage, soil and water relationships, and soil mechanics. It maintains a library.

The Faculty of Natural Resources has the following departments. The Department of Reclaiming the Arid Zones and Hills investigates soil conservation and watershed management; it has laboratories for both these fields. The Department of Forestry and Forest Economics conducts studies relating to the forests of Iran; it has laboratories for dendrology, forest exploitation, forest genetics, forest protection, and typology of forest soils. The Department of Wood Technology conducts investigations of Iranian wood and has laboratories for wood protection and wood technology.

The Faculty of Veterinary Medicine has a Laboratory of Icthyology which investigates fish pathology and Iranian fishes; it has laboratories for Icthyology and taxidermy.

The following establishments are attached to the University of Tehran. The Animal Husbandry and Research Institute; this has laboratories for artificial insemination and skin technology. The Institute of Geographical Research; this conducts geographical surveys and has a laboratory for transformation of aerial photographs into maps; it also maintains a library. The Institute of Geophysics; this conducts research into astrophysics, cosmic particles, geo-electricity, geo-magnetics, gravimetry, the ionosphere, satellite tracing, and the tidal crust. The Institute of Experimental Medicine and Medical Research; this studies experimental pharmacodynamics and experimental physiopathology; it also maintains a library. The Institute of Public Health Research; this is attached to the Faculty of Medicine and studies the prevention of epidemic diseases and public health. The Cancer Research Institute; this has laboratories for cytogenetics, electron microscopy, and experimental tumours, and also maintains a library. The Tehran University Nuclear Centre; this conducts research into isotopes, neutrons, and nuclear reactions; it has laboratories for agriculture, animal radiobiology, carbon 14, metallurgy, nuclear chemistry, nuclear physics, radiobiology, radiochemistry, radioisotopes, and solid-state physics; it also maintains a library. Other attached institutes include the Institute for Economic Research, the Institute of Communications Research, and the Institute of Hydro-Science and Water Resources Technology.

Tehran University of Technology has extensive laboratories and research facilities. Its departments include those for industrial engineering, mathematics, chemistry, physics, electrical engineering, metallurgy and mechanical engineering. It also has a computer centre.

The University of Tabriz (formerly Azarabadegan) has facilities for medicine, science, agriculture, engineering and pharmacology.

Mottaheddin University (formerly Farah Phalavi) is named after a young woman revolutionary who was killed during the revolution. Located in Tehran, it is a women's university with faculties for sciences, psychology and teacher training.

The University of Mashhad (formerly Ferdowsi) has faculties for medicine, dentistry, science and pharmaceutical and nutritional sciences.

The University of Shiraz (formerly Pahlayi) is mainly a science and technology university. Its Faculty of Arts and Sciences has a Department of Geology, which studies the geology of Iran and adjacent countries, a Department of Biology, which studies animal and plant biology and has seven laboratories, and a Department of Mathematics, which conducts research. The Faculty of Medicine has a Department of Medical Research on Radioisotopes whose interests include food hygiene. It has a laboratory for biochemistry. Other faculties include those for engineering, agriculture, veterinary medicine and dentistry. The Geotechnic Institute is attached to the university.

Isfahan University. This has faculties of medicine, science, and pharmacy. Each faculty maintains a library.

Jundi Shapur University. This is under state control, and has schools of agriculture, medicine, and nursing. Its Faculty of Agriculture has a Department of Agronomy and Horticulture which conducts scientific and technical surveys for increased production. It also has a Department of Research on Soils of Khuzistan, whose interests cover alkaline and saline soils, groundwater survey, plant nutrition, and salt-tolerant plants.

The University of Mazandaran (formerly Reza Shah Kabir) has been turned into a regional institution and all colleges and institutes of higher education in the Mazandaran area have been brought under the administration of the university. The university has faculties for basic sciences, social sciences and humanities.

Agricultural Science and Research

Agricultural research is conducted by the Ministry of Agriculture which supports the following institutes:

The Bureau of Statistics carries out economic surveys and scientific research on agriculture.

The Plant Pests and Diseases Research Institute conducts research on pests and diseases of plants and agricultural products. It has laboratories for citrus pests, fruit-tree pests, industrial plants and cotton pests, jute pests, and sugar-cane pests.

Razi Institute. The interests of the institute include preparation of sera and veterinary diseases. It has laboratories for antiparasitic drugs, entomology, mycology, helminthology, vaccines, and protozoology.

The Seed and Plant Improvement Institute conducts scientific surveys of seeds, plants, and fruit plants.

The Soil Institute of Iran conducts water and soil surveys. It has laboratories for plant chemistry, soil chemistry, soil microbiology, soil physics, and water chemistry.

State Animal Husbandry Institute. The institute's interests include milk technology, dairy products, birds, goats, and sheep. It has laboratories for milk technology, nutrition, and wool, and it maintains a library.

Sugar Beet Improvement Research Centre. The centre undertakes measurement of different elements of sugar beet, and also studies in plant breeding (sugar beet), and sugar-beet pests and diseases. It has a laboratory for investigation of sugar-beet seeds, and it maintains a library.

Industrial Science and Research

Industrial research is conducted by the Ministry of Economy and the Ministry of Water and Power.

The Ministry of Economy maintains the Centre for Scientific and Industrial Research in Tehran. The centre has done considerable work to support local manufacturing activities and has produced a number of innovations, including a new design for chicken incubators and new techniques for manufacturing copper wire and various household electrical appliances. The centre is also interested in standardization of agricultural, industrial and mineral products.

The Geological Survey of Iran, under the Ministry of Economy, investigates the geology of Iran and conducts surveys of mineral deposits.

The Ministry of Water and Power maintains the following departments and institute:

Ground Water Department. The department covers the fields of excavation, geodesy, geology, geophysics, hydrochemistry, photogeology, and pumping. It has laboratories for soil, technology, and water, and it maintains a library.

Institute of Hydro-Science and Water Resources Technology. This is responsible for the training of engineers and technicians. It has laboratories for physics and chemistry of water, and it maintains a library.

Surface Hydrology Department. Established in 1945, the department conducts surface hydrological resources surveys. It has laboratories for sediments and water and it maintains a library.

The National Iranian Oil Company also has a research and laboratories department, which is conducting research on air pollution, crude oil evaluation, oil chemistry, petrochemicals, petroleum products, pilot plant and suppression and erosion.

Medical Science and Research

Medical research is conducted by the Ministry of Public Health, which is responsible for the following institutes:

Firouzgar Medical Centre. The centre's interests include medical research, nutrition, and training of nurses. It maintains a library.

Food and Nutrition Institute of Iran. The institute's interests include food habits, food materials, measurement of water elements, and nutrition and nutrition diseases in Iran. It has laboratories for biochemistry, food industries, food materials, microbiology, and physiology.

Other Research

The Department of Environment in Tehran has an ambitious programme for the conservation of Iranian wastelands and wildlife, cleaning up the Caspian Sea and Iranian rivers, and air pollution in Tehran and Isfahan. The department has introduced new environmental legislation for dumping

of industrial waste, lead-free petrol and conservation of parks and wildlife. It maintains laboratories for pollution monitoring and research.

The Atomic Energy Organization, based in Tehran, is supervising the
completion of four partly-built reactors: two have a capacity of 1,200 MW
at Bushehr on the Persian Gulf, the others are 900 MW stations near
Ahwaz on the Karun river. Work on the reactors had started under the
Shah's regime but was suspended by the Revolutionary government. They
will now be completed using Iranian scientists and engineers. Nuclear
research in Iran is carried out at the Isfahan Nuclear Technology Centre
and the Nuclear Research Centre in Tehran. The Isfahan Nuclear Technology Centre is concentrating on uranium enrichment and reactor design.

The Nuclear Research Centre conducts research in nuclear physics and
has facilities for maintaining radioactive samples for use in medical research.
Since the revolution it has developed facilities for producing irradiated
iodine and technetium, which are widely used in the diagnosis and treatment of cancer and renal diseases in Iran.

Iraq

Demographic and Economic Background

Iraq is situated in the north-east of the Arabian peninsula. It has boundaries with Turkey to the north, Iran to the east, Kuwait to the south, Jordan and Saudi Arabia to the south-west and Syria to the north-west. Geographically the country can be divided into four regions: the mountainous regions of the north-east; the barren, semi-desert area of the south-west; the desert of the north-west; and the fertile plains and marshes of the region between the Euphrates and Tigris rivers. The area between the two rivers is among the most fertile land in the Middle East. The total land area is 435,000 km² and in 1979 the population was 12.6 million, increasing at the annual rate of 3.3 per cent.

Over half of the economically active population of Iraq works in agriculture but it provides only 8 per cent of the GDP. In 1979, Iraq's GDP was US$30.71 billion, most of it from oil revenues. In the 1976–80 development plan, agriculture was given priority, but the sector could absorb only 20 per cent of the funds allocated to it. While the government has spent heavily on farming cooperatives, rural infrastructure, transport and electricity, agricultural productivity in 1977 was less than in 1961. Nevertheless, the government aims to make Iraq an exporter of agricultural commodities, although in the near future it will continue to be dependent on the import of cereals.

The 1976–80 development plan devoted 40 per cent of the total expenditure to industry. Under the plan vast sums have been spent in setting up turnkey industrial complexes, like the iron and steel plant at Khar-al-Zubair and the fertilizer plant near the Syrian border. However, shortage of skilled manpower, particularly managerial skills, and endless bureaucratic bottlenecks have produced serious problems in the industrial sector. The cement industry is one of the few where productivity is good.

The 1981–85 development plan aims at more radical changes in the national economy and in the structure of the Iraqi society as a whole. The Political Report of the Eighth Regional congress of the Arab Baath Socialist Party, the ruling party of Iraq, has made the following four points the basis of Iraq's economic policy:

1. Expansion of the socialist sector in agriculture (state farms, collectives and cooperatives). To develop this sector so as to become the prevail-

ing and leading sector. Individualistic forms of agriculture must be discouraged in order to increase production, accelerate socialist transformation and raise the standard of living of farmers.

2. All foreign trade must be controlled by the state, which will centrally control the internal trade in which the public sector prevails. Due consideration will be given to the urgent requirements of the development plan which might necessitate some exceptions.

3. Consolidating the prominence of the public sector in industry and actively work accordingly to move away from state capitalism in this sector to a socialist democracy. The private sector will have to be further coordinated so that it can play its positive role in the development plan.

4. Public services will have to be directed in accordance with the requirements of development and socialist transformation.

Science Planning and Organization

Science policy and planning in Iraq is the responsibility of the Foundation of Scientific Research, which is attached to the Ministry of Higher Education and Scientific Research. The basic tenet of Iraq's science policy is to import technology from a wide range of sources at the most competitive prices, indigenous research, and scientific cooperation between the Arab countries.

The Foundation for Scientific Research was established in 1963 when it was called the Supreme Council of Scientific Research and was under the auspices of the University of Baghdad. It was renamed in 1966 and brought under the control of the prime minister's office. At present it is attached to the planning board. It is governed by a council and administered by a president.

According to its charter, the foundation acts for 'the advancement of pure and applied research, in particular that which is connected with industry, agriculture, public health, petroleum and other fundamentals of the national economy within the general plan of the State'. The objectives of the foundation are: the elaboration of a national science policy; the preparation of a national plan for research activities; coordination of research on a nationwide basis; facilitating and conducting research through its research institutes and centres or on contract basis, or through other scientific institutions; financing and promoting research programmes; awarding grants and financial assistance to researchers and scientific establishments; creating research centres, and cooperating with similar scientific establishments.

The foundation has several research departments, including agriculture and industry, and a number of research units such as a science policy unit, a space research unit and an energy unit. The following institutes and centres are attached to the foundation:

1. Institute for Applied Research on Natural Resources.
2. Petroleum Research Institute.

3. Building Research Centre.
4. Dates and Date Palm Research Centre.
5. Biological Research Centre.
6. Agricultural Research Centre.
7. Scientific Documentation Centre.
8. Directorate General of Youth Scientific Welfare.

The foundation is also responsible for the activities of several Iraqi national committees, especially those of oceanography and for the International Hydrological Programme, and other *ad hoc* committees. The foundation organizes scientific conferences, seminars and symposia in many different fields of science, technology and humanities.

In addition to the Foundation for Scientific Research and its affiliated research centres and institutes, research is also carried out under the Ministry of Agriculture, the Directorate-General of Industry, the Iraqi Atomic Energy Commission and at the Universities of Baghdad, Mosul and Basra.

Academic Science and Research

There are six universities in Iraq: al-Mustansiriyah University in Waziriyah, Baghdad, the University of Baghdad, the University of Basra, the University of Mosul, the University of Sulaimaniya and the University of Technology in Baghdad.

The University of Baghdad was founded in 1957. It was organized from a number of colleges which had been established in Baghdad between 1908 and 1955 and was reorganized in 1969. Other colleges have been established since the reorganization. In 1970 the university came under the jurisdiction of the Ministry of Higher Education and Scientific Research. The governing body is the university council, which is composed of the president, the vice-president, the deans of all the component colleges, and a representative of the students. Since the university is a state institution, it provides free education to all its students. The following colleges make up the university, the dates of the foundation being in parentheses.

The College of Science (1949) includes departments of physics, mathematics, biology, chemistry, and earth sciences. The College of Engineering (1942) has departments of civil, electrical, mechanical, chemical and agricultural engineering, architecture, and petroleum and minerals engineering. The College of Engineering Technology (1960) includes departments for building and construction, machine engineering, and electricity. The College of Medicine (1927) has departments covering most aspects of medical science; the College of Pharmacy (1936), the College of Dentistry (1953), and the College of Nursing (1962) cover other fields of health research. The College of Agriculture (1950) includes the departments of plant protection, plant production, food technology, soils, animal production, farms administration, and communes; the College of Veterinary Medicine (1955) undertakes undergraduate and postgraduate work in animal health. Other colleges in the university having interests outside the scientific field are the College of Law and Political Science (1908), the College of Administration and Economics (1947), the College of Arts (1949), the College of Physical Education (1955), the Academy of Fine Arts (1967), and the College of Education (1971). The latter College of Education is seeking to fulfil the country's needs for teaching staff and, apart from language and arts courses, is training teachers in education and teaching methods, educational psychology, home economics, mathematics, physics, chemistry, and biology. In 1974 this college had a total of 1,180 students, but it is expanding each year. The total number of students in the university in 1974 was 22,289.

Apart from the constituent colleges, the university has the following research centres: Educational and Psychological Research Centre, Economic and Administrative Research Centre, Palestinian Studies Research Centre, Urban and Regional Planning Centre (for graduate studies), the Psychology Clinic, the Medical Research, and the Natural History Research Centres; there is also a supervisory committee controlling studies in librarianship and documentation.

The University of Mosul was founded in 1964 from colleges which were formerly part of the University of Baghdad. In 1947 it became a separate university under the jurisdiction of the Ministry of Higher Education and Scientific Research. It has colleges for agriculture and forestry, engineering, medicine, and sciences. The College of Agriculture and Forestry, which is located at Hamam al-Alil, has the following departments: the Forestry Department, which is carrying out research in afforestation without irrigation, watershed management, production of seedlings, and forest entomology; the Animal Production Department, which is concerned with animal breeding and nutrition, meat technology, and artificial insemination; the Soil Sciences Department, whose interests lie in soil-water-plant relations with emphasis on soil fertility and plant nutrient uptake; the Field Crops Department, which is concerned with plant breeding research and with farming on arid land; the Food Technology Department, which carries out studies on the preservation and nutritional value of different foodstuffs; the Plant Protection Department, which is interested in plant diseases and carries out research work on agricultural pests, including insects – it also studies the effects of beneficial insects; the Horticulture Department which studies the effect of plant growth regulators on sexual and asexual reproduction of horticultural crops, and considers the adaptation of new fruit and vegetable varieties suitable to the area; the Veterinary Medicine Department, which is concerned with veterinary bacteriology, brucellosis in cows, and all aspects of animal pathology; and the Agricultural Economics Department, which is concerned with farm management, marketing, cooperative societies, and agricultural extension activities.

The College of Medicine has departments for general medicine, general surgery, gynaecology and obstetrics, microbiology, pathology, pharmacology, public health and forensic medicine, anatomy and microanatomy, and physiology and biochemistry.

Attached to the university are the Centre for Applied Scientific Research, the Centre for Applied Agricultural Research, the Centre for Applied

Medical Research and the Institute for Testing and Engineering Consultation.

The Centre for Applied Scientific Research was founded in 1974 and conducts research in production engineering, textiles, agriculture and geology. It provides scientific and technical assistance to a number of industrial establishments, such as the Sugar Factory of Mosul, the Mosul Dairy Project, the Cement Projects at Baghdad and Hamman al-Alil, the Mosul Textile Industry, the Modern Tannery Project and the Sulphur Mining Project in Mishraq.

The Centre for Applied Agricultural Research was founded in 1973 to identify the agricultural problems peculiar to northern Iraq. It is concerned with the problems of irrigation, weed control and parasites.

The Centre of Applied Medical Research was established in 1978 to encourage the university to do community-oriented medical research. It conducts research on bacteriology, parasitology, physiology and herbal medicine.

The University of Basra, like the University of Mosul, was founded in 1964 from colleges which were formerly part of the University of Baghdad. In 1967 it became an independent university governed by a university council and under the control of the Ministry of Higher Education and Scientific Research. It has colleges of science, engineering and medicine and a School of Higher Studies and Scientific Research. Attached to the university is the Centre for Marine Sciences.

The al-Mustansiriyah University, which is also known as the Free University of al-Mustansiriya, was founded in 1966 and is a privately controlled establishment located in Baghdad. It has colleges for sciences and for technology, and an Institute of Agricultural Cooperative Studies.

The University of Sulaimaniyah was founded in 1968 and is under the control of the Ministry of Higher Education and Scientific Research. It has colleges of sciences and arts, engineering, and agriculture.

The University of Technology was formerly the College of Engineering Technology of the University of Baghdad. It was made an independent university under the Ministry of Higher Education and Scientific Research in 1974. It has departments for mechanical, electrical and chemical engineering, applied sciences, building and construction, production and metallurgy and control and systems.

Agricultural Science and Research

Agricultural research is carried out at the Agricultural Research Centre of the Foundation for Scientific Research, the Date and Date Palm Research Centre, the University of Mosul's Centre for Applied Agricultural Research, and the Ministry of Agriculture.

The Ministry of Agriculture has a number of directorates covering the areas of the country's agricultural activities. The Directorate-General of Agricultural Extension covers educational and extension services. The Directorate-General of Animal Production has divisions for cattle and buffaloes, sheep, artificial insemination, nutrition, poultry, natural and irrigated pastures, and agricultural technology. In addition to the divisions, there are four experimental stations: the main station at Abu Chraib; a southern station at Basrah; a station at Bakrajo in the northern mountain area; and a station at Aski Kalak, also in the northern mountains. The main areas of research in the stations are the breeding, management, and production of cattle, sheep and poultry. The Directorate-General of Field Crops has divisions for seed crops (wheat and barley, white and golden maize, and legumes), cotton (cotton research station, cotton ginning section, and fibres inspection), and industrial crops (oil crops, sugar crops, jute and linseed, tobacco, medicinal plants, stone weeds, and weed control). The Directorate-General of Horticulture has sections which deal with fruit production, vegetable production, date palms, nurseries, and horticultural technology. The Directorate-General of Plant Protection has departments for entomology, plant pathology, pest control, plant quarantine, plant technology, and beekeeping and silkworms. The Directorate-General of Soil and Land Reclamation has divisions for research, soil surveying and land classification, land reclamation and utilization, soil and water conservation, and technology and pilot plants. The Directorate-General of State Farms controls the following state farms: Sweira Farm, Shattrah Farm, the Medicinal Plant Farm, Abu Ghraib Farm, Haweeja Farm, Latifiyah Farm, and Bakrajo Farm; the directorate also controls a seed production and certification project. The Sugar Cane Administration of Iraq also comes under the control of the Ministry of Agriculture.

Nuclear Science and Research

The Iraqi Atomic Energy Commission (IAEC) was founded in October 1956. Its administrative organ is the Secretariat-General, which is responsible for the commission's programmes and the implementation of its decisions and policies. The commission has ordered a 600 MW reactor from France and plans to purchase three more 600 MW reactors by the year 2000.

The commission controls the Nuclear Research Institute (NRI) which is centred around a 2 MW swimming-pool reactor which became critical on 11 December 1967. Recently, NRI has acquired a more advanced reactor, a 70 MW Osirak reactor, from France. The IAEC also established the Institute of Radiology and Nuclear Medicine in 1969 and the Ministry of Health's Radioisotope Institute at Mosul. The IAEC is also responsible for implementing bilateral treaties which have been signed with the Soviet Union, France, Brazil and Italy. It was a founding member in 1963 of the Middle East Regional Isotopes Centre for Arab States, in Cairo, and is a participant in the governing body of this centre and in its training programme.

Research at the NRI is directed towards producing radioisotopes for local problems in medicine, agriculture and industry. The NRI has studied corrosion in pipelines, undertaken chemical analysis of industrial materials and used radioactive sources for the study of groundwater sources. It has departments for nuclear reactors, nuclear physics, chemistry, biology and agriculture, engineering and instrumentation, nuclear geology, radio-isotope production, and health physics.

The Nuclear Reactor Department of the institute is responsible for the operation and maintenance of the reactor (which was designed and constructed by nuclear experts from the Soviet Union), in order to make use of the ten experimental channels of the reactor in research activities and in the irradiation of various medical and industrial isotopes. The department also carries out research programmes in reactor and neutron physics, which include the analysis of reactor noise and power spectrum to determine the reactor's transfer function and other parameters, heat transfer studies, optimum fuel loading, development of the reactor control system, spatial neutron flux and power distribution in the reactor, and neutron radiography.

The Nuclear Physics Department of the institute is divided into four groups. The Experimental Nuclear Physics Group carries out research in the fields of nuclear spectroscopy and angular distribution of gamma rays; measurements of gamma-spectra resulting from the inelastic scattering of fast neutrons from natural elements and pure isotopes are carried out using Ge(Li) detectors with a 4096 multichannel analyser and a computer code. The Solid-State Physics Group uses a double axis neutron diffractometer to identify crystal structures for different alloys and materials, and to measure diffraction parameters of irradiated samples; an X-ray diffraction laboratory is used by the group for crystal and powder studies of various materials. The Theoretical Physics Group deals with elastic neutron interactions by using separable potential forms for two-body scattering so that it can be used in Faddeev three-body equations and inelastic neutron interactions by using Hauser-Feshbach formalism. The Neutron Activation Analysis Group uses a pneumatic system with which it is possible to irradiate samples near the reactor core in order to determine the amount of various elements in parts per million (ppm). This method was used in measuring the amount of mercury in meat during the 1971 mercury poisoning outbreak in Iraq, the amount of arsenic in Iraqi tobacco, fluorine concentration in water, and in tracing of rare elements in the study of underground oil migration.

The Department of Chemistry has five units which carry out research indicated by the general policy of the International Atomic Energy Agency. The Analytical Chemistry Unit provides a general service for the institute and for some other government departments; this included the analysis of 4,000 samples of food poisoning by mercury in 1971, the analysis of lead samples for the Nuclear Physics Department, the analysis of reactor water, and the analysis of radioactive materials from Iraqi phosphate and carbonate ores. The Inorganic and Radiochemistry Unit is concerned with the study of aqueous and non-aqueous stable and radioactive complexes using various methods such as solvent–solvent extraction; it is also engaged in the preparation and identification of thorium and uranium compounds; preparations are also being made for research in the chemistry of nuclear fission and radiochemical analysis. The Organic Chemistry Unit is actively engaged in the preparation of new organic compounds which are capable of producing complexes with some elements capable of preventing the damage caused by ionizing radiation to the human body or biologically active complexes; this unit is also concerned with preparation of labelled compounds as well as the study of their mass and infrared spectral parameters. The Radiation Chemistry Unit studies radiation effects on certain materials which are widely used in industry, such as wood and textiles, and studies hot atom reactions, such as the reaction of nuclear recoil tritium with different types of molecules. The Structural Chemistry Unit is mainly concerned with the analysis of crystal structure by means of X-ray diffraction of different inorganic and organic complexes using the heavy atom method.

The Biology and Agriculture Department has five major laboratories. Both the Biochemistry and Microbiology Laboratories investigate the effects of radiation on the chemical composition of dates and grains, e.g. proteins, free amino acids, sugars, pectins, and carotenes. Research is carried out to study the nature of radiation resistance in some microorganisms, and to locate the initial events responsible for lethal damage in these cells. The Entomology Laboratory carries out research concerning the control of insect pests, e.g. saw-toothed grain beetles and fig moths, by preventing their reproduction through sterile male techniques or direct killing, using radiation in order to protect Iraqi dates and other stored foodstuffs. The Plant Breeding Laboratory is concerned with the use of radiation to find genetic mutants with good-quality and high-yielding strains of barley, linseed and sesame; research on the improvement of date quality by irradiation of pollen grain is also undertaken. The Plant Genetics and Morphogenesis Laboratory conducts research on the use of radiation for growth stimulation and to determine genetic changes in wheat and rice in order to obtain new varieties resistant to diseases, salinity, and drought, and giving a high-quality yield.

The Engineering and Instrumentation Department is concerned with the design, development, and maintenance of the electronic and mechanical instruments which are used in other departments of the institute and, to a lesser extent, it provides similar services to other government institutes.

The Nuclear Geology Department of the institute is primarily concerned with prospecting for radioactive uranium and thorium-bearing deposits throughout Iraq and with determination of the percentage of such elements in ore samples.

The Radioisotopes Production Department is engaged in the preparation of radioisotopes and labelled compounds used in the medical, agricultural and industrial fields. It also produces seventeen standard radioactive sources for the calibration of nuclear instruments used for teaching and identification purposes, and it imports those radioisotopes which are not produced in the institute according to the requirements of universities, health establishments, and the research scientists in the institute. It also exports some of its radioisotope production to some other Arab countries.

Lastly, the Health Physics Department of the Nuclear Research Institute carries out studies which are primarily concerned with the safety and protection of personnel in the institute from radioactive hazards. The department is also engaged in several research programmes which include the total body burden of natural and industrial radioactivity with the use of a whole-body counter, the measurement of daily intake of I-125 and I-131, and with environmental studies of radioactive pollution.

Scientific and Technical Information Services

The Iraqi Scientific Documentation Centre was established in 1972 in the Foundation for Scientific Research in Baghdad. Services of the centre are available to the scientists and technologists involved in research and development, including those engaged in universities, research centres, government establishments and industries. The centre also cooperates with experts and consultants working on projects of the United Nations Development Programme.

The objectives of the centre are: to build up a modern scientific and technical library which will meet the needs of researchers; to collect each scientific and technical publication published in Iraq or which deals with or refers to Iraq; to offer bibliographic and current awareness services; to establish a combined catalogue of all scientific and technical periodicals in the centre and in other libraries in the country; to classify and index collections of scientific books, monographs and reports collected by the centre; to provide reading room facilities and to develop a collection of bibliographic and reference works; to translate works from less common languages into languages known to researchers; to schedule, prepare and participate in national and international meetings and conferences; to train necessary staff for the centre and for other libraries; and to establish a reprographic and printing unit necessary to the centre. It is intended that the scientific and technical library will be developed into a national scientific library.

Jordan

Demographic and Economic Background

Most of Jordan consists of the north-western corner of the great Arabian plateau, which extends unbroken into Syria, Iraq and Saudi Arabia. The West Bank of Jordan has been under Israeli occupation since 1969. The country's only port is Aqaba at the innermost point of the Gulf of Aqaba, which extends north from the Red Sea. Jordan's total area is approximately 98,000 km² and in 1979 its population was estimated to be 3.1 million. Of the total area of 'East Bank' Jordan, 91 per cent is classified officially as arid. This is either sand or rock desert and has little agricultural possibility. The agricultural sector provides just under 10 per cent of the GDP, while the industry and services sectors provide 32 and 60 per cent respectively. Vegetables and fruits are the main agricultural products, but wheat and other cereals are also grown. The emphasis is on drip and sprinkler irrigation methods, but hydroponics and dry-farming techniques are also used quite extensively. Under the last development plan (1976–80), Jordan's industrial sector grew at the annual rate of 22 per cent, and the five major industries in Jordan – potash, fertilizer, phosphates, cement and petroleum – all expanded rapidly. Plans to recover potash from the Dead Sea, set up a major fertilizer complex in Aqaba, and expand the mining of phosphate rocks have all received a push from the new development plan.

The second five year development plan (1981–85) envisages an annual increase of 10.4 per cent in the country's GDP and a sharp increase in domestic revenues. Some 49 per cent of the total investment under the plan will go into commodity-producing industry and tourism. The plan divides the country into five self-contained planning regions: Amman and vicinity, the Jordan river valley, the north, around the city of Irbid, the Aqaba area in the south, and the central desert region around Ma'an. The development plans for each region are based on indigenous resources and manpower and 50 per cent of the funds are expected to come from the private sector.

The regionalization philosophy of the plan is based on the success of the Jordan Valley project. The Jordan Valley, a 140-km stretch of fertile land that lies along the length of the River Jordan, is fed by a number of streams and rivers. The valley has a tropical climate and much of it is over 1,000 feet below sea level. The valley is already hailed as a farming

Eden: the narrow strip of rich soil which consists of only 0.6 per cent of Jordan's total land area is now producing half of the country's fruit and vegetables and 90 per cent of its export crops. The agricultural success of the valley is due to an irrigation network consisting of dams and canals. The Ghor Canal runs parallel to the River Jordan and channels water to farmlands throughout the valley. Feeding the canal are the US$35 million King Talal Dam, Kufrain Dam, Shueib Dam, Ziglab Dam, Sultani Dam, Katranch Dam, Sama Sdud Dam and Um Jmal Dam. The US$900 million Maqarin Dam, the Wadi Araba Dam, Hasa Dam and Rumeil Dam, are all due for completion by 1985. The success of the Jordan Valley project has been just as much due to social planning: the Jordan Valley Development Authority divided the valley into thirty-six communities and provided each community with complete infrastructure including homes, schools, clinics, water and power. The same approach will be applied, under the new development plan, to the other four planning regions.

Science Policy and Planning

The National Planning Council and the Royal Scientific Society, together with the Ministry of Education and the Ministry of Agriculture, are responsible for science policy and planning in Jordan. Originally science planning was the responsibility of the Jordanian Scientific Research Council, which was established in 1964. However, after a reorganization in 1972, the council was finally abolished in 1976.

The National Planning Council is the only institution which is empowered by law to formulate national plans. The council was established in 1971 to formulate long-range plans for economic, social and manpower development of Jordan, to negotiate agreement with foreign countries for technical assistance and the transfer of technology, to identify manpower needs of the country and to set up a system for the evaluation and monitoring of the long-range plans. In February 1979, a Conference on Science and Technology Policy in Jordan was held and the council was entrusted with formulating and supervising the implementation of science and technology policies. The council will cooperate with the Royal Scientific Society and various ministries to formulate an integrated national policy for science and technology. The 1981–85 development plan states that the council will be reorganized to improve its capabilities for formulating a national science and technology policy. It also states that a science and technology fund will be established with private and public contributions and expenditure on science and technology will be increased to between 3 and 5 per cent of the GNP, with 30 per cent earmarked for research and development, to facilitate the task of the council.

The basis of the science and technology policy will be the recommendations of Jordan's Science and Technology Policy Conference of 1979. The conference recommended:

1.   That the role of each scientific and technological institution in Jordan

be defined with regard to the research they conduct and service they render so that unnecessary duplication of research effort is avoided.

2. That contract research and development for the production sector should be encouraged and the necessary mechanism for its implementation be established in all scientific institutions.

3. That appropriate management techniques compatible with research requirements should be introduced through training, revised procedures and expert advice.

4. That a suitable technical information system be introduced in Jordan.

5. That performance of research and development by the production sector be encouraged and strengthened through a variety of means, including tax incentives and the establishment of research associations.

Government Science and Research

The Royal Scientific Society (RSS) is the main research institution in the country. It was established in 1970 as an independent, non-profit, research and development organization. The charter of RSS, formulated in 1973, states that the society's objective is 'to carry out research, conduct studies and offer scientific and technological consultation, especially that which related to the economic and social development of the Kingdom and to the proper utilization of the country's resources, with the purpose of increasing the national income and improving the standard of living of the citizens'. The society's functions are:

1. To follow up the latest advances in science and technological development in the world; to establish laboratories for scientific research, applications and experimentation; and to conduct research and studies on the feasibility and launching of pilot industries.

2. To extend to the government and private organizations technical services and consultations for the organization of scientific research, technological development, and planning.

3. To mobilize Jordanian scientists and technologists to work in applied research, and to help find scholarship opportunities for outstanding Jordanians to attain higher degrees abroad.

4. To provide translations, publications and documentation for scientific research.

5. To cooperate with indigenous and foreign organizations, societies and establishments interested in scientific research, development and planning, and so enhance scientific research and benefit by its results.

The RSS functions under a board of trustees presided over by Crown Prince Hassan ibn-Talal. A director-general looks after the daily operations of the society. Research is carried out in the Computer Systems Department, Mechanical Engineering Department, Economic Research Department, the Education Department, the Electrical Engineering Department and the Building Research Centre. There is also an Electronic Services and Training Centre.

The Computer Systems Department takes cognisance that Jordan, as a developing country, is in need of accurate and rapid information to use as a basis for proper decision-making. The aims of the department are: to provide data processing services and technical consultation in the electronic computation area, to implement modern data collection methods, to effect rapid and accurate preparation, processing and analysis of the data gathered, and to use electronic computers in order to serve Jordan's growing project needs; to train Jordanian personnel and develop their capabilities in the data processing area; and to plan, develop and implement sound electronic computer systems to meet the present and projected requirements of Jordan and her neighbouring Arab countries.

The Mechanical Engineering Department participates in setting up an infrastructure for conducting applied engineering research in the areas of mechanical engineering and industrial chemistry in Jordan. Its aims are: to conduct research related to mechanical engineering; to test industrial materials and products related to Jordan's needs; to provide consulting services aimed at the development of local industries; to work towards the improvement of technical manpower; to solve technical problems related to the development of industry and technology in Jordan; to follow up technical progress in developed countries, and to effect a transfer of such technology relevant to the needs of Jordan. The department has a section for research and development which is concerned with solar energy application, machine design, and engineering drawing; a vocational training section; an industrial programme and studies section, which is also concerned with standards; an industrial chemistry section, which carries out projects in organic and inorganic chemistry, spectrography, and fuels and lubricants; a building materials section; and an engineering laboratory, where present studies are directed towards strength of materials, measurement and calibration, and metallography. In the future it is proposed to establish facilities for research on plastics and rubber, paper and textiles, glass and ceramics, paints and lacquers, and stress analysis.

The Economic Research Department is responsible for carrying out economic research and studies that are believed to contribute to the economic and social development of Jordan. The specific functions of the department are: to develop a significant economic research capability with a trained research staff which can analyze Jordan's economic problems and suggest solutions; to conduct research on Jordan's economic achievement and on specific policy issues in areas such as public finance and fiscal policy, monetary policy and money markets, foreign trade and the balance of payments, industrial development potential, agricultural development, labour market and manpower policies, income distribution and policies, and economic relations between Jordan and her neighbouring countries; and to collect data, carry out statistical inference, evaluate such data and statistics, and publish the results of economic research, as well as prepare training programmes and provide consultative services to public, private and industrial sectors in Jordan.

The Education Department aims at keeping up to date with the latest developments and research in the scientific, educational and technical fields and to adapt them to meet the needs of education in Jordan. In carrying out its responsibilities the department initiates innovative work in Jordan in the field of science, mathematics, and languages, which is not carried out by any other educational centre, such as the Ministry of Education or the University of Jordan. The department is especially concerned with acquiring the most modern teaching systems and making them available to Jordanian teachers, either by providing them in translation, or by conducting intensive courses in general and technical English, French, and other languages. Training courses for teachers are offered in science, mathematics and technical education, and the department cooperates with other educational research centres in Jordan, and Arab world, and other countries.

The Electronics Engineering Department aims at actively participating in the scientific and technological development of electronics engineering through conducting research and development, initiating pilot production operations, and providing technical consultations. The department consists of two major divisions: the first is concerned with research and development and includes all systems and products development laboratories; it is staffed with qualified engineers whose key members have received industrial experience abroad; the second division is concerned with production having been established as a pilot production facility capable of producing in marketable quantities. In addition to its primary role in prototype production, this division has facilities for drafting and layout, machine and plastics shops, printed circuit board production, and an electronics assembly line. The department provides technical consultation services in the areas of communication systems, and in electronics laboratory equipment, including specifications and operation.

According to the 1981–85 development plan, RSS has two major problems: lack of a permanent source of income and shortage of necessary facilities and qualified personnel. The plan has allocated a total of JD 6.2 million to the RSS and envisages the setting up of general advisory bodies to strengthen the linkage between local industry and the RSS and to ensure a fixed source of income and increase revenues from contractural research. To overcome the shortage of facilities, the plan has provisions for the expansion of mechanical engineering and industrial chemistry laboratories, the computer centre and Electronic Services and Training Centre and facilities of the Building Research Centre.

Academic Science and Research

Jordan has two universities: the University of Jordan and Yarmouk University. A third university will be established in Mu'ta.

The University of Jordan was established in 1962 as an autonomous institution. The university has ten faculties, including sciences, medicine, nursing, agriculture and engineering. In 1972, the university established a deanship for scientific research and graduate studies whose responsibilities included the development of a research plan for the university's various faculties. This plan has yet to be produced. Only the Faculty of Agriculture conducts research; its research is concerned with 'plastic agriculture', dry farming, ground sterilization using solar energy, and irrigation.

Yarmouk University in Irbid was established in 1976 and has faculties for science and arts, engineering, medicine and graduate studies. There is also a teaching hospital.

Jordan also has two further universities in the occupied West Bank. Bethlehem University is a private university founded in 1973. It has a College of Arts and Sciences and a School of Nursing. Birzeit University was founded in 1924 as a small, private school. In 1934 the school became 'Birzeit College' and in 1975, after the June 1967 Arab–Israeli war, when the need for the establishment became obvious, the college was changed officially to Birzeit University. At present the university has faculties for science and engineering. Within the ten-year plan of the university (1977–87) faculties for education and health sciences will also be established.

Agricultural Science and Research

The Directorate of Research and Agricultural Extension of the Ministry of Agriculture is responsible for agricultural research in the country. It was established in 1952. It has research programmes on dry farming, irrigation, horticulture, livestock and poultry, fisheries, afforestation and soil surveys and land classification. Under the 1981–85 development plan a National Centre for Agricultural Research will be set up by 1985 and an Agricultural Research Unit for the Ghors will also be established.

Medical Science and Research

The Supreme Health Council, founded in 1977, is responsible for medical research in the country. The council is composed of nineteen members with the Prime Minister as president and the Minister of Health as vice-president. The Directorate of Planning and Foreign Relations at the Ministry of Health acts as a secretariat to the council. The council will develop research programmes on curative and preventive medicine, pharmaceuticals, family planning and rural health care. Under the 1981–85 development plan, a Public Health Laboratory will be set up in Amman by 1983, and a Pharmaceutical Control Laboratory by the end of 1982.

Kuwait

Demographic and Economic Background

Kuwait is situated at the head of the Arabian Gulf, bordering Iraq. In 1979, Kuwait's population was 1.3 million; the average growth rate for the 1970s was 6 per cent. This population occupies an area of 18,000 km².

In the period prior to the discovery of oil, Kuwait's economy was based on fishing, pearling and transit trade. Since oil was first exported in 1946 the country's economic growth has become highly dependent on petroleum and the oil-related sector. Oil revenues now constitute around 70 to 80 per cent of the GDP and 95 to 98 per cent of the government budget. With the exception of petroleum the Kuwaiti economy is facing serious obstacles due to the small size of the country, harsh climatic conditions, poor soil fertility for large-scale agricultural expansion and short supply of fresh water.

However, oil revenues have ensured rapid economic development for the small Gulf state. In 1979, Kuwait's GDP was a staggering US$23.3 billion. The increase in income has produced a parallel expansion in finance, government and service sectors and has led to a sharp increase in the number of immigrants into the country due to the shortage of local manpower. Immigrant and expatriate manpower represents over 60 per cent of the total population of Kuwait.

The current development plan (1981–86) is aimed at producing 'auto-motivated economic growth' and an 'increasing income and production rates'. According to Kuwait's National Paper to UNCSTD, the main features of Kuwait's economic development strategy are:

1. The development of manpower by training, planning and organizing manpower requirements, promoting female participation in the workforce, increasing productivity and linking the latter to wage rates.
2. Economic diversification and broadening the productive base through the use of capital intensive technology together with the adaptation of modern technology to local needs, the establishment of a plan for industrialization based on rapid technological development and the creation of a suitable climate to encourage investments in the local sectors.
3. Economic coordination and integration among the various sectors based on the creation of linkages and the facilitation of movement

among the various sectors, the reduction of production bottlenecks and the promotion of regional and Arab cooperation in joint development projects.
4. The creation of a pollution-free society enjoying economic maturity and a social system based on sound values.

Science Policy and Planning

Kuwait does not have a body responsible for science and technology, and a science and technology plan was not included in the 1976–81 development plan. However, science and technology have been pursued in Kuwait within the broad framework of the economic development strategy described above. The Kuwait Institute for Scientific Research has now been given the responsibility of producing a national science plan.

Organization of Science and Research

All institutions concerned with science and technology are State-controlled and financed by various government departments.

The Kuwait Institute for Scientific Research (KISR) is the main scientific institution in the country. It was founded in February 1967 by the Arabian Oil Company Ltd (Japan) to conduct research on petroleum, arid zone agriculture and marine biology and fisheries. The institute was run jointly by the company and the government of Kuwait. In 1973, the government of Kuwait completely took over and the research programme of the institute was enlarged to include energy, water studies, pollution and the geological and geographical mapping of the country. In 1976, KISR was reorganized and expanded and its budget increased many-fold.

Research at KISR is project-oriented and based on the goals and objectives of the institute. The overall objective is described in the institute's constitution as the promotion of 'scientific and applied research, particularly where industry, energy, agriculture and other major resources of the national economy are concerned, and with a view to servicing the objectives of the national economic and social development and to rendering advice to the government of the scientific research policy of the State'. These objectives are pursued by undertaking the following responsibilities to:

1. Carry out scientific research and undertake studies relating to the advancement of national industry and to matters referred to it by the ministers.
2. Follow up modern developments in scientific and technological progress in order to furnish scientific and industrial data and information to government departments, industrial concerns, and those engaged therein.
3. Study and discover resources of natural water wealth and devise methods for their exploitation; and for improvement of agricultural

processes, promotion of water wealth, elimination of pests, as well as making studies conducive to the preservation of the environment.
4. Encourage Kuwaiti citizens to engage in scientific research and promote the spirit of research in the rising generation.
5. Establish and maintain relations with scientific and technological research institutes and centres in Kuwait and in other countries of the world, and exchange therewith information and know-how with a view to achieving worldwide cooperation. (From Mohamed A. Omar and Mohamed Afzal, Kuwait Institute of Scientific Research, *Proceedings of the Symposium on Science and Technology for Development in Kuwait*, edited by K. Behbehani, M. Girgis and M. S. Morzouk, Longman, London 1981.)

Research at KISR is divided into four core programmes: energy, food resources, natural resources and environmental studies. The energy programme is largely concerned with solar energy and has three focus areas: solar heating and cooling of buildings, agricultural applications of solar energy and solar thermal conversion and photovoltaic conversion. The food resources programme also focuses on three areas: food technology, arid zone agriculture and mariculture. The natural resources programme deals mainly with materials development and the development of petroleum and petrochemical products. The environmental studies programme is concerned with thermal pollution in the Arabian Gulf as well as investigations into oil and air pollution and the use of remote sensing in identifying locations of pollutants.

KISR has a wide-ranging cooperation agreement with the United States National Science Foundation. The agreement, signed on 9 June 1980, is designed to provide opportunities for exchanging ideas, information, skills and techniques in all fields of the natural sciences, engineering and mathematics. The two countries will 'collaborate on solving scientific and technological problems of mutual interest and benefit'.

Academic Science and Research

The University of Kuwait was inaugurated in 1966 after six years of preparatory work. The university has an independent budget and is administered by a university council which is also Kuwait's Supreme Council for Higher Education, and which is responsible to the Minister of Education, who is the university's chancellor. The university has colleges of science, engineering and petroleum, medicine, law, arts and education, and commerce, economics and political science, and a college of graduate studies. The College of Graduate Studies was established in 1977, and postgraduate studies and research commenced in 1978. Research at the university is limited to oceanography, petrochemicals, food substitutes, energy, medicine and environmental science. The university provides numerous advisory services to various government organizations, such as the Ministry of Education (development of scientific curricula), the Ministry of Electricity (nuclear energy) and the Ministry of Health (pharmaceutical use of desert plants, nutritional problems and cancer research). The university publishes the annual *Bulletin of the Faculty of Science.*

Agricultural and Water Science and Research

The Department of Agriculture of the Ministry of Public Works has an Agricultural Experimental Station, which was founded in 1953 to carry out research in agricultural disciplines, including soil conservation and irrigation, plant protection, arid zone research and animal husbandry. The station now has five areas of research: agriculture, animal husbandry, veterinary medicine, public gardens and afforestation and fisheries. Kuwait has a high temperature and a low rainfall climate and very little in the way of fertile soil. For this reason the station gives particular attention to field studies on soil and water, hydroponic agriculture and the planting of trees and desert plants and the maintenance of afforestation.

The Water Resources Development Centre was established in 1968 in cooperation with UNEP. In 1973 the centre was completely taken over by the Government of Kuwait, with UNEP providing only technical and advisory assistance. The centre has a laboratory for water analysis, which is used for training university graduate chemists in techniques of water analysis. The research and development section of the centre investigates and advises the government on various types of desalination plants and their suitability for operation in Kuwait, on chemical treatment of existing distillers, and on corrosion prevention.

Material Science and Research

The Government Research Station was established in 1953. It has a soil-testing section, which is responsible for testing soil at foundation level of all buildings in Kuwait according to the rules of the municipality and a chemistry section which has a laboratory for analysing materials chemically. The centre is responsible for handling scientific problems faced by the building industry in Kuwait, running physical and chemical tests on all materials used for building, construction and industrial projects, conducting site tests for building foundations and testing the safety of buildings in Kuwait. The centre also offers technical consultancies for construction problems in Kuwait.

Scientific and Technical Information Services

The National Scientific and Technical Information Centre (NSTIC) was established in 1976 after the recommendation of the 1976 CASTARAB conference. The centre was developed from the Documentation Information Division of KISR which was set up in 1973. NSTIC aims to become the national focal point of specialized subject-oriented information centres and libraries in Kuwait and as a national depository library for technical and statistical reports. It also aims to function as a regional scientific and technical centre for the Gulf. The technical library of NSTIC has 20,000 books of specific interest to KISR and other scientific institutions of Kuwait. The periodicals library contains 1,000 titles, supported by more than 3,600 titles cited in the *Union List of Scientific and Technical Periodicals in Kuwait*, which is prepared and published by NSTIC to provide access to fourteen special and academic libraries in Kuwait. The computerized *Union List* is updated annually. NSTIC has also published the *Regional Union List of Scientific and Technical Periodicals in the Gulf Area*. NSTIC offers a number of specialized services, including facilities for retrospective search, current awareness and selective dissemination of information. The centre also runs training programmes in information science and librarianship.

Scientific Societies and Association

The Kuwait Foundation for the Advancement of the Sciences was established in 1976 and supports scientific research and development projects across a wide range of disciplines.

Lebanon

Demographic and Economic Background

Bordered by Syria to the north and east, and Israel to the south, Lebanon forms a strip of about 193 km in length, varying from 48–56 km in width along the eastern Mediterranean coast. The total area is about 210,400 km², and the population numbers approximately 2.7 million.

The country is not a great oil producer, but an important revenue is obtained from transit fees for oil originated in Saudi Arabia and Iraq which is transported by pipelines which terminate at the Lebanese ports of Sidon and Tripoli. Agricultural products provide cash crops, the most important being grain, cotton, tobacco, and fruits. Only just over one-quarter of the country is cultivated. Chief industries are oil refining, food processing, and cement, and the production of consumer goods is rapidly expanding. Since the civil war and the flare-up of 1978, there are signs of greater State involvement in the economy. A £L14 billion reconstruction plan, spread over five years, is emphasizing public works and industrial development.

Science Policy and Organizations

Lebanon does not have a specific science policy. The National Council for Scientific Research (NCSR) is the government body concerned with science and technology in the country. Established in 1962, the NCSR reports directly to the prime minister and is responsible for the national science policy, overseeing scientific research and promoting science and technology activities in the country. The council promotes research in agriculture, biomedical science, engineering sciences, environmental studies and marine sciences. The council is supporting several solar energy projects, the most important of which is the establishment of a radiometric network of ten stations for the measurement of available solar energy in Lebanon. Other solar energy programmes of the council include water heating, distillation, double-effect distillation and photovoltaic conversion.

Most of the research in Lebanon is conducted in the independent universities. However, the Ministry of Agriculture has an Agricultural Research Institute working on cotton and grains. The International Centre for Agricultural Research in Dry Areas has a regional office in Beirut.

Academic Science and Research

There are four universities in the Lebanon which have faculties for sciences or medicine. One other, the *Université Saint Esprit de Kaslik*, has no scientific interests.

The American University of Beirut was founded in 1866 as the Syrian Protestant College. Four years before this date American missionaries in Lebanon and Syria had suggested the founding of a college of higher learning and medical training to the American Board of Commissioners for Foreign Missions.

The State of New York granted a charter for the university in 1863, and the guiding principle of the Syrian Protestant College was: 'This College is for all conditions and classes of men without regard to colour, nationality, race or religion. . . .' The name of the college was changed by the Board of Regents of the State University of New York on 18 November 1920, and since then it has been called the American University of Beirut. Today it is still a private, non-sectarian institution of higher learning, which presents a programme in international education and research which is unusual among the universities of the world.

In the Faculty of Arts and Sciences, the scientific departments and their activities are briefly described below. The Department of Biology, apart from its undergraduate teaching course, has programmes in endocrinology, molecular biology of development, cell and molecular biology, advanced genetics, concepts of modern ecology, and chemical, physical and biological oceanography. The Department of Chemistry has advanced programmes for the structure of inorganic compounds, chemistry of the less common elements, chemistry of the coordination compounds, mechanisms of inorganic reactions, advanced organic chemistry, organic stereochemistry, physical organic chemistry, heterocyclid chemistry, chemistry and technology of high polymers, quantum chemistry, statistical thermodynamics, chemical kinetics, and electrolytes. The Department of Geology has advanced programmes for geochemistry, geophysics, mineral deposits, petroleum geology, photogeology, micropalaeontology, and hydrogeology. The Department of Mathematics has undergraduate and graduate programmes in all branches of mathematics and statistics. The Department of Physics has programmes in all branches of physics, including nuclear physics, solid-state physics, optics, astrophysics, theoretical elementary particle physics, experimental low-temperature physics, magnetic resonance, and molecular spectroscopy. In addition to the departments, the Faculty of Arts and Sciences has a Centre for Behavioural Research, a Centre for English Language Research and Teaching, an Economic Research Institute, a Graduate Centre for Middle Eastern Studies, a Science and Mathematics Education Centre for the training of prospective science and mathematics teachers, and a special University Orientation Programme which aims to meet the needs of students who qualify for entrance to the university but who have a deficiency in English language skills.

The Faculty of Medical Sciences includes four schools – the School of Medicine, the School of Pharmacy, the School of Nursing, and the School of Public Health. The School of Medicine has departments for anaesthesiology, bacteriology and virology, biochemistry, clinical pathology, human morphology, internal medicine, obstetrics and gynaecology, ophthalmology, otorhinolaryngology, pathology, paediatrics, pharmacology and therapeutics, physiology, radiology, and surgery; there is also a nutrition research programme, and special preventive medicine and public health courses. The School of Pharmacy has departments for pharmaceutical chemistry, pharmacodynamics and toxicology, pharmacognosy, and pharmacy. The School of Nursing carries out programmes for the provision of qualified nurses in the medical, surgical, maternal and child, mental health and psychiatric, and public health fields. The School of Public Health has departments for community health practice, environmental health, epidemiology and biostatistics, health services administration, and tropical health.

The Faculty of Engineering and Architecture has the following departments: the Department of Architecture, which carries out advanced studies on regional planning, transport planning, and urban design; the Department of Civil Engineering, which undertakes advanced programmes in many fields but is especially concerned with water resources development, water pollution control, waste disposal and industrial wastes, and marine pollution; the Department of Electrical Engineering, which carries out advanced work on digital systems and circuits, process control, network analysis and synthesis, semiconductor devices, power systems, biomedical instrumentation and equipment, biological control systems and their analogues, communication systems and circuits, and information theory; and the Department of Mechanical Engineering, which carries out studies in hydrodynamics and viscous flow, gas dynamics, advanced thermodynamics, industrial engineering, systems analysis, turbomachinery, thermal conduction and radiation, and convective heat transfer.

The Faculty of Agricultural Sciences has departments for agricultural economics and sociology, animal production and protection, plant production and protection, food technology and nutrition, and soils and irrigation. There is also a programme in general agriculture. All departments of the faculty carry out research programmes of great significance to the agricultural sector in the Lebanon.

The Lebanese University, situated at Bir Hassan, Beirut, was initially founded as a teacher training college but later, in 1953, it was reorganized by decree as a full university. It is an autonomous State institution under the patronage of the Minister of Education. It is governed by the University Council and the Councils of the Faculties. Faculties include those for literature and the humanities; sciences; law and political sciences; business administration; and education. There is also an institute for information sciences.

The Faculty of Sciences has sections for mathematics, physics, chemistry, and natural sciences (including general biology, molecular biology, geology, plant anatomy and physiology, vertebrate and invertebrate zoology, plant systematics and reproduction, biochemistry, microbiology, human anatomy and histology, human physiology, general ecology, and heredity and evolution).

The Beirut Arab University was founded by the Muslim Benevolent Society in 1960 and is associated with the University of Alexandria in Egypt. The governing board is composed of the rector, the deans, a representative of the University Board of Alexandria, and two representatives of the Muslim Benevolent Society. It is financed by the founding society. It has a Faculty of Engineering and Architecture, but the engineering work undertaken in the faculty is confined to structural engineering associated with the study of architecture.

The St Joseph University was founded in 1881 by the Society of Jesus and its title was confirmed by the Pope in the same year. It is a private institution governed by the University Council and it receives some aid from the French government. It has a Faculty of Medicine, which includes departments for dentistry, pharmacy, and nursing and midwifery; there is also a School of Engineering.

Scientific Societies and Associations

The Arab Physical Society is a regional body that promotes research and development work in physics. The society was established in 1974 after a number of preparatory meetings between physicists from Syria, Iraq, Egypt, Kuwait and Lebanon. The society organizes conferences – two of the most noted conferences organized by the society include the First International Conference on Physical Chemistry held at the University of Damascus in October 1975 and the First International Conference on Solar Energy held in Benghazi, Libya, in October 1976 – and publishes the journal *Al Physia*.

Libya

Demographic and Economic Background

Libya lies along the southern coast of the Mediterranean and has borders with Tunisia in the north-west, Algeria in the west, Niger and Chad in the south, the Sudan in the south-east, and Egypt in the east. The country covers an area of 1,759,000 km² and, in 1979 had a population of 2.9 million. More than one-third of Libya's population consists of pastoral nomads.

The Libyan economy depends exclusively on the export of crude oil; the principal oil-producing areas are Zeltan, Dahra and Beda. Agriculturally, three zones are recognized: Mediterranean, sub-desert and desert. Only the Mediterranean zone is suitable for agriculture and the main products are dates, olives, citrus fruits and cereals. Irrigated agriculture is practised in the sub-desert and desert zones. Apart from oil, industrial activity is centred on foodstuffs, weaving, textiles, clothing and leather, cement and construction materials, chemicals, engineering and electronics. The three year plan of 1973–75 and the 'Five-Year Plan for Economic and Social Transformation 1976–80' initiated vast expansion of agriculture and industry in Libya. In 1979, the GDP of the country was US$24.57 billion.

The US$62.5 billion 1981–85 development plan gives emphasis to industrial (particularly heavy industrial) and agricultural development, with the annual growth rate of 7 per cent. Oil production will be cut and the contribution of the oil sector to the economy will be allowed to fall from the present 65 per cent to under 50 per cent. The long-term aims of Libya's economic development strategy are agricultural self-sufficiency and a diversification of the industrial sector with decreasing reliance on the export of crude oil.

Government Science and Research

Science policy and planning in Libya is the responsibility of the Supreme Board of Planning. The Arab Development Institute in Tripoli, established in 1972, promotes scientific activities in the country and acts as a national scientific research council. It has extensive laboratories and funds research in a number of disciplines, particularly solar energy, for which it has a

centre where research on solar collectors, thermal performance, water
and space heating, desalination and solar water pumping is being conducted.

However, the major government research organization is the Industrial
Research Centre, which was established in Tripoli in 1970. It has three
general departments: the Geological Research and Mining Department, the
Technical and Economic Department, and the Financial and Administrative
Affairs Department. The objectives of the centre are defined by its establishing law: '. . . The Centre shall be concerned with promoting the
national economy of the Libyan Arab Republic with respect to all the industrial research aspects, and it shall be regarded as the key organ for the
implementation of the Development Plan in this field through rendering
the technical and economic services to the agencies engaged in industry,
whether these be governmental or private, in the areas of investment,
raising of production quantitatively as well as qualitatively, raising production sufficiency, and providing expertise and advice to effect the achievement of the industrial development objectives . . .'

The Industrial Research Centre specifically undertakes the following
functions:

1. The carrying out of technical and economic studies, the most significant of which are:
   (a) Provision of information, technical references, data and guide-
       books in order to answer queries, and to publish technical extracts
       which cover the available references and to give a periodical sum-
       mary of recent data;
   (b) Studies pertaining to marketing, which include the technological,
       economic and social aspects;
   (c) Feasibility studies related to industrial enterprises whether such
       studies are required for the public or for the private sector;
   (d) Studies related to organization and planning such as organizational
       structure, employment procedures, selection of site, factory design,
       laying down the production plan, and handling the raw materials
       and cost accounting;
   (e) Studies connected with the raising of the production capacity
       whether they be technological, economic, social, or physiological;
   (f) Drawing up specifications and standards in respect of raw materials
       and industrial products in preparation for their approval and legal
       issue by the appropriate agencies;
   (g) Studies related to product quality control, equipment, testing,
       problem solving, and elimination of bottlenecks.

2. The carrying out of analysis and tests, both generally and specifically,
   which cannot be carried out by the laboratories of the producing units;
   applying provisions related to production quality and conformity to
   specifications, either on request of the producing units or as an arbitra-
   tion between disputing parties.

3. Carrying out applied research and industrial tests connected with new
   products or with the development of existing products; adapting pro-

cesses and methods of production to local conditions; and using local raw materials in order to reduce production costs.

4. Undertaking geological research work and exploration for mineralogical and petrological materials, in order to determine their nature, sites, and extraction potential, as well as the economics of extraction, transport, and utilization.

5. Taking over the training of personnel in the field of research work relevant to the objectives of the centre.

The Libyan National Oil Company is actively pursuing a research policy aimed at establishing Libya as an exporter of petroleum products. It has research projects on the production of methanol, ethylene, ammonia, heavy water and an extensive research programme on the extraction of protein from crude oil.

The Ministry of Food and Mineral Resources has a Marine Research Centre at Bab el-Bahr, near Tripoli, which was founded in 1969. The centre has extensive laboratories and carries out research on physical and chemical oceanography, phyto- and zooplankton, fish biology, benthos, and marine biology.

Academic Science and Research

Until 1973, Libya had only one university – the University of Libya. Today the country has two universities: Al Fateh University, Tripoli, which was founded from existing faculties of the University of Tripoli; and the University of Gar Younis, Benghazi, which was established from the Benghazi campuses of the University of Libya. Both universities are biased towards science and technology and are being rapidly expanded.

Al Fateh University has faculties for science, engineering, agriculture, petroleum, medicine, pharmacy and education. The Faculty of Engineering has an extensive solar energy programme focusing on solar insulation, solar stills and solar cooling. The Faculty of Agriculture has research programmes on irrigation, arid zones, and poultry farming.

The University of Gar Younis has nine faculties, including faculties for medicine, science, engineering, dentistry and agriculture. It has a limited solar energy research programme.

Nuclear Science and Research

The Atomic Energy Commission, established in 1973 and under the Ministry of Atomic Energy, which was set up in 1981, is responsible for nuclear science and research in Libya. It is building a Nuclear Research Centre with Soviet assistance at the Al Fateh University. The centre will contain a 10 MW research reactor.

The Ministry of Atomic Energy is supervising the construction of a 440 MW VVER Soviet reactor on the Mediterranean coast.

Morocco

Demographic and Economic Background

Morocco came into being, in its present form, in 1956 following the union of French and Spanish protectorates in North Africa with the international zone of Tangier. It is situated in the north-west of the African continent and has coastlines on the Atlantic Ocean in the west and the Mediterranean in the north. Other borders are with Algeria in the east and Spanish Sahara in the south. Total area is approximately 445,500 km². In 1979, the population was estimated to be 19.5 million.

Agriculture is the most important sector of the economy; 65 per cent of the active labour force is engaged in agriculture, livestock rearing, or fishing. Chief crops are wheat, barley, and maize. The other important sector of the economy is mining; the most important mineral is phosphate rock, of which Morocco is the third largest world producer and exporter after the United States and the Soviet Union. Other minerals include iron ore, coal, lead, and manganese.

Morocco has been facing an acute economic crisis over the last five years. The country launched a new five year 'economic recovery' plan in 1981. The plan lays emphasis on industrial revival, rural development and a reduction in food and energy imports. Stress on import substitution involves an expansion of farm production, especially cultivation of sugar cane, cereals, edible oilseeds, citrus fruits and fresh vegetables. The plan also wants to promote small- and medium-sized industries to manufacture domestic hardware consumer goods, electric components, ready made cloth for local markets and export, and motor vehicle parts. New light industrial development is to be diverted from the main Mohammedia–Casablanca axis to generate employment in the provinces and the countryside with small, labour-intensive industry. The plan is also placing emphasis on discovering and exploiting new mineral resources. It is recognized that the worldwide need for metals and energy products will have a proportional effect on industrial development and exports in Morocco. For this reason extra effort is being placed on discovering and exploiting new resources such as lead-zinc, copper, antimony, petroleum, and natural gas, without neglecting minerals which exist in Morocco but which have not yet been fully explored, such as molybdenum, wolfram, tin, uranium, and nickel. Great hopes are entertained for discovering petroleum after the expansion of prospecting activities on the continental plateau.

Government Science and Research

Morocco does not have a formal science policy nor a science policy and planning body. However, the *Centre National de Coordination et de Planification de la Recherche Scientifique et Technique* (National Centre for Coordination and Planning of Scientific and Technological Research) has been planned and is in the process of formation. The proposed centre will be responsible for formulating a National Science and Technology Plan and for coordinating the research activities of the country's various institutes and centres.

At present, the government funds for scientific research and development are channelled through the Ministries of Agriculture and Agrarian Reform, Commerce and Industries, Public Health and Education. All the universities and technical institutes come under the Ministry of Education, which also manages the *Institut Scientifique Chérifen* (Moroccan Scientific Institute), the only multi-disciplinary research institute in Morocco.

The Moroccan Scientific Institute operates in close collaboration with the Faculty of Science of Mohammed V University in Rabat. The institute is organized into seven laboratories for geology, geography and cartography, cryptogamy, phanerogramy, zoology, entomology, and geophysics. In addition, there are a number of regional stations, and they include the biological station at Ifrane, the seismological observatories at Ifrane, Berrechid, and Tiouine, and the Saharan research station at Aouinet-Torkoz.

Academic Science and Research

Morocco has four universities: Mohammed V University in Rabat, Hassan II University in Casablanca, Mohammed ben Abdullah University in Fez and the Quaraouyine University, also in Fez. The Quaraouyine University, founded in 859, is the second oldest university in the world (after al-Azhar University in Cairo) and is a religious institution. Mohammed ben Abdullah University, founded in 1973, specializes in languages, history and philosophy. Hassan II University was established in 1976 and although it has a faculty for medicine, it is largely a social science institution. Only Mohammed V University teaches science and technology subjects and has programmes for scientific research.

The Mohammed V University was founded in 1957 as a state institution under the Ministry of Education. It has faculties for sciences and medicine, a School of Engineering and a Scientific Research Centre. The Faculty of Science carries out teaching and research in departments for animal biology, plant biology, physics, chemistry, mathematics and geology. The Faculty of Medicine houses the National Institute of Health (see p. 182). The School of Engineering has departments for mechanical, electrical and civil engineering. The Scientific Research Centre coordinates the activities of the various university institutions in the field of research and publication and carries out practical and applied research on behalf of Morocco's technical ministries. The centre includes a documentation service, a publication service, and a service for promoting links between scientific institutes and centres in the country.

Agricultural Science and Research

The *Direction de la Recherche Agronomique* (Agricultural Research Director-ate) of the Ministry of Agriculture and Agrarian Reform is responsible for the *Institut National de la Recherche Agronomique* – INRA (National Insti-tute for Agronomic Research). The institute, with headquarters in Rabat, controls agricultural research stations throughout the country. The insti-tute's objectives are:

1. To carry out all scientific research necessary for the development of agriculture.
2. To carry out exploratory studies prior to the establishment of national agricultural plans.
3. To undertake studies and testing of new and improved methods of cultivation.
4. To undertake all experimental steps necessary concerning processing and conservation of plant and animal products.
5. To ensure efficient diffusion of information relative to agricultural research in Morocco and overseas.
6. To advise all national organizations and individuals concerned in the agricultural sector in Morocco.

The institute is divided into departments for general and administrative services, research, external services, documentation, plant control and propagation, nutrition research, and laboratories for analysis and chemical research.

The Research Department has nine central stations for basic research which carry out work in pedology, phyto-ecology, bioclimatology, agri-cultural genetics and botany, plant chemistry and physiology, technology, animal biology and pathology, and cultural improvement. The results of work at these nine central stations are fundamental to the success of the twenty-two central stations for specialized research, each of which studies all problems concerning each category of cultivated plant or animal species – improvement of variety, adaptation to different soils, cultural techniques, water needs, protection against disease, processing and conservation, smoking, etc. The special stations are concerned with cereals and legumes, sugar plants, textile plants, oil-bearing plants, forage crops, citrus fruits, olives, vines, date palms, various fruit trees, market-garden plants, ornamen-tal and perfume plants, cattle, sheep, goats, poultry, cattle feeding, and forestry research.

The Department for External Services has twenty-eight experimental stations which carry out practical work necessary for research in the lab-oratories of the Research Department. In addition to these stations, the

Department for External Services has twenty-eight centres for inspection of various products.

The institute makes the results of its research and practical work known through all possible channels, broadcasts, conferences, and direct education. It also publishes a review *Al Awamia*, and *Cahiers de la Recherche Agronomique*, and *Technique et Productions Agricoles*. The institute exchanges information and research results with over 500 similar scientific establishments in seventy-two other countries.

The *Institut Agronomique et Vétérinaire Hassan II* (Hassan II Agricultural and Veterinary Institute) also comes under the direction of the Ministry of Agriculture and Agrarian Reform.

The *Office de la Recherche Scientifique et Technique d'Outre-Mer* – ORSTOM (French Office for Overseas Scientific and Technical Research) has established two missions in Morocco – a pedological mission in Rabat, and an oceanographic mission in Casablanca. The oceanographic mission is attached to the *Institut des Pêches Maritimes* (Institute of Marine Fisheries), which is affiliated to the *Office National des Pêches* (National Fisheries Office). The Institute of Marine Fisheries carries out research in marine biology, physical oceanography, marine meteorology, marine pollution, the evaluation of fishery resources, and on the processing of marine products.

Medical Science and Research

The Ministry of Public Health has a Technical Services Department which is concerned with applied research in public health, hygiene, and epidemiology. The ministry is also responsible for the *Institut National d'Hygiène* (National Institute of Health), which has departments for bacteriology, parasitology, and toxicology. The ministry also supports the *Institut Pasteur* (Pasteur Institute of Morocco) with financial contributions, although research activities are under the direction of the Pasteur Institute in Paris. The Pasteur Institute has two branches in Morocco; the Casablanca branch carries out work in virology, bacteriology, parasitology and epidemiology, and produces vaccines and sera; the Tangier branch carries out microbiological research.

Mineral Science and Research

The *Bureau de Recherches et de Participations Minières* (Prospecting and Mines Office) is a public agency which stimulates prospecting and facilitates cooperation between the State and the individual in the exploitation of mineral deposits. The office carries out large-scale prospecting work and provides mining enterprises with technical and financial support. Work is concentrated on the search for oil in various parts of the country, and on prospecting for ore deposits with the exception of phosphates.

The *Division de la Géologie* (Geology Division) of the Ministry of Commerce and Industries, Mines and Merchant Marine, has its central office in Rabat and six regional offices in Oujda, Midelt, Meknes, Quarzazate, Marrakech, and Agadir. The division is composed of departments for geological cartography, mineral deposits research, geophysics and geochemistry, and laboratories. The Department of Geological Cartography has laboratories for palaeontology, micropalaeontology, petrography, and geochronology, as well as a design and photographic office. The Department for Mineral Deposits Research has a section for the study of metallic substances; a section for non-metallic substances of use to industry, the section also studies the current and future needs for such materials; a geotechnology section; and a mineralogy laboratory. The regional offices are attached to the Department for Mineral Deposits Research and are responsible for documenting and prospecting for mineral deposits in their own areas. The Geophysics and Geochemistry Department coordinates all effective research of the division. The Laboratories Department has laboratories for chemistry and geochemistry and provides an analytical service for the whole Division of Geology using methods such as optical spectrography, X-ray fluorescence, fluorimetry, X-ray diffraction, differential thermal analysis, atomic absorption, electrolysis, colorimetry, etc.

The *Office Chérifien des Phosphates* – OCR (Moroccan Phosphates Office) is a State-owned industrial and trading enterprise which was established by decree in 1920. The decree gave the State exclusive rights in prospecting, mining and sales of the ore deposits; the general manager is appointed by decree and the supervising board of directors comprises several government ministers and is under the chairmanship of the prime minister. The office is subject to the same fiscal rules as apply to private companies; it contributes to the State budget with part of its dividends, the rest being used for self-financing. During the 1973–77 five year plan, the office aims to increase its existing producing areas, and to diversify its interests by expanding the activities of its subsidiary companies *Maroc Chemie* (for the production of solid fertilizers), and *Maroc Phosphore* (for the production of phosphoric acid). Long-term plans include the building of a petrochemicals–fertilizers complex and the construction of new ports for handling the shipping. Most of the work of the company is concerned with mining and manufacture; there is a research and planning section under the Commercial Branch; a research and technical control division under the Production Branch; and a training section under the Personnel Branch which is concerned with the training of skilled engineers, chemists, and technologists.

Pakistan

Demographic and Economic Background

The Islamic Republic of Pakistan covers an area of 804,000 km²: it is bordered by Iran to the west, Afghanistan to the north-west, the disputed area of Kashmir to the north-east, and India to the south-west; its southern flank lies on the Arabian Sea. Much of the country is mountainous, but to the south-east are the plains formed of the alluvium of the Indus and its tributaries. Much of the soil is poor, and would be unfit for agriculture without irrigation. In 1979, Pakistan's population was 79.7 million; it has a rapid growth rate of 3.1 per cent.

Although Pakistan has made great industrial and scientific strides, the economy is dominated by agriculture. About half the population is engaged on the land. Much of the soil is poor, but extensive irrigation allows agricultural activity. The main crops are cotton, maize, rice, sugar cane, tobacco and wheat. The country also produced hides and leather and fish for export. There are a variety of industrial products (cement, fertilizers, engineering goods) but manufactured foods and raw materials form a significant part of the import bill. Much of the research and development is aimed at finding indigenous substitutes for some of these import bills.

Under the martial law government which came into power in July 1977, Pakistan's economy is being changed from the existing capitalistic interest-based economy to an interest-free economy. The initial Islamic economic reforms package introduced by the military government included the introduction of zakat ('poor-due') and ushr (public assistance tax) under government auspices and the enforcement of measures to replace the interest-based system in three principal financial institutions – the National Investment Trust, the House Building Finance Corporation and the Investment Corporation of Pakistan. The package was extended in 1981 to make modaraba, sharing of profits and risks in business, the basic linch-pin of Pakistan's economy. The new laws require all companies, banks and financial institutions to register themselves as modaraba companies. The forty-three article Modaraba Companies Ordinance specifies the operational requirements of such companies and restricts their businesses to ventures formally approved by a newly constituted religious board. The 'Islamization' of Pakistan's economy is expected to continue for the next few years.

Science Policy and Planning

Pakistan's achievements in the development of its scientific establishments are remarkable. On Partition in 1947, it started a long way further back than almost any other Asian country at its independence. It inherited almost none of the scientific institutions and personnel geographically operating or located in Pakistan, little of the basic survey data, and only a modicum of the modern scientific heritage developed within the sub-continent. Nor did it have institutions adequate to train the scientific personnel that a science programme would require. This was particularly true in agriculture, where economic development was both possible and essential. Before 1947 there were only two universities, Punjab, which was then mainly an examining institute and laid no great stress on science, and Dacca, now in Bangladesh. To expand science, Pakistan had to expand the training institutions and at the same time change their practices and constitution.

The first major research efforts were in agricultural research, in connection with cotton and jute (the jute crop being exclusively in what was then East Pakistan and, now lost to the economy of Pakistan). Commodity committees were established in 1948–49 and at about the same time a Food and Agricultural Research Council was set up. The early 1950s saw the establishment of government scientific and industrial research programmes and, subsequently, the creation of research councils for scientific and industrial research, medical research, and atomic energy research and development.

In the early days after partition a great deal of effort, reflected in the first two five year plans, was directed towards building up facilities: laboratories, importation of scientific equipment, and training of research manpower. New institutions were created for research, coordinating and directing councils established, and new universities founded.

Before 1962, no central science policy machinery existed. In 1959 a major enquiry conducted by the internationally representative Pakistan Scientific Commission reviewed the development in Pakistan and recommended increases in the autonomy of the various research councils, accompanied by the development of a science policy apparatus. In response to this recommendation, the National Science Council was established in 1962 as the highest advisory body to the government of Pakistan on all matters concerning science and technology. The council was given the additional responsibility of coordinating research and development activities of the main research councils in the country. In 1973, the National Science Council was replaced by the Pakistan Science Foundation, which has now become the main alternative funding agency for science and technology.

Under the military government, Pakistan has developed a national science and technology policy, through involvement of about 300 of the country's scientists, engineers, technologists and industrialists. The new policy operates on four recognized functional levels. Level one is described as the 'decision-making, planning and inter-ministerial coordination level'. Here, the policy calls for establishing a broad-based National Council for Science and Technology (NCST), headed by the chief executive of the country, to give science and technology a positive direction; strengthening of the Ministry of Science and Technology, which will also act as the secretariat for the National Council for Science and Technology; establishment of Science and Technology Departments in the provinces to act as provincial focal points for science and technology activities; and the creation of science and technology sections in the Federal Planning Commission and Provincial Planning and Development Departments for integrating the science and technology programme with social and economic development plans.

Level two concerns the 'promotion and sectoral financing of research and development'. Here the policy is to provide a statutory base for research councils to acquire an autonomous character, increase their funding and establish new research councils; set up a Committee of Chairmen of Research Councils for regular exchange of information, coordination and tackling multi-disciplinary problems; establishing autonomous multi-disciplinary science councils in the provinces; and strengthening of the Pakistan Science Foundation as a major alternative source of funding.

Level three concerns the performance of research councils and institutes. At this level, the policy is to establish research-cum-training and research-cum-production units in the institutes; to increase the non-salary operative expenditure to at least 50 per cent of the budget; promoting research and postgraduate work in the universities; to establish research and development units in major industries and research and development associations in cottage industries; and establish a research development corporation to provide risk funds for undertaking pilot plant and field scale trials of new technologies.

Level four is concerned with science and technology services. Here plans are to strengthen science and technology information bases; to create new services such as equipment manufacture and repairs, a national engineering laboratory, facilities for remote sensing, electronics data processing and consultancy services; to create services to study mechanisms of technology transfer; to develop indigenous capabilities in design, development and construction; and to strengthen the appropriate technology development organizations and transfer of appropriate technologies to rural communities.

Under the new science and technology policy, research and development establishments will be created for barani (rain-fed) agriculture, veterinary sciences, water management, oceanography and marine resources, roads, buildings, ship design and naval construction, power, natural resources, pilot plant design, electronics, systems analysis and computer sciences, health sciences, appropriate technology, transfer of technology and research utilization, solar energy and metallurgy. There will be seven new centres of excellence; almost every Pakistani university will have a centre of excellence when the new science policy is implemented.

Science Organization

Pakistan has a well developed infrastructure for science and technology. The existing infrastructure, together with institutions that will be set up under the dictates of the new science policy is shown in Figure 3.2. The main scientific institutions of the country are: Pakistan Science Foundation (PSF); Pakistan Council for Scientific and Industrial Research (PCSIR); Pakistan Agricultural Research Council (PARC); Pakistan Medical Research Council (PMRC); Irrigation, Drainage and Flood Control Research Council (IDFCRC); Appropriate Technology Development Organization (ATDO); Council for Works and Housing Research (CWHR); and Pakistan Atomic Energy Commission (PAEC). Although administratively attached to various ministries, these are autonomous bodies funded directly by the government. The Ministry of Science and Technology coordinates the activities of PSF, PCSIR, PMRC, IDFCRC, ATDO, and CWHR. The chairmen of PAEC and PARC report directly to the president. The activities and organization structure of each institution is described below, under appropriate sections.

Funding and Promotion of Science

The Pakistan Science Foundation (PSF) is the main organization responsible for funding research projects and institutions that do not get a direct budget from the government and for promoting science and technology activities in the country. It was established on 30 June 1973 as a financing agency for:

1. The establishment of comprehensive scientific and technological information and dissemination centres.
2. The promotion of basic and fundamental research in the universities and other institutions, on scientific problems of national significance relevant to the socio-economic development of the country.
3. The utilization of the results of scientific and technological research, including pilot plant studies to prove the technical and economic feasibility of processes found to be promising on a laboratory scale.
4. The establishment of science centres, clubs, museums, herbaria and planetaria.
5. The development of learned bodies, scientific societies, associations and academies, engaged in spreading the cause of scientific knowledge in general or in the pursuit of a specific scientific discipline or technology in particular.
6. The organization of periodical science conferences, symposia and seminars.
7. The exchange of visits of scientists and technologists with other countries.
8. The grant of awards, prizes and fellowships to individuals engaged in developing processes, products and inventions of consequence to the economy of the country.
9. Special scientific surveys not undertaken by any other organization and collection of scientific statistics related to the scientific effort of the country.

The foundation was also given responsibility to review and evaluate

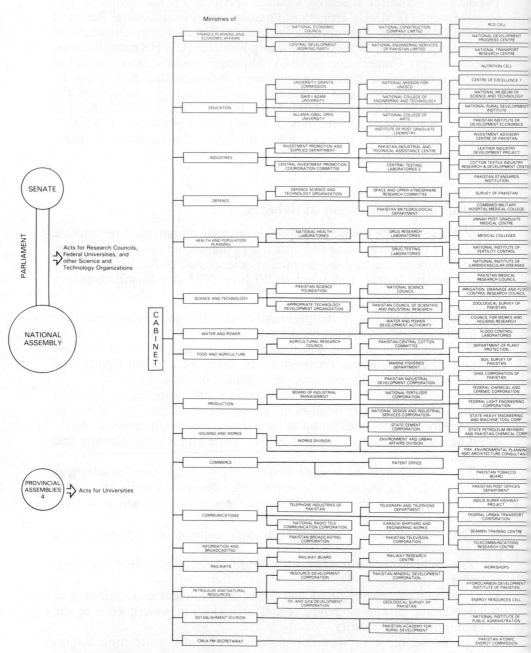

Source: Pakistan's National Paper to the United Nations Conference on Science and Technology for Development, Vienna 1979.

Fig. 3.2 Science and Technology Organization in Pakistan

Zone of Provincial Governments

Zone of the Citizens and the Scientific Community
National, Regional, Local and Disciplinary Societies, Associations and Learned Bodies

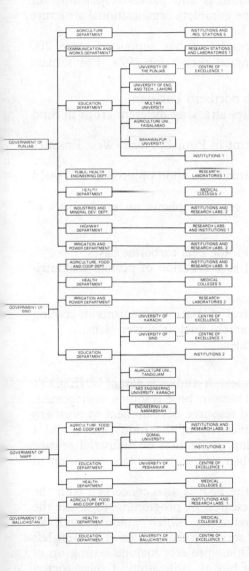

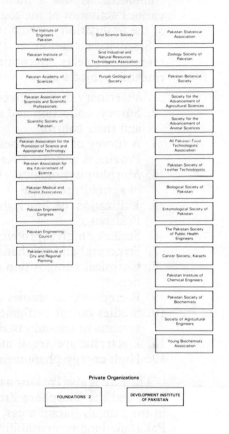

independent research in the country, maintain a national register of professional scientists and technologists, including Pakistani scientists working abroad, and cultivate scientific cooperation with similar bodies in other countries.

The foundation is administered by a chairman, who is also the chairman of the foundation's board of trustees and who is assisted by an executive committee. It has a number of committees and panels responsible for various activities of the foundation. The complete organizational structure of the foundation is given in Figure 3.3.

Since its inception in 1973, the foundation has supported some 200 research projects. According to its annual report for 1979, PSF's main research projects are:

1. Veterinary disease investigations in northern Pakistan.
2. Survey, collection and study of mites attacking different crops in Sind and their control.
3. A survey of the diseases of silk-worms in Punjab, North-West Frontier Provinces and Azad Kashmir.
4. Morphophysiological effect of gamma irradiation on growth and yield of agriculture crops.
5. Utilization of brackish water for growing plants on sandy belts of Pakistan.
6. Studies on glycoprotein hormones.
7. Structural and synthetic studies on some beta carboline bases.
8. Chemical composition of hair root as a criterion of protein malnutrition.
9. Bacteriological studies on tuberculosis.
10. Studies on the settlement and control of marine organisms in cooling systems of coastal installation at Karachi nuclear power plant.
11. Electronic spectra of metallic hydrides.
12. High energy phenomenology.

The PSF is also backing a number of research studies as part of UNESCO's Man and the Biosphere Programme. These include resource management in the Punjab Barani areas, ecology and resource development in northern Pakistan, long-term stability and productivity of the Indus Basin, and a number of research studies on pollution, utilization of industrial sewage and waste and ecological effects of urban and metropolitan expansion in Pakistan.

In addition to promoting research, the PSF is also concerned with the industrial utilization of the results of research. A programme to utilize the results of research in coarse-grain production, which would provide an additional 2 to 5 million tons of grain sorghum from lands at present left fallow, has been recently completed. Other projects include setting up of prototype plants for the production of biogas, utilization of solar energy for small-scale appliances, design and construction of a prototype electric power generator utilizing water-wheels in selected areas of North-West Frontier Province, design and fabrication of multi-purpose self-propelled low-cost reapers, utilization of discarded banana plants for the preparation

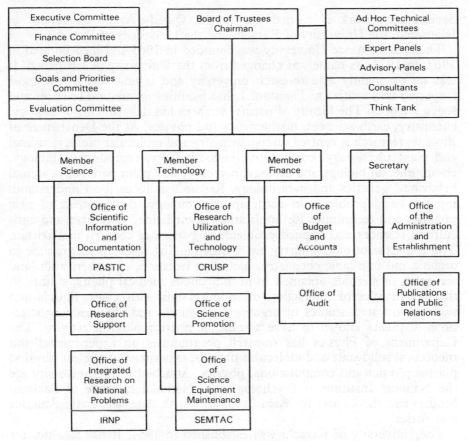

PASTIC: Pakistan's Scientific and Technological Information Centre.
CRUSP: Centre for Research Utilization and Special Projects.
IRNP: Integrated Research on National Problems.
SEMTAC: Science Equipment Maintenance Technical Assistance Centre.

Source: Pakistan Science Foundation, *Annual Report 1980.*

Fig. 3.3 Pakistan Science Foundation: organizational structure

of pulp suitable for papermaking and utilization of pine needles for the preparation of pulp for paper and textile manufacture are presently being backed.

The PSF has also prepared detailed schemes for setting up a National Science Centre at Islamabad, establishing the Pakistan Museum of Natural History and promoting a number of scientific and professional associations. It also runs the National Talent Pool scheme and grants a number of awards and fellowships.

Academic Science and Research

Universities in Pakistan are mainly teaching institutions but research and development work is carried out at the Quaid-e-Azam University in Islamabad, the University of Karachi and the University of Punjab.

The Quaid-i-Azam University was founded in 1965 and incorporated in 1967. In 1977, its name was changed from the University of Islamabad. It was set up mainly as a research university and is now one of the most respected universities in Pakistan. It has faculties for natural sciences and social sciences. The faculty of natural sciences has departments of biology, chemistry, earth sciences, mathematics and physics. At the Department of Biology, research is centred on biochemistry and molecular biology, animal and plant physiology, comparative endocrinology, reproductive biology, environmental biology and ecology, mycology and plant pathology, animal behaviour, genetics and parasitology. Research is focused on understanding the basic problems in contemporary biology, development of new methods and techniques for application in medicine, veterinary and agricultural sciences and applied problems of particular concern to Pakistan. The Department of Chemistry has a wide-ranging research programme in organic and inorganic chemistry, including isolation, characterization and screening of steroids obtained from indigenous medical plants, studies in thermodynamics of interaction of solid crystals with gases, liquids and vapours, infrared studies of organic compounds and chemical investigations of plants known to have significant pharmacological activity. The Department of Physics has research programmes on experimental and theoretical solid-state and molecular physics, experimental nuclear physics, plasma physics and computational physics. Attached to the university are the National Institute of Psychology, the National Institute of Pakistan Studies and the Centre for Area Study of North America, Latin America and Africa.

The University of Karachi was established in 1951. It has faculties for pharmacy, science, medicine, and engineering and technology. Attached to the university are the Basic Medical Sciences Institute, the School of Medical Technology, the School of Paediatrics, the School of Physiotherapy, the Ojha Institute of Tuberculosis and Chest Diseases, the Institute of Marine Biology and the Hasein Ibrahim Jamal Postgraduate Institute of Chemistry. The last institute is among the leading research centres in Pakistan. Research at the institute is focused on pharmacochemicals studies and the synthesis of potential therapeutic agents. Among the institute's discoveries is the first synthesis of two dimeric alkaloids which occur in the leaves of *Vinca rosea*, commonly known as sada bahar. These alkaloids have been found to be extremely useful in the treatment of acute leukaemia in children, cancer of the lymphatic system, cancer of the foetal membrane and other malignant conditions, but as they occur in the plant only in traces, their extraction and synthesis is very expensive. The institute is working on economic ways of extracting the alkaloids.

The University of Punjab is the oldest university in Pakistan, having been established in 1882. It has faculties of engineering, medicine, pharmacy and science, with disciplines which include astronomy, botany, chemical technology, chemistry, geology, physics, statistics and zoology.

The university has over a hundred affiliated colleges and a noted Centre of Excellence on Crystallography.

Other universities in Pakistan are: the University of Baluchistan, founded in 1970 in Quetta, with facilities for teaching chemistry, geology and physics; the University of Sind which was founded in 1947 in Karachi and transferred to Hyderabad in 1975 and now has forty affiliated colleges, including a college of engineering; the University of Peshawar, founded in 1950, which has a faculty of science and constituent colleges for, among others, engineering, medicine and agriculture, and has a Forest Museum attached to its Pakistan Institute. Four new universities were established in 1974 and 1975. These are: Bahauddin Zakariya University in Multan, Gomal University in Dera Ismael Khan, Islamia University in Bahawalpur and the Allama Iqbal Open University in Islamabad. Pakistan also has a number of technical universities, the oldest of which is the Pakistan Agricultural University which was established in Faisalabad in 1909 as the Punjab Agricultural College. It has faculties of agricultural science and technology, veterinary science, animal husbandry and agricultural economics and rural sociology. Other technical universities are NED University of Engineering and Technology in Karachi, the University of Engineering and Technology in Lahore, Mehran University of Engineering and Technology in Nawabshah and Sind Agricultural University in Tandojam. An Islamic University was established in Islamabad in 1981. There are technical colleges in Karachi – the Polytechnic National College of Engineering and Technology, the Swedish Pakistan Institute of Technology, and Rawalpindi.

Agricultural Science and Research

The Pakistan Agricultural Research Council is the main organization responsible for agricultural science and research in Pakistan. It is responsible for planning, coordinating, financing and formulating the national strategy of agricultural research. The council also has in-house research facilities where research is focused on priority areas such as the problem of barani (rain-fed) agriculture.

Efforts to promote agricultural research in Pakistan go back to 1948, a year after the birth of Pakistan, when a Food and Agriculture Committee was set up to study the agricultural needs of the country and recommend areas of research. In 1964, the Food and Agricultural Commission was replaced with the Agricultural Research Council (ARC). In 1978, the ARC was reorganized, given an autonomous status and renamed the Pakistan Agricultural Research Council (PARC).

The PARC consists of a chairman, four full-time members and twenty-two part-time members. The Federal Minister of Food, Agriculture and Cooperatives is the president of the council. The council is administrated by the chairman, who has complete powers to approve, expand, diminish, redirect or relocate the research projects. The council has a wide-ranging mandate. Its main functions are:

1. To serve as the technical arm of the Ministry of Agriculture.
2. To identify problem areas, develop and finance closely coordinated programmes of agricultural research.
3. To establish research centres as and when necessary to fill the gaps in the overall research programme.
4. To act as a clearing house of information on agricultural research.
5. To maintain national registers for research workers in agriculture and research projects undertaken anywhere in the country.

The council's research programmes are based on a system that involves both the researchers and the users of research in identification and solution of problems through formulation of coordinated and objective-oriented research projects. The system uses Coordinated Agricultural Research Planning (CAREPLANS), and Current Research Information Systems of Pakistan (CRISP), as the linch-pin of its strategy. CAREPLANS is based on the philosophy that coordinated research is best kept on target by continuous input from users of research, doers of research and administrators and eminent scientists. Briefly, the system involves:

1. Technical committee composed of eminent scientists is appointed by the council, on the advice of the concerned member. The member acts as a chairman of the committee and produces an advisory report regarding the development of research programmes in his research division.
2. Status review committee composed of farmers, extension agents, suppliers and other users of research, is appointed by the member. The committee identifies the grass-root problems of a given commodity.
3. Scientific panel is appointed by the member as an *ad hoc* body to transform the report of the status review committee into proposed research objectives/projects/programmes.
4. Executive board approves the proposed projects and return these to the member.
5. Principal investigator is selected by the member to prepare project outline.
6. Principal investigator's panel is a group of principal investigators for contributing projects in a coordinated commodity research programme. The panel provides technical guidance, for the plans, direction, accomplishments and reporting of the coordinated commodity research programme.
7. Scientific reviewer reviews the project and produces a 'scientific review'.
8. Financial review officer reviews the project for financial legality and conformity to PARC financial rules.
9. Research coordination directorate of PARC is charged with the responsibility of overseeing CAREPLANS and CRISP, and providing liaison with principal investigator's donor, PARC and research divisions.

After a project has attained approved status through all the above stages, it is fed into CRISP, and notified to all concerned.

CRISP is a computerized information system based on research management by objectives and provides exact information on accomplishment rather than on activity. The system can generate inventories of investigators, establishments, commodity analysis and research problem areas, along with finances allocated to various projects. CRISP is a key element in the planning and management of research at PARC.

Research areas at the council are divided into nine directorates, one each for crops, animal husbandry, soil and irrigation, fisheries, agricultural economics, range management and forestry, research information, pest management and research coordination. The last directorate is concerned solely with research projects under the United States PL 480 scheme. At the national level, PARC is coordinating research projects on: wheat, barley and triticales; rice; maize, millet and sorghum; oilseeds; potatoes; forage and fodder; pulses; sugarcane and sugarbeet; horticulture; spices, medicinal and aromatic plants; research and development of farm machinery; post-harvest technology; water management and soil salinity; soil fertility and micronutrients; barani research system; integrated control of insect pests.

In-house research at the PARC is focused on:

1. Pest management studies and research for the development of an integrated pest control programme for paddy rice, maize, cotton and sugarcane.
2. Estimation of the consumptive use of water for major crops in Pakistan under optimum management conditions.
3. Honey bee management.
4. Special crops: jute, tea, coffee and ginger.
5. Improvement of dairy animals.
6. Fisheries production.
7. Storage stability of pesticides and their residues on crops.
8. Long-term effects of gamma rays on some pests of stored cereals.
9. Economically important plant families of Pakistan.
10. Plant introduction.

There are three research institutes and eight research units under the council:

1. National Agricultural Research Centre.
2. Arid Zone Research Institute.
3. Cereal Diseases Research Institute.
4. Vertebrate Pest Control Centre.
5. Locust Research Station.
6. Federal Pesticides Laboratory.
7. Radioisotope and Radiation Laboratory.
8. Plant Pathology Division.
9. Food Storage Division.
10. National Insect Museum.
11. National Mycological Herbarium.

The National Agricultural Research Centre is located just outside

Islamabad, near Rawal Dam. It has a 1,400-acre research site and a complex of laboratories. The centre undertakes research in areas neglected by other institutes and where the research can best be done at central institution, such as the problems of barani areas. The centre also provides analytical facilities to provincial research organizations.

The Arid Zone Research Institute has its headquarters in Quetta and three substations are Bahawalpur, Dera Ismael Khan and Umarkot. It is developing techniques for efficient land use and increasing agricultural productivity in arid areas of Pakistan.

The Cereal Diseases Research Institute is located in Islamabad and has substations at Muree and Karachi. It conducts research on cereal diseases as well as diseases caused by viruses, nematodes and bacteria. The institute has developed a disease-resistant variety of wheat and is working on varieties of other crops.

PARC publishes a bimonthly popular journal, *Progressive Farming*, a quarterly research journal, *Agriculture Pakistan*, a newsletter, *PARC News*, an Urdu magazine, *Jadeed Ziraet*, and the proceedings of its scientific symposia, workshops, seminars and conferences.

Medical Science and Research

The Pakistan Medical Research Council, located at the Jinnah Postgraduate Medical Research Council, Karachi, promotes and applies research in all aspects of medicine and public health and coordinates Pakistan's research in these fields. Current research sponsored by the council includes protein-calorie malnutrition and its impact on physical and mental development, liver diseases, collection of data on various types of tumour, malabsorption, thalassemia, immunology in relation to cancer and vitamin-A levels in patients suffering from malignant diseases. The council publishes *Pakistan Journal of Medical Research* (quarterly).

Jinnah Postgraduate Medical Centre is a teaching and research institute with an attached hospital. Research is carried out at the Basic Medical Sciences Department and by postgraduate students. Ongoing research projects include head injuries, burns to children, mental retardation, schizophrenia, rehabilitation of pregnant diabetic women, urolithiasis, oral carcinoma, early steroid treatment, prosthetics and orthotics, and eye diseases. Most of these projects are supported by the PL 480 scheme.

The National Health Laboratories in Islamabad have a wide-ranging research programme focused on health problems of Pakistan.

The Hamdard National Foundation is an independent organization that promotes education and thinking on 'Eastern medicine'. Under its founder and president, Hakim Mohammad Said, the foundation has fought for, and gained official recognition for, *Tibbi* medicine. The foundation is responsible for the standardization of *Tibbi* medicine and for developing a nationally recognized structure for training of doctors of Eastern medicine. Hamdard has its own research laboratories where research on traditional remedies and herbal plants is conducted. Hamdard Tibbia College (Academy of

Eastern Medicine) in Karachi is administered by the foundation. The president of the foundation is chairman of the Government of Pakistan's Board of Unani and Ayurvedic System, which is responsible for maintaining the standards of Eastern medicine in the country. The foundation publishes the noted learned journals, *Hamdard Islamicus* and *Hamdard Medicus*.

Industrial Science and Research

There are two organizations devoted to industrial research: PCSIR and ATDO.

Pakistan Council for Scientific and Industrial Research – PCSIR

PCSIR is an autonomous and the largest scientific and technological organization in Pakistan. Established in 1953, PCSIR is administered by a council of twenty-one members nominated from the federal government, provincial governments and public and private industries. The governing body of the council consists of a chairman and three members – one each for technology, science and finance; together, these four members of the council are responsible for general administration and supervision of the affairs of the council (see Figure 3.4).

The headquarters of PCSIR is in Karachi and the research and development operations are carried out through four subsidiary laboratories located in Karachi, Lahore and Peshawar. The council also manages the National Physical Standards Laboratory, which is located in Islamabad and operates the Pakistan Swiss Training Centre, which grants diplomas in precision mechanics and instrumentation and is situated in Karachi.

The research laboratories of the council are divided into divisions, which in turn are organized into groups around specific areas of research or major projects. The research divisions at the council's four laboratories are:

1. Karachi Laboratories, which comprise research divisions for: (a) agro and industrial chemicals; (b) applied physics, electronics and instrumentation; (c) plastics and polymers; (d) marine foods and applied biology; (e) chemical engineering and design; (f) pharmaceuticals and fine chemicals; and sections for (i) workshop, (ii) industrial liaison, (iii) laboratory services.
2. Lahore Laboratories, which comprise research divisions for: (a) ore processing and metallurgy; (b) glass and ceramics; (c) industrial organic chemicals; (d) food technology and fermentation; (e) chemical engineering and design; (f) chemical standards and testing; (g) oils and fats; and sections for (i) workshop, (ii) instrumentation, (iii) industrial liaison, (iv) inorganic industrial chemicals.
3. Peshawar Laboratories, which comprise research divisions for: (a) minerals and inorganic industrial chemicals; (b) fruit technology; (c) natural fibres; (d) natural drugs and fine chemicals; and sections for

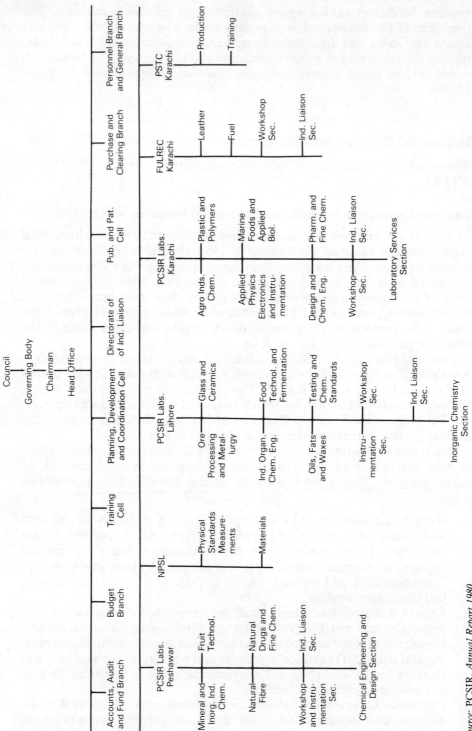

Fig. 3.4 Organization chart – PCSIR

(i) workshop and instrumentation, (ii) industrial liaison, (iii) chemical engineering and design.

4. FULREC, which comprises research divisions for: (a) leather; (b) fuel; and sections for (i) workshop, and (ii) industrial liaison.

Research at PCSIR is divided into two broad programmes. The long-range research programme aims at: (a) systematic evaluation, development and utilization of indigenous materials, including their adaptation to conventional or new uses; (b) developing projects in accordance with the national plans for industrial development; and (c) initiating projects aimed at developing new or improving existing technical capabilities. Long-range programmes are initiated after surveying particular industries and identifying problem areas. Such surveys are conducted frequently; in 1979–80 the council made the following surveys:

1. Requirements of industry for standards.
2. Process equipment manufacture units.
3. State-of-the-art of oilseed processing technology.
4. Spoilage of mango and banana production in Sind.
5. Cottage-scale carpet manufacturing units.
6. Treatment provided by *Hakims* (doctors of Eastern medicine) through medicinal plants and the problems of quality control associated with the practice of *Tibbi* medicine.
7. State-of-the-art of indigenous leather industry.

The short-range research programme includes applied projects aimed at the creation of new products and processes and uses or development of process know-how for currently imported products or development of suitable substitutes. In 1979–80, the council completed the following projects and offered them to Pakistani industry:

1. A process for the production of cement from rice husk.
2. A plant for the dehydration of vegetables.
3. A system for the control of transistorized traffic signals.
4. Small-scale plants for the beneficiation of low-grade chromite and graphite ores.
5. A process for the manufacture of phosphatic pesticides.
6. A process for the manufacture of acid-proof bricks.
7. A process for the manufacture of soft drink tablets.
8. A plant for the manufacture of adhesive for chipboard.

In addition to research and development work, the council also provides consultancy services to trade and industry. These services range from development of products and processes to meet specific needs of the client, evaluation and testing of materials and products, and repairs of scientific instruments and providing guidelines for quality control and designing small- to medium-scale industrial plants and assessing imported turnkey plants.

The PCSIR has long-standing plans to expand its activities and establish a number of single-purpose technological research institutes. Proposed institutes are: Institute of Minerals Technology; Institute of Glass and

Ceramics Technology; Institute of Leather Technology; Institute of Agro-Industrial Chemicals and Chemical Technology; Institute of Fuel Technology; Institute of Nutrition and Food Technology; Institute of Pharmaceuticals and Fine Chemicals Technology; and the Institute of Oils and Fats Technology.

The areas of activity of the PCSIR laboratories at Karachi, Lahore, and Peshawar are listed below.

KARACHI LABORATORIES

Agro-Industrial Chemicals Research Division

1. Process know-how for the manufacture of known pesticides – malathion, maleic hydrazide; new pesticides work being undertaken on heterocyclics (herbicides and weedicides), amido-metallic complexes (fungicides and chemosterilants), dithio-caramates (fungicides/rubber accelerators), aluminium phosphides (rodenticides).
2. Pot and pan method for producing pulp; agricultural wastes; de-inking of printing paper.
3. Improving decorative qualities, scratch and stain resistance of natural marble.
4. Electrical insulating materials, varnishes and potting compounds.
5. Naval paints; protective coatings for underground pipes (sponsored projects); corrosion-inhibiting products.
6. Aqueous and emulsion paints, cold setting urea and phenol-formaldehyde based coating; electroless coatings; plating of plastics.
7. Phthalocyanine and silica-cored pigments.
8. Dyes (disperse, urea-resorsinol) and wetting agent and its salt for textile industry.
9. Production of sodium sylphahydrate, thioglycolic acid and its salts.
10. Preparation of polyvinyl formal and butyral.
11. Direct conversion of methane to formaldehyde.
12. Recovery of chemicals from bittern; survey of industrial effluents.

Item 2 is one outcome of work undertaken in 1974 to identify and develop projects which could be suitable for the establishment of small production units in villages, and which would be based on as simple a technology as possible. Success has been achieved in developing a simple cottage-scale method for the production of paper pulp from banana stump. A demonstration model has been put in operation in the laboratories, and the know-how has been released to a plantation owner who is going ahead with fabrication of a large unit for the plantation.

Other industrial processes which this division has developed concern foam concrete; additives; lightweight structural concrete; di-octyl phthalate plasticizer for polyvinylchloride; self-emulsifiable degreasing compositions; electrodes copper plating composition; decolourizing carbon from rice husks; scarlet red G-1 dye base; composition for inhibiting scale deposits in condensers; composition for boiler feed water treatments; and algaecide for cooling water-tower treatments.

Many of these processes aim to avoid imports and the associated drain on foreign exchange.

Pharmaceuticals and Fine Chemicals Research Division
1. Screening of medicinal plants for anti-cancer, anti-diabetic, anti-fertility and anti-microbial activities.
2. Utilization of slaughter house wastes: enzymes-proreolytic from mucosa and pancreatin from beef pancreas; microorganisms producing proteolytic enzymes; enzymes; hormones (insulin) from beef pancreas.
3. Synthesis of nikethamide, vitamin D8, diazepam, metamizol, diphenhydramine hydrochloride, phenobarbitone, phenyl butazone, niclosamide diphenyl hydantion, chlordia zepoxide and its derivatives.
4. Synthesis of furan derivatives; sulfonyl ureas; heterocyloic nitrogen oxides.
5. Antibiotics – bacitracin, griseofulvin, improved strains of penecillium.

One of the industrial processes developed by the division concerns cholic and de-oxycholic acids. Bile acids, such as cholic and de-oxycholic acids, are used in pharmaceutical preparations as hydrochloretics and digestants. They also find use as the starting material for the manufacture of corticosteroids. The source of these acids, the bile of slaughtered animals, is so far being collected, concentrated, and exported at a very low price, while much higher-priced bile products are imported. A pilot plant for production of these chemicals was designed, fabricated and put into operation in 1974.

Physics and Physical Chemistry Research Division (including Electronics Instrumentation and Maintenance)
1. Fabrication of X-ray generator for X-ray crystallography work; adaptation of X-ray spectrometer for extending its detectability and sensitivity.
2. Batteries; development of technology of production of nickel-cadmium batteries; design and fabrication of batteries for flash guns; mercury cell.
3. Design and fabrication of traffic signals.
4. Preparation of high-quality optical mirrors and optical glass surfaces.
5. Adaptation of NMR spectrometer for solid-state work; fabrication of regulated power supply unit for the instrument.
6. Design and fabrication of: induction and ignition coils; vapour discharge tubes; standard Weston cells (a primary voltage reference standard); hygrostat; polarograph; pH meter; thermal control units; humidity control circuits, electronic flash gun; thermal protective device for electrical equipment.
7. Crystal and molecular structure of organic compounds; studies on: (a) various aspects of liquid structure; (b) crystal growth, solid-state reaction hygroscopicity and phase transition reaction; (c) physico-chemical problems relating to reverse osmosis membrane.
8. Development and production of citrate and borate buffers; reference electrodes.

9.   Improved formulations for nickel plating.

A major industrial project of this division has the objective of developing the know-how for the manufacture of batteries. Spent nickel-cadium batteries are reconditioned as part of this programme.

Applied Biology Research Division
1.   Biological evaluation of insecticides, fungicides, fumigants, nemacides, chemosterilants, insect repellents and attractants.
2.   Screening of indigenous plants for their insecticidal and fungicidal properties.
3.   Studies on deterioration of: (a) stored grains by fungi; (b) raw and finished industrial materials (cellulose, leather, wool, etc.).
4.   Survey of: (a) plant pathogenic fungi of Pakistan; (b) plant parasitic nematodes of Sind.
5.   Increasing the effective range of systemic pesticides through incorporation of physiological promoters.
6.   Mutation and breeding of grain legumes to improve yield and protein content.

Future work is contemplated on:
1.   Survey and studies of stored-grain mites in Pakistan.
2.   A comprehensive study of fungal deterioration of grains in storage in Pakistan.
3.   Studies on fungi in connection with soil and water relationship, with special reference to those causing root rot of cotton.
4.   Chemosterilization of fruit flies in Pakistan.
5.   Survey and studies on the resistance in insects against pesticides.
6.   Studies of synthetic mutants in some grain legumes, induced through mutagenic agents, with special reference to high-quality yield of amino acids and proteins.
7.   Studies on the toxic residue of pesticides on or in foodstuffs.
8.   Survey and studies of plant parasitic nematodes in Pakistan.

Pilot Plant Design and Process Development Research Division
1.   Granulation of fertilizers in a rotary cylinder.
2.   Continuous nitration of hydrocarbons.
3.   Vinyl acetate from acetylene.
4.   Manufacture of carbon black.
5.   Manufacture of phosphorus from phosphate rock.
6.   Acetone from ethyl alcohol.

Design, fabrication and pilot plant studies relate to:
1.   Cholic acid and deoxycholic acids from bile; the pilot plant for the production of cholic acid and deoxycholic acids (cf. Pharmaceuticals and Fine Chemicals Research Division above) has been designed, fabricated, and put into operation; the pilot plant investigations have been scaled up to study the economics and the designing aspects.

2. Sodium chromate from low-grade indigenous chromate ore: for the production of sodium chromate, fabrication of a pilot plant has been completed and the economics of the process are being evaluated.
3. Cholesterol based on spinal cord of slaughtered animals: on the request of M/s Charter Chemicals, Karachi, who acquired the lease right of the process for the production of cholesterol developed by these laboratories, a semi-commercial experimental plant has been designed and fabricated for them.
4. Air-drying vehicle for paints from turpentine oil: with the available equipment in the laboratories, a pilot plant study has been completed and the economics of the process are being evaluated.

Anhydrous aluminium chloride has been manufactured by the division in order to replace imported material. Likewise, compressed wood fish-plates for electric railway tracks have been produced which can replace imported insulating materials.

Fish Technology Research Division
1. Production of fish hydrolysates: the division plans to undertake pilot-plant studies, next year.
2. Improvement in the existing techniques of fish meal production.
3. Production of soft drink tablets: work continues on studying suitable and economic packaging.
4. Spoilage of fish – the mechanism and methods for extending storage life are being studied.

Fish Protein Concentrate (FPC) is an industrial process, work upon which was started in 1960. It is based on production of deodorized powder having 90 to 95 per cent protein starting material, being non-bony fish, and deodorization by solvent extraction. The powder, produced at laboratory scale, has been incorporated in food items such as wheat flour, biscuits, macaroni and spaghetti up to 10 per cent without imparting odour or affecting baking quality. A 100 lb/day pilot plant is expected from United States AID for scaling-up the studies. In the meantime, soluble FPC from 'trash' fish has been produced based on enzymatic hydrolysis of the whole fish. On simplification of the technology, local fabrication of plant will be no problem, and the capital investment will be economical. The soluble FPC is slightly odorous but this will not matter in a variety of products such as soluble syrup and proposed sugar-coated pills, and also in insoluble pre-cooked FPC for incorporation in various food products.

Oil and Fats Research Section
1. Sulphochlorination of hydrocarbons and their utilization: (a) detergents; (b) emulsifying agents.
2. Plasticizers.
3. Essential oils/oleo-resins of spices. For example, oleo-resins have been prepared from red chillies, onion, garlic, black pepper and ginger, and essential oils from onion, garlic, ginger, turmeric and clove. The

essential oils find use in beverages, bakery, pickles, seasoning of food products, and pharmaceuticals.

LAHORE LABORATORIES

Food Technology and Fermentation Division
1. Dehydration and preservation of vegetables.
2. Leaf protein concentrate: this involves extraction of protein from forage crops using sugarcane juice and filtration.
3. Detoxide mustard seed cake: developing a process for the production of detoxified mustard seed cake for the monogastric animals.
4. Utilization of cellulosic waste: the project involves chemical, physical and biological degradation of cellulosic wastes such as bagasse, wheat and rice husk and extraction of protein from such wastes and their use in producing biogas.
5. The production of calcium gluconate by *Aspergillus niger* WRL 51 and *Pencillium chrysogenum*. A fermenter has been designed and manufactured for the process.
6. Production of amylolytic enzymes for industrial use.
7. A general purpose fermentation and pilot plant: a complete pilot plant with fermenters ranging from laboratory to 1,000 gallons has been designed, fabricated and installed; the plant has been used in the production of processed yeast cake.

The Food Technology and Fermentation Division has also established a Aflotoxins Regional Research Centre and a Regional Mycotoxin Centre. The division also organizes training courses in aflotoxins analysis techniques for private industries, universities and research centres and institutes.

Ore Processing and Metallurgy Research Division
1. Beneficiation and utilization of chromite ores: the project involves setting up a prepackaged plant for working out the cost economics of ore-beneficiation, and improving the chromium to iron ratio. A pilot plant has been in operation since 1978.
2. Pilot plant flotation study on graphite ore of Azad Kashmir and Malakand.
3. Recovery of alumina, iron oxide and titania from ziarat laterite: this project is being tackled by reducing the ore in a rotary kiln at the fusion point to produce iron globules and vitreous slag. On cooling, iron is recovered by crushing and magnetic separation. The non-magnetic portion on digestion with alkali separates alumina, and the residue on treatment with sulphuric acid dissolves-out titania. The objective is not to set up a complete pilot plant, but only units for critical steps and to determine the commercial viability of the method.
4. Evaluation, beneficiation and utilization of indigenous low-grade iron ores: the project utilizes Chichali iron ore in determination of the exact mineral assemblage in the ore and liberation studies, flotation of

iron minerals to remove maximum amount of silicates from the concentrates; removal of potash, phosphates and fluxes from the concentrate; and induration and sintering iron ore concentrate.

5. Research and development work on Saindak copper ore.
6. Electrolytic production of magnesium metal: the project aims at developing electrochemical technology for the production of magnesium metal that could also be adopted for the production of sodium, calcium and potassium.

The division also has a number of projects from local industry which involve:

1. Determinative mineralogy, ore microscopy and chemical analysis of samples; plant scale research directed towards evaluation and beneficiation of minerals. Particular attention to be given to copper, chromium, manganese and fluorite ores.
2. Studies on design and performance of unit operations required for mineral processing with particular reference to equipment needed for beneficiation of ores.
3. Minerals utilization – production of bentonite suitable for drilling and use as insecticide; production of hydrofluoric acid from fluorite and related chemicals; manganese chemicals from manganese ore, etc.
4. Improving foundry practice: Ferrous and non-ferrous castings procured in the country are not of good quality; specialized alloy castings are of very low quality. This is due to lack of quality control in the metallurgical operations as well as sand mould-making practice.
5. Small-scale manufacturing facilities for extraction of non-ferrous metals.

Glass and Ceramics Research Division
1. *Raw materials.* Systematic evaluation of indigenous raw materials; their utilization by existing industries or by developing new applications thereof. This is a continuing activity and studies are being concentrated on the following minerals:

   (a) Glass sands – particularly that of Thana Bulla Khan;
   (b) Clays – ball clays, bentonite, fullers earth, etc.;
   (c) Refractory minerals, such as magnesite, chromite, serprentine, quartizite, dolomite, etc.;
   (d) Feldspars and tale.

2. *Special types of glasses*

   (a) Opal and alabastar glasses;
   (b) Signal glass;
   (c) Pyro-ceram (glass-ceramics).

3. *Special kinds of ceramics*

   (a) Electro-ceramics as used in condensers, resistors, transformers, based on clays, alumina, porcelain, cordierite, barium titanate and ferrites;
   (b) Technical ceramics, such as spark plugs, chemical porcelain, etc.

4. *Structural ceramics*
   (a) Sand-lime bricks;
   (b) Acid-resistant materials for process industry.
5. *Refractories*
   (a) There is a constant demand from consumers for refractories that will give improved service at increasingly higher temperatures. Work is being directed along lines which will help improve the quality of locally manufactured refractories and in setting up new industries based on magnesite dolomite, etc., the demand for which is sure to rise three- to four-fold with establishment of steel mills in the country;
   (b) High-temperature refractories, based on pure oxides of various carbides bonded with oxides and other materials;
   (c) Development of different types of plastic and refractory mortars.
6. *Miscellaneous products*
   (a) Abrasives – production of materials and end-products based on ceramic bonds;
   (b) Low- and high-temperature graphite crucibles.
7. *Manufacturing techniques.* Design, fabrication and operation of down-draught kiln.
8. *Development of laboratory glass ware.*
9. *Optical glass.* At present the country's needs in this field are being met through imports. The project involves highly sophisticated technology in the quality control of the final products with regard to the homogeneity and freedom from a number of defects. The project is designed to develop technical know-how for the manufacture of this product from indigenous raw materials and is expected to go into trial operation soon.
10. *Development of refractories.* Refractories are used in various industries such as iron and steel, cement, abrasives, ceramics, power generation and fertilizers. Presently about 50 per cent of various refractories are being produced in the country, while the rest are being imported. The demand, however, will increase many-fold with expansion of cement, glass, iron and steel industries. Evaluation of the locally produced refractories as well as an assessment of the availability of the raw materials used in the manufacture of refractories in the country has been carried out and the development work of a range of refractories has also yielded encouraging results, eg technical know-how has already been leased out to local industries for the production of magnesite refractories. Laboratory-scale studies on the composition of various refractories have been carried out. Pilot plant studies will follow after the installation of machinery and a suitable hydraulic press, so that bulk production and performance evaluation can be undertaken.
11. *Rapid hardening cement.* This is a gypsum-based product which can acquire a compressive strength of about 3,000 psi within an hour. It is self-levelling and is used for quick runway repairs. Preparative work on the laboratory scale has been completed and a pilot plant of 1 ton

per day capacity has been designed and partly fabricated; the pilot plant has been in operation since 1978.

12. *Preparation of steatice bodies.*
13. *Development of bone-china from indigenous raw materials.* Studies on the development of bone china from such indigenous raw materials as are abundantly available (the two principal raw materials being the ash obtained after burning animal bones, and natural materials such as phosphates, bauxite clays, quartz and feldspar) have been carried out. Test samples have been prepared and preliminary evaluation has given encouraging results.
14. *Acid-proof bricks.* Know-how for the production of acid-proof bricks has been developed by the Glass and Ceramics Division. The process is based on indigenous raw materials.

Oils and Fats Research Division
1. Development of erucic acid-free species of *Cruciferae* for the production of nutritionally superior oil: Sarson (brassica) is one of the primary oil crops of Pakistan but the presence of high levels of erucic acid in its oil causes problems in hydrogenation and storage. Also heart tensions have been observed in animals fed on diets containing this acid. This project involves both wild and cultivated crucifers for selecting a variety that yields either erucic acid-free or low erucic acid content.
2. Recovery and utilization of rice bran oil for edible and industrial purposes.
3. The chemistry and importance of the essential oil of the *Umbelliferae* family: the plants of the *Umbelliferae* are extensively used for various ailments and their remarkable medicinal value is fully recognized by the traditional people of Pakistan. Either different parts of the plant such as roots and seeds or their components such as oils or aqueous distillates known as 'Araks' are employed as medicines. These oils are considered to be antispasmodic, astringent, stimulant, carminative, diuretic, stomachic and flatulent. Some of the species have also been used against fall in blood pressure and in liver, heart and many other diseases.

In view of the importance of this family of plants the following work has been carried out:

(a) An overall picture of the occurrence, distribution and commercial importance of the *Umbelliferae* species has been recorded.
(b) Out of the 174 species which reportedly occur in Pakistan, 75 have been collected and preserved in the herbaria of these laboratories.
(c) Twenty-three wild or imported and introduced species have been successfully grown in areas close to their habitats or in the PCSIR Laboratories, Lahore.
(d) Physico-chemical values and chemical composition of the essential oils of fifty-two species of the family have been determined. The methods used for analysis of the essential oils have employed column chromatography, thin-layer chromatography, gas-liquid chromato-

graphy, mass spectrometry, infrared and ultraviolet absorption, nuclear magnetic resonance and various classical chemical techniques.

(e) Bacteriostatic bacteriocidal properties of the essential oil of seventeen species have been studied.

(f) Fungicidal fungistatic activities of four oils have been investigated.

(g) Chemical analysis of the seeds of twenty-six species have been carried out for their ash, moisture, carbohydrate, protein and lipid contents.

Additional work which is still in progress on the species of this family includes studies on (i) chemical analysis of the remaining essential oils, (ii) chemical composition of the lipids, (iii) insect repellency of the seeds and the essential oils, (iv) food preservative value of the essential oils and (v) their medicinal properties.

4. Production of the nickle catalyst used in the vegetable *ghee* industry: *ghee* is the national fat of Pakistan. It is produced by the hydrogenation of vegetable oils using nickle as a catalyst. The catalyst is imported and this project aims to develop a process for the indigenous manufacture of the catalyst.

5. Production of synthetic fats through chemical and biochemical reactions.

6. Studies on chemical composition of oils and fats from local resources for possible industrial application.

The Oils and Fats Research Division also provides consultancy services to the Ghee Corporation of Pakistan and acts as the corporation's quality-control agent.

Industrial Organic Chemical Research Division

1. Industrial exploitation of juniper berries of Pakistan; the juniper berries are found in Baluchistan, where the reserves are believed to be the second largest in the world. The berries contain 1.5 per cent of essential oils which can be used in essences for flavouring of beverages. The berries also contain 30 per cent sugar. The project aims at developing processes to extract oil and sugar from the berries.

2. Production of sodium carboxymethyl cellulose.

3. Physical and chemical studies of various mint varieties.

4. Development of technical know-how for the commercial production of dye-stuff in Pakistan.

5. Steroidal drugs from indigenous sources: steroidal drugs, such as contraceptive-steroids, anabolic steroids and sex hormones, are produced from diosgenin, which can be extracted on commercial scale from the tubers of *Dioscorea delotoides*, which grows wild in the northern regions of Pakistan. Another important source of diosgenin is found to be fenugreek seed (*Metht*), which is extensively cultivated throughout Pakistan. The project aims at developing a process for the commercial extraction of diosgenin and other sapogenins from such indigenous sources.

Chemical Standards and Testing Research Division
1. Development and pilot plant production of analytical-grade chemicals.
2. Production of sodium sulphate from gypsum and rock salt.
3. Purification of commercial grade indigenous caustic soda to analytical grade.
4. Development and modification of analytical methods for industrial quality control.

In addition to the above division, the Lahore Laboratories also have a Chemical Engineering Design and Development Division and a Solar Energy Research Group. The former division assists the other divisions of the laboratories in design, fabrication and setting up pilot plants both for experimental and commercial purposes. The Solar Energy Research Group has research projects on solar water heating, solar vegetable dehydrators, and solar air-conditioning of houses, and is preparing a plan for a National Solar Energy Institute.

PESHAWAR LABORATORIES

Natural Products and Fine Chemicals Research Division
1. Preparation of berberine chloride from indigenous plant sources.
2. Synthesis of anti-tuberculosis drugs. The synthesized drugs have the following characteristics:
   (a) Easy diffusibility at the site of infection;
   (b) Bactericidal rather than bacteriostatic action;
   (c) Inexpensive and easy to manufacture.
      About a hundred new biologically active compounds have been synthesized and tested *in vivo* against some pathogenic bacteria. Based on the results thus obtained structural modification has been carried out in a number of compounds to bring the desired effect in the drugs. About thirty such compounds have been synthesized and their pharmacological screening is underway.
3. Survey of useful plants of Pakistan.
4. Taxonomic studies of trees, shrubs and climbers of Pakistan.

Mineral and Inorganic Industrial Chemical Research Division
1. Mineralogy, beneficiation and utilization of phosphorite deposits of Hazara.
2. Chlorination method for recovery of alumina, iron oxide and titania from ziarat laterite.
      Pakistan has considerably large deposits of laterite in the Ziarat area. It has a low percentage of alumina and the non-availability of coke in the country may make the conventional methods for the extraction of alumina uneconomical. A relatively new approach has been adopted, which is a combination of reduction chlorination and oxidation–chlorination processes. The metallic oxides are converted into volatile chlorides in a fluidized bed. The chlorides are separated by fractional condensation and subsequently reconverted to oxides. Laboratory-scale investi-

gations have been completed and work on the chlorination project has been carried out to determine parameters needed for the design of a pilot scale furnace.

3. Barium chemicals. Barytes is abundantly available in Hazara (North West Frontier Province) and Khuzdar (Baluchistan). Laboratory-scale experiments have been followed by preparation of larger batches of chemicals by improving existing facilities to prepare bulk samples for consumer evaluation. Based on the data collected during these operations, a half a ton a day pilot plant has been designed and fabricated. This consists of a large-size gas-fire rotary furnace, rubber-lined leaching and mixing vessels, and a newly designed PVC rotary vacuum filter and a shelf dryer. Various units required for reduction and subsequent processing of barytes are being installed.

4. Study on the production of rice husk cement. Rice husk can be used as a building material when mixed with cement and cast into blocks. The tough structure of the husk and the fact that it entraps air in its folds makes it a useful lightweight insulating material. The structural strength of such blocks is however low and they cannot be designed to take any appreciable stress. There is also the danger of organic decay.

This difficulty can, however, be overcome by using the rice husk, which contains over 20 per cent silica if the husk is properly burnt. The ash thus obtained gives a fairly high strength to cement blocks. For example, a 1:1 mix of cement and rice husk ash gives 250 lb/in^2 tensile strength and a thermal conductivity of 0.4×10^{-3} cal cm sec^{-1} C, which is less than half that of ordinary concrete. Rice husk ash can therefore be advantageously used in insulating concretes. This material has the added advantage of being light in weight and resistant to fire, insects and decay.

A very recent breakthrough has come by the production of active silica, when husk is burnt under very controlled conditions. This active silica, when mixed with lime, gives a cement which is not only as good as Portland cement, but has also the additional property of producing acid-resistant concrete.

PCSIR undertook this study and has been successful in producing rice husk ash cement on a 2 cwt a day scale. This development will lead to the setting up of small- to medium-scale cement plants, based on indigenous technology, especially in the neighbourhood of the rice milling areas of the Sind and Punjab provinces.

5. Characterization and technical evaluation of Dera Gazi Khan clays.
6. Geochemistry of Kohat limestone.

Natural Fibre Technology Research Division
1. Improved wool spinning machines for cottage-scale industries. A foot-operated spinning wheel for wool, which is a major improvement over traditional hand-spinning methods, has been developed. The machine has also been found useful for conversion of waste fibres resulting from wool processing and carpet shearing into coarse woollen yarn. The machine is now being introduced into rural areas.

2. Finishing of woollen products: the project aims at conducting pilot plant studies to test the fibre characteristic and loom performance with reference to woollen fibres and their effect on the quality of products.
3. Utilization of indigenous vegetable fibres.
4. Dyeing of indigenous wools and their blends.
5. Production of paper pine needles.

Fruit Technology Research Division
1. Development of rural technology for dehydration of vegetables and fruits and the production of date vinegar.
2. Studies on sorghum.

The Peshawar Laboratories also have an Industrial Liaison Division to improve linkage between research and industry. PCSIR publishes *Newsletter* and frequent reports on specific projects for Pakistani industry.

Appropriate Technology Development Organization – ATDO

ATDO is an autonomous body under the Ministry of Science and Technology. It was established in 1974 to promote appropriate technology, simplify technology to the level at which it can be understood and practiced by people without resorting to costly and time consuming elaborate training, to link production with employment, to mobilize people to undertake planning and execution of projects themselves, to help set up village workshops for fabrication of agricultural tools, carry out repairs and manufacture small industrial plants and to establish an effective marketing and distribution system for supporting village industrial and agricultural production.

The organization is governed by a general council and administered by a vice-chairman. Its head office is in Islamabad with four regional offices in Karachi, Lahore, Peshawar and Quetta, and two field offices in Sukkar and Dera Ismail Khan.

ATDO has a small budget (approximately US$500,000 per year) and a staff of forty. However, it has had considerable success in diffusing and developing small-scale agricultural and industrial tools for rural areas. ATDO has developed a small-scale hydroelectric plant based on water-wheels, screw-type cane-crushing machines, some thirty *gobar* gas plants for the production of fuel and nitrogen-enriched fertilizer and has set up a number of small-scale industries including hand-made matches and hand-operated spinning mills. It has also developed windmills and subsoil irrigation techniques which are now successfully operating in northern Pakistan.

ATDO's ongoing programmes include:

1. Food and agriculture: dehydration of vegetables and fruits, screw-type cane crushing machines, under-soil irrigation and low-cost grain storage units.
2. Agro implements: development of bullock-driven earthmoving tools, paddy driers, oil expellers and multi-hopper seeders.

3. Recycling of organic and agricultural waste: production of paper pulp from banana stem, fertilizer and fuel from biomass, insecticides from tobacco waste and petroleum hydrocarbons and utilization of wheat and maize bran as fertilizer, mazri fibres for ropes and rice husk for cement.

4. Small-scale industry: developing plants for hand-made matches, cottage-level chalk and candle manufacturing, wool-spinning machines, electronic industry, manufacture of dry battery cells, small-scale smelting plants, mini cement plants, production of *Patoo* cloths, production of carpets with portable frames, handlooms for terry towel units, hand-made paper, mini glass plants, production of domestic appliances and manufacture of leather sandals.

5. Energy: production of windmills, cheap hydel sets, water turbines, solar energy appliances, small steam turbines, electric motors, trolley buses, low-cost vehicles and rural electrification with flour mill diesel engines.

6. Health and habitation: development of low-cost housing, primary schools, housing schemes, village roads, slum improvements, rehabilitation of eroded lands, and training health guides.

7. Social realization: *mistry* mobilization, creating entrepreneurship in rural population, and motivating rural women to develop home technology.

Nuclear Science and Research

The PAEC is the main body responsible for nuclear science and research in Pakistan. The PAEC was established in 1955 as a semi-governmental body but soon became an autonomous organization. It was fundamentally changed in 1965 when it became a statutory body. The commission consists of a chairman, a secretary, three full-time members (for technology, science and finance) and four part-time members, including the chief scientific adviser to the president. The PAEC is administered by the chairman, who reports directly to the president.

The work of the PAEC is divided into two divisions: research and development and nuclear power projects. The research and development division oversees the work of several centres: the Pakistan Institute of Nuclear Science and Technology (PINSTECH) at Nilore, near Rawalpindi; the Nuclear Institute for Agriculture and Biology (NIAB), Faisalabad; and the Atomic Energy Agricultural Research Centre, Tandojam; the Atomic Energy Minerals Centre, Lahore; the Institute of Radiotherapy and Nuclear Medicine, Peshawar; and the Atomic Energy Medical Centres at Karachi, Lahore and Multan. The nuclear power projects division is responsible for the Karachi Nuclear Power Plant (KANUPP) and the 600 MW power plant being built at Chasma.

The KANUPP was established with Canadian technical and financial help and went critical in November 1972. In March 1976, a heavy water upgradation unit was added to the 137 MW plant. KANUPP has a staff of forty-five engineers and over 250 technicians.

The Chasma Nuclear Power Plant (CHASNUPP) is being built entirely by Pakistani engineers. The 600 MW plant on the bank of the Indus near Chasma is expected to be operational by 1983. Following CHASNUPP, PAEC plans to build, using indigenous resources only, one nuclear power plant every alternate year till 1990, followed by a much faster rate of installation in the 1990s.

Pakistan Institute of Nuclear Science and Technology – PINSTECH

PINSTECH is the oldest and most respected nuclear research centre in Pakistan. It has a 5 MW swimming pool research reactor, which went critical in December 1965, and achieved full power in June 1966. PINSTECH has four laboratories: radiation detection and measurement laboratory, shielding and reactor physics laboratory, reactor simulation laboratory and control systems laboratory. Ancillary facilities include an IBM 360-44 computer, a library and a well-equipped workshop. The research and development programme at PINSTECH covers nuclear and solid-state physics, radiation chemistry, radiochemistry, radioisotopes production, analytical chemistry, nuclear engineering, fuel cycle technology, electronics, radiation and isotopes application, and health physics.

PINSTECH is responsible for training Pakistan's nuclear scientists, engineers and technicians. It has a Centre for Nuclear Studies, which offers postgraduate courses. PINSTECH also arranges specialized courses in electronics and industrial radiography and some courses are run in collaboration with Quaid-i-Azam University in Islamabad. It also supplies specialized equipment, through its Radiation and Isotope Application Division, to industry, universities and research organizations. PINSTECH supplies over half the national requirements of radioisotopes for use in medicine.

Nuclear Institute for Agriculture and Biology – NIAB

NIAB is located on the Faisalabad–Jhang Road on the outskirts of Faisalabad. Its building complex is spread over 6.8 ha and there is an attached experimental farm of over 80 ha. Research work at the NIAB was started in 1970, but the institute was not formally inaugurated until April 1972. It has six divisions: mutation breeding, entomology, plant nutrition, soil biology, biochemistry, and natural products and food science. It has well-equipped laboratories and three radiation sources: a Mark IV irradiator, a gamma cell 222 and a gamma beam 1508. Research at NIAB is focused on wheat, triticale, rice, cotton, grain legumes, pest control, trace element nutrition of important crops, transformation and uptake of super-phosphate, isotope-aided transformation of carbon and nitrogen in the soil, economic utilization of salt-affected soils, physiology of salt tolerance, symbiotic and asymbiotic biological nitrogen fixation, chemical composition of groundwater, extension of shelf life of fish, fruits and vegetables, mutagenic effects of processed food, disinfestation of cereal grain by radiation, fungal spoilage of stored grain, replication and repair of radiation-damaged DNA, chemical

Table 3.2 Details of optimum plan for power generation in Pakistan for the period AD 1980–2000

	Year											
	1980	1981	1982	1983	1984	1985	1986	1987	1988	1989	1990	2000
Peak demand (MW)	4,379	4,844	5,341	5,869	6,434	7,037	7,682	8,371	9,108	9,895	10,735	22,690
Installed capacity (MW)												
(i) Hydro	2,897	3,247	3,247	3,247	3,247	4,372	4,372	4,372	7,372	7,372	4,772	7,272
(ii) Thermal	3,330	3,476	3,476	3,476	3,476	3,476	3,446	3,446	3,446	3,446	3,082	3,195
(iii) Nuclear	137	137	737	737	1,337	1,337	1,337	1,937	2,537	3,737	4,937	15,937
Total (MW)	6,346	6,860	7,460	7,460	8,060	9,185	9,155	9,755	10,355	11,555	12,791	26,404
Annual energy generation (GWh)												
(i) Hydro	15,233	15,988	16,477	18,016	18,020	24,147	24,178	24,179	24,179	24,179	26,180	38,180
(ii) Thermal	6,736	8,425	7,857	7,834	6,743	4,540	7,240	6,876	6,834	4,612	2,867	1,693
(iii) Nuclear	1,048	1,048	3,738	4,998	9,055	8,301	8,960	12,945	16,860	23,219	27,378	79,384
Total (GWh)	23,017	25,461	28,072	30,848	33,818	36,988	40,378	44,000	47,873	52,010	56,425	119,257
Annual plant factors												
(i) Hydro	60.0	56.2	57.9	63.3	63.3	63.0	63.1	63.1	63.1	63.1	62.6	59.9
(ii) Thermal	23.1	27.6	25.8	25.7	22.1	14.9	23.8	22.6	22.4	15.1	10.6	6.1
(iii) Nuclear	87.3	87.3	57.9	77.4	77.3	70.9	76.5	76.3	75.9	70.9	63.3	56.9

Source: 'Nuclear Power in Pakistan', PAEC, Islamabad (n.d.).

pesticide residues, and isolation, purification and characterization of antibiotics from indigenous microbes.

Institute of Radiotherapy and Nuclear Medicine – IRNUM

Established in 1975 at Peshawar, IRNUM is the latest acquisition of
PAEC. It is a teaching and research institution which awards postgraduate
degrees in collaboration with the University of Peshawar. Research at
IRNUM is carried out in cooperation with the PCSIR laboratories at
Peshawar and the National Health Laboratories in Islamabad. Research is
focused largely on indigenous drugs, radiation therapy and treatment of
cancerous diseases such as leukaemias, squamias and squamous cell carcinomas.

Atomic Energy Agricultural Research Centre

This was inaugurated in 1963, and is concerned with plant genetics and
breeding, plant physiology, soil science, and entomology. A division of
microbiology is also planned. Its research programme covers virtually all
aspects of agriculture, but particularly the evolution of improved varieties
of grain and cash crops, plant development, pest eradication, evaluation of
fertilizers and fungicides, and investigation into salinity development,
water-use efficiency, and soil fertility problems. Its facilities are available
also to workers at the Agricultural Research Institute and the Agricultural
College in Tandojam.

Atomic Energy Minerals Centre – AEMC

This was formerly the Directorate of Nuclear Minerals, and was established
in 1971. Its five divisions are prospecting, exploration, mining, chemistry,
and chemical engineering. The last-mentioned division has designed and
fabricated a pilot plant for the extraction of uranium from the ore from
the Dera Ghazi Khan region, where extensive mining operations are being
undertaken by the centre with UNDPSF assistance.

Medical Centres

PAEC has established medical centres at Karachi, Jamshoro, Multan, and
Lahore. That at Lahore dates from 1963 and is based in the Mayo Hospital.
It is staffed by three doctors trained in nuclear medicine, a physicist, a
radiopharmacist, and other technical and laboratory staff. It is undertaking
research using radioisotopes for the investigation of some locally prevalent
conditions, notably endemic goitre.

Defence and Space Research

The Defence Science and Technology Organization (DSTO), which is
attached to the Ministry of Defence, is responsible for defence research in
Pakistan. The DSTO itself is not a research organization but promotes
defence research in other organizations such as PCSIR. Among the defence-

related projects completed by the PCSIR laboratories are a patented
process for reconditioning strategic war weapons and a process for the
manufacture, from indigenous materials, of an important ingredient required for flashless explosives.

The Pakistan Space and Upper Atmosphere Research Commission
(SUPARCO), also attached to the Ministry of Defence, was established
in 1961. In 1962, SUPARCO launched Pakistan's first rocket, Rahbar, and
since then it has launched 150 experimental rockets. In 1981, SUPARCO
was given complete autonomy and a Space Research Council was set up
under its administration. The government has also approved a ten year
research plan for the council. The plan focuses on radio communication
and analysis of satellite data, and is geared to putting Pakistan's first satellite into orbit.

Scientific and Technical Information Services

The Pakistan Scientific and Technological Information Centre (PASTIC),
formerly Pakistan National Scientific and Technical Documentation Centre
(PANSDOC), is being established with the help of UNDP. PANSDOC
was established in 1956 and changed into PASTIC in 1973. Under a new
plan of expansion and improvements, developed by the PSF, PASTIC
has acquired a national centre in Islamabad and four sub-centres have been
set up in Quetta, Karachi, Lahore and Peshawar. A Science Reference
Library has also been established in Islamabad. PASTIC has also been
made the national focal point for the United Nations International Referral
Systems situated in Nairobi, Kenya, for gathering, transmission and retrieval
of bibliographical and institutional information, especially in the field of
ecological and environmental research and development. Among the
services rendered by PASTIC and its sub-centres are: document supply
services to scientists in the form of photocopies of the desired literature;
abstracting and indexing of scientific literature; current awareness services;
preparation of special bibliographies; and translation of scientific and technical papers and documents into English. The information network system
of PASTIC is shown in Figure 3.5.

Scientific Societies and Associations

The Pakistan Association for the Advancement of Science, established in
the year of independence, 1947, is the most respected and active scientific
society. It has branches in most cities, offers a number of fellowships,
organizes conferences and symposia and runs a 'science house' (Ismail
Aiwan-i-Science) in Lahore. It publishes the *Pakistan Journal of Science*
and the *Pakistan Journal of Scientific Research*.

The Scientific Society of Pakistan was founded in 1954 and is located
at the University of Karachi. It publishes the Urdu magazines, *Science
Bachon-ke-liay* and *Jadeed Science*.

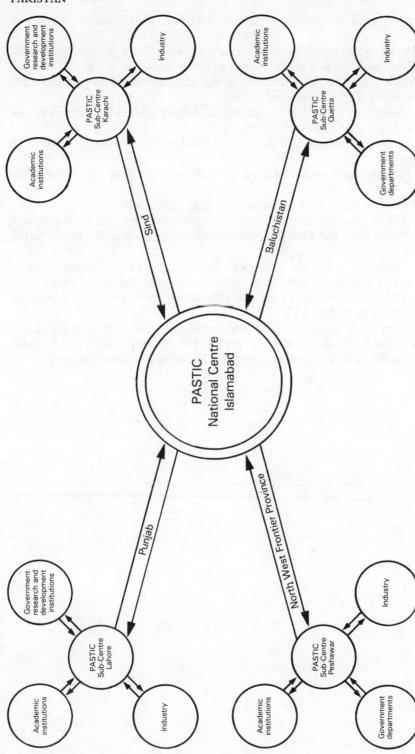

Source: Pakistan Science Foundation study on PASTIC, Islamabad 1980.

Fig. 3.5 PASTIC internal network

The Zoological Society of Pakistan publishes the *Pakistan Journal of Zoology*.

The Pakistan Botanical Society publishes the *Pakistan Journal of Botany*.

The Biological Society of Pakistan publishes *Biologia*.

The Society for the Advancement of Agricultural Sciences publishes the *Pakistan Journal of Agricultural Sciences*.

The Society for the Advancement of Animal Sciences publishes the *Pakistan Journal of Animal Sciences*.

The Pakistan Biochemical Society publishes the *Pakistan Journal of Bio-Chemistry*.

The Punjab Geological Society in Lahore publishes the *Journal of Geology*.

The Pakistan Medical Association is based in Karachi.

The All-Pakistan Homoeopathic Association was founded in Karachi in 1949. It publishes the *Pakistan Homoeopathic Journal* and *Homoeopathic Light*.

Other national scientific societies include the Pakistan Academy of Sciences, the Pakistan Association of Scientists and Scientific Professions and the Pakistan Association for the Promotion of Science and Appropriate Technologies (PAPSAT).

Profession associations include the Pakistan Society of Leather Technologists, the Pakistan Society for Public Health Engineers, the Pakistan Institute of Chemical Engineers, and the Pakistan Statistical Society.

Saudi Arabia

Demographic and Economic Background

Saudi Arabia, the largest country of the Arabian peninsula, occupies 1,600,000 km². It is bound on the east by the Persian Gulf and the Gulf of Oman, on the west by the Red Sea, and on the north by the deserts of Jordan and Iraq. In 1979, Saudi Arabia's population was 8.6 million, with an annual growth rate of 4.5 per cent.

The name of Saudi Arabia is synonymous with oil: it supplies 16.6 per cent of the world's crude oil and its 1980 oil revenues were a staggering US$84.466 billion. It is not surprising that the Saudi economy is firmly based on export of oil, with agriculture accounting for less than 1 per cent of the GDP. Only 0.2 per cent of the land is cultivable and most of the country is covered by vast stretches of desert. Traditionally, dates were the main crop of the country, but now wheat is grown in sufficient quantities to meet about a third of domestic needs. Since 1971, the manufacturing sector has expanded rapidly from 300 firms to over 900 in 1980. The new industrial towns of Yanbu and Jubail, concentrating on petrochemicals, have been developed to ensure that Saudi Arabia also becomes a producer of petroleum products.

Economic development of Saudi Arabia is based on six goals, which are stated in the third development plan (1980–85):

1. To maintain the religious values of Islam, by applying, propagating and fostering God's *Sharia* (Islamic law).
2. To ensure the defence of the religion and the country, and maintain the internal security and social stability of the Kingdom.
3. To continue balanced economic growth by developing the country's resources, by increasing the income from oil over the long term by conserving finite resources, thereby improving the social well-being of all citizens and providing the economic strength to attain all the other fundamental goals of development.
4. To reduce dependence on the production of crude oil as the primary source of national income.
5. To develop human resources through education, training and the raising of health standards.
6. To complete the basic infrastructure which is required for the attainment of these other goals.

The US$300 billion third development plan is based on three medium-term objectives to be pursued within a specific framework of policy measures. It describes the objectives and the policy framework in the following words.

Structural change of the economy. This will be induced by:

1. Adopting oil and gas production levels which ensure the maximum sustainable lifetime for these resources, while generating sufficient revenue which, together with available monetary reserves, will be sufficient to cover the financial requirements for domestic development.
2. Directing a major proportion of the Kingdom's capital and manpower to the producing sectors, such as agriculture, industry and mining, to ensure diversification of the economic base. A key element will be the maximization of domestic value-added from crude oil production through hydrocarbon industries.
3. Reducing the percentage share of physical infrastructure in total investment after completion of the continuing commitments from the second plan period, except when needed to support productive activities. New investments will be concentrated in those areas with proven potential for growth of productive activities.
4. Adopting sound yet flexible fiscal and monetary policies which permit the attainment of development goals without incurring excessive rates of inflation.

Participation and social welfare in development. These will be attained through:

1. Promoting among the Saudi population an awareness of the Kingdom's development goals and needs, providing guidance for their contribution to the achievement of these goals, and supporting Saudi society to deal with the problems of rapid economic and social change.
2. Stimulating the potential of all regions through a system of national, regional and district development service centres.

Economic and administrative efficiency. These will be increased through:

1. Improving the administrative organization and procedures of the government in order both to utilize manpower more efficiently and to improve individual performance and responsibility.
2. Adopting incisive manpower development policies with the objective of replacing foreign manpower by Saudis to the maximum possible extent, through increasing the number and the skills of the Saudi labour force and raising its productivity, both by greater efficiency within sectors and by intersectoral mobility.
3. Preserving national fixed capital by improving routine repair and maintenance programmes.
4. Ensuring sufficient allocations of manpower and finance to operate infrastructural plant and machinery at full capacity.
5. Limiting the level of government civilian expenditure so that it should not exceed a total of SR 783 billion, including inflation, and allocating

expenditure levels to sectors in accordance with the priorities of the strategy.

The plan gives major emphasis to industrialization and agriculture. The indigenous hydrocarbon industry will be developed in Yanbu and Jubail producing everything from petrochemicals and fertilizers to light industrial products such as soap and washing powder. Once the basic heavy industrial structure has been set up, smaller industries will be promoted with cheap energy and chemical raw materials at hand. In agriculture, numerous projects have been initiated under the plan to increase the irrigated land from 121,000 ha to 171,000 ha. Emphasis is also given to developing rural infrastructure to prevent the drift to the cities and raise food production. The plan also envisages an overall expansion of universities and research and development activities in the Kingdom.

Science Policy and Organization

Saudi science policy is intricately linked to its development planning. Its basic thrust is to provide research and development support to the plan's main goal of minimizing the reliance on oil exports as the chief source of national wealth. According to Saudi Arabia's National Paper to UNCSTD, the country is emphasizing applied research in areas of direct relevance to its development goals. It identified ten priority areas for research:

1. Reclamation of arid and saline land.
2. Development and utilization of water resources, including technology of exploration, climatic modification and desalination.
3. Technology of industrial processing.
4. Exploration for, and processing of, minerals.
5. Housing and the technology of building and construction.
6. Establishment of basic and applied research centres and laboratories.
7. Technology of technical training.
8. Production and conservation of energy.
9. Information technology.
10. Technology of transport and communications.

These priorities are reflected in the organizational structure of SANCST, which is the main science policy and planning body in the Kingdom. SANCST was established in December 1977 as an autonomous centre attached administratively to the prime minister and with the responsibility of promoting and encouraging applied scientific research and coordinating the activities of Saudi scientific research organizations and centres with the Kingdom's development requirements. SANCST's by-laws state that the centre will undertake to:

1. Conduct applied scientific research programmes in the fields that serve the economic and social development objectives of the Kingdom.
2. Establish and manage an information centre which collects and disseminates data on the scientific and technological manpower resources

in the Kingdom in order to utilize this labour force in implementing scientific and technological development policies.

3. Establish and operate laboratories for applied scientific research in areas of importance to the Kingdom.

4. Provide assistance to the private sector in the development of productive agricultural and industrial research that will help increase the GNP.

5. Support joint research programmes between the Kingdom and international scientific foundations in an effort to keep pace with scientific developments in the world by awarding research grants and undertaking joint research projects.

6. Establish and manage an information centre maintaining data on national and international scientific institutions. It will also organize seminars and publish research papers as a means of furthering the centre's objectives.

7. Formulate a scientific research plan which will specify national objectives for achieving scientific advancement. The plan shall be subject to the approval of the council of ministers.

8. Award scholarships to develop the necessary skills for conducting research work.

9. Award grants to individuals and scientific organizations to undertake applied research work.

10. Coordinate with government agencies, scientific organizations and research centres in the Kingdom to enhance research, information and expertise exchange, and to avoid duplication of effort. To achieve this goal, a liaison committee shall be formed consisting of experts from government agencies and organizations associated with the centre's activities. This committee will provide the centre with advice in developing the framework of the national scientific plan.

SANCST is governed by a seven-man board of directors, with the chairman of the board as the chief executive officer of the centre responsible for the administration of the organization. It has four directorates: for scientific research, national research institutes, science and technology infrastructure, and science awareness and technology transfer. The organizational structure of SANCST is given in Figure 3.6

The Directorate for Scientific Research is responsible for creating conditions that promote research and provides grants to existing scientific centres in the country. It will have divisions of engineering, mathematics, natural sciences and life sciences.

The Directorate for National Research Institutes is responsible for setting up research centres and laboratories in areas of national importance. The directorate is establishing five institutes for:

1. Arid land research.
2. Energy research.
3. Industrial research.
4. Natural resources and environmental research.
5. Petroleum and petrochemical research.

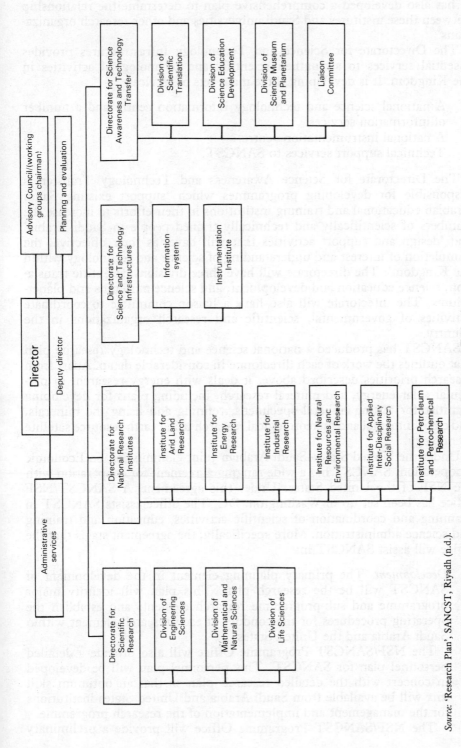

Source: 'Research Plan', SANCST, Riyadh (n.d.).

Fig. 3.6 Organizational structure of Saudi Arabian National Centre for Science and Technology

It has also developed a comprehensive plan to determine the relationship between these institutes and Saudi universities and other research organizations.

The Directorate for Science and Technology Infrastructures provides essential services to strengthen scientific and technological activities in the Kingdom. It is developing three main sets of services:

1. A national science and technology information centre and a number of information services.
2. A national instrumentation centre.
3. Technical support services to SANCST.

The Directorate for Science Awareness and Technology Transfer is responsible for developing programmes which 'support existing Saudi Arabian educational and training institutions in their efforts to increase the numbers of scientifically and technically trained people in Saudi Arabia' and 'design and support activities that will have, as their objective, the stimulation of interest and understanding of science and technology within the Kingdom'. The directorate will have three divisions: scientific translation, science education and development, and science museums and planetariums. The directorate will also have a liaison committee to coordinate activities of governmental, scientific and research organizations in the country.

SANCST has produced a national science and technology research plan that outlines the work of each directorate in considerable detail. Apart from research priorities described above, it deals with energy research, in particular solar energy, and mineral research, including plans for developing facilities for testing mineral specimens, refining and using the minerals, and environmental and meteorological research using earth resource satellite technology.

Under the United States–Saudi Arabian Joint Commission on Economic Cooperation, SANCST has a wide-ranging agreement for cooperation with the NSF of the United States. Under this agreement, A SANCST/NSF office has been set up in Washington, DC. The office assists SANCST in planning and coordination of scientific activities, education and training and science administration. More specifically, the agreement states that the office will assist SANCST in:

1. *Development.* The primary planning element in the development of SANCST will be the research plan. This plan will identify major programme and sub-programme research elements and establish the operating procedures for the conduct of each research element within Saudi Arabia and the United States.

   The NSF/SANCST Programme Office will also provide a detailed personnel plan for SANCST. This personnel plan will be developed in concert with the detailed research plan so that an optimum skill mix will be available from Saudi Arabia and United States institutions for the management and implementation of the research programme.

   The NSF/SANCST Programme Office will provide a preliminary

plan for the design of the permanent SANCST headquarters and national laboratories. A final design for SANCST permanent structure will be submitted to SANCST for review and approval.

Pursuant to meeting these objectives, and in consultation with SANCST, the NSF/SANCST Programme Office will carry out approved detailed studies, analyses, and conferences in each planning area including overall consideration of the organization and management of SANCST. The Saudi Arabian Government will authorize dispersal of required funds from the Dollar Trust Account for these purposes.

2. *Planning and coordination of scientific activities.* The NSF/SANCT Programme Office will assist SANCST in:
   (a) Planning and establishing priorities for SANCST programme development;
   (b) Planning and establishing priorities for Saudi Arabia's scientific activities in accordance with the Kingdom's socio-economic development plans and its indigenous capabilities to conduct such activities;
   (c) Establishing policies regarding technology transfer and Saudi Arabia's support of basic and applied research;
   (d) Planning regional and international scientific cooperation programmes;
   (e) Establishing policies, programmes and mechanisms for coordination with other Saudi Arabian agencies, the academic community and the private sector relating to science and technology;
   (f) Planning cooperative science projects.

3. *Education and training.* The NSF/SANCST Programme Office will assist SANCST in:
   (a) Identifying Saudi Arabian scientific and technical training needs as they relate to Saudi Arabia's socio-economic development plans;
   (b) Providing assistance to other Saudi Arabian agencies in developing scientific curricula and technician training programmes;
   (c) Providing training and orientation to SANCST and other Saudi Arabian personnel in the United States and other countries;
   (d) Conducting seminars, symposia, and other scientific meetings on subjects of concern to Saudi Arabian scientists.

4. *Science administration.* The NSF/SANCST Programme Office will assist SANCST in:
   (a) Obtaining pertinent information concerning the establishment, operation, and evolution of institutions similar to SANCST;
   (b) Planning all phases of the phased and evolutionary development of SANCST including (i) technical management and support staff requirements, (ii) facility and equipment needs, (iii) budgetary planning, and (iv) information system needs;
   (c) Administering arrangements for scientific research done for Saudi Arabia;

(d) Developing scientific information systems to serve Saudi Arabia's needs;

(e) Publishing newsletters and other publications on scientific matters of concern to Saudi Arabia;

(f) Developing capabilities to plan, manage, and evaluate scientific research programmes and activities of Saudi Arabia.

Academic Science and Research

Saudi Arabia has six universities: King Saud University in Riyadh, the University of Petroleum and Minerals in Dahran, King Abdul Aziz University in Jeddah, King Faisal University in Dammam, Imam Mohammad Ibn Saudi Islamic University in Riyadh, and the Islamic University of Medina. The last two universities are purely religious institutions and do not teach science and technology subjects. The remaining four universities are active in research and development.

King Saud University was founded in 1957 by royal decree. Later its name was changed to the University of Riyadh. In 1981, the university was once again given its original name. The university has colleges for arts, science, administrative sciences, pharmacy, agriculture, engineering, education, medicine, dentistry, allied medical sciences and graduate studies. Attached to the university is an Arabic language institute.

The College of Arts may be said to have some scientific interests since it contains laboratories and workshops for the maintenance of antiquities from the archaeological areas of Saudi Arabia.

The College of Science was founded in 1958 and has departments for physics, botany, zoology, geology, chemistry and mathematics. It has twenty-eight laboratories and encourages pure and applied research work in industrial and agricultural fields and has research programmes for solid state physics, nuclear physics, optics, plasma physics, plant ecology, plant physiology, microbiology, applied statistics, operations research, physiology, arthopoda and parasites, and various branches of chemistry.

The College of Pharmacy has departments of pharmaceutical chemistry, organic chemistry, pharmacology, analytical chemistry, pharmaceutics and pharmacognosy. In addition to pure research in pharmaceutics and medical analysis, the college cooperates with other government departments, such as the criminal laboratory of the General Security Department and the central laboratory of the Ministry of Health, on applied research projects.

The College of Agriculture has departments for agricultural economics and rural sociology, plant protection, soil and land reclamation, agricultural industries, animal production, agronomics, and veterinary sciences. The college also runs the al-Ghathat Experimental Farm and has a well-equipped experimental and statistics laboratory, an automatic pasteurization plan and a food canning plant. There is also an experimental laboratory for the dairy and food industries. The college has research programmes on crops, gardens, plant pathology, insects and pesticides and offers technical advice to private factories and government organizations.

The College of Education is paying particular attention to training of science teachers in physics, chemistry, biology and mathematics.

The College of Engineering was founded in 1962 as a joint project between the Government of Saudi Arabia and UNESCO. It was annexed to the university in 1968. It has departments for mechanical, electrical, chemical, civil and petroleum engineering and architecture. The college also has a research centre which was established in 1974. In 1981, the research centre had sixty-two research projects ranging from picture processing from digital computers, formation and characteristics of sand dunes, various branches of solar energy, analysis of traffic flows in Riyadh, evaluation of local raw materials as building materials, to housing in arid zones, development of semiconductor devices, stability studies of induction motors and a range of studies on heat transfer.

The College of Medicine has departments for physiology, otolaryngology, internal medicine, pathology, forensic medicine, ophthalmology, gynaecology and obstetrics, surgery and hygiene. The college has its own hospital, King Abdul Aziz Hospital, and has a number of locally oriented research projects.

The College of Allied Medical Sciences has departments of nursing, clinical laboratory sciences, radiological sciences, rehabilitation science, community health, biomedical technology and dental health. It also has a research centre which operates a few health-related research projects.

The College of Graduate Studies is responsible for general policy formulation, coordination and implementation of graduate programmes in all King Saud University colleges and institutes.

The King Saud University Press publishes the *Bulletin of the Faculty of Science* (annual), *College of Agriculture Research Bulletin* (annual), and research reports of the Research Centre of the College of Engineering.

The University of Petroleum and Minerals at Dahran, was established as the College of Petroleum and Minerals in 1963. In 1975, it was granted a full university status. The university is unique in Saudi Arabia in that it is advised by a consortium of American universities specially set up for the purpose by the Government of Saudi Arabia in 1971. The consortium consists of nine American institutions: the University of Alabama, California Institute of Technology, Colorado Schools of Mines, Massachusetts Institute of Technology, University of Michigan, Milwaukee School of Engineering, Princeton University, University of Rochester and Westworth Institute. The consortium has guided the development of the university from a college to a fully-fledged technological university and advises the university's eleven-man board of administration in its education and research programmes. Every five years the consortium carries out an evaluation of the university's academic performance using procedures and standards of the Engineers' Council for Professional Development which accredits engineering programmes in the United States and Canada.

The university is divided into six academic units concerned with instruction and research: the preparatory programme, the College of Applied Engineering, the College of Engineering Science, the College of Science,

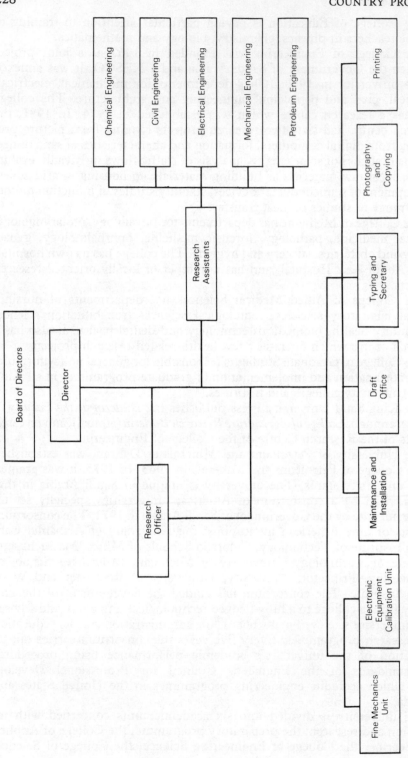

Source: 'Annual Report', Research Centre, Riyadh, 1980.

Fig. 3.7 Organization structure of the Research Centre, College of Engineering, King Saud University

the College of Industrial Management and the graduate school. Although their function, administration and student bodies are quite separate, these six academic units share common facilities and utilize a common faculty with similar disciplines in other programmes or colleges. Collectively, the four colleges have seventeen academic departments, including architectural engineering, chemical engineering, electrical engineering, mechanical engineering, petroleum engineering, chemistry, physics, earth sciences, mathematical sciences and general studies.

The university has one of the major data processing facilities in the Kingdom and services both internal university needs and on a fee basis is available to external governmental and industrial agencies. It also has one of the best technical libraries in the Kingdom, with some 100,000 technical volumes and monographs and 3,000 current journals. Because the university has access to the libraries of the consortium universities, its library can secure virtually any material from America or Europe within two weeks by airmail and specific items directly by teletype.

Research at the university is carried out at all academic colleges, but specifically at the Research Institute, which has research programmes in six functional areas: petroleum and gas technology, geology and minerals, environment and water resources, energy resources, metrology and standards and business studies. In the area of petroleum and gas, the activities at the institute include oil testing, combustion engines, petroleum production, gas utilization, petroleum economics, geophysics and petroleum geology. The geology and minerals research programme covers crystallography and mineralogy, petrology, sedimentation and stratigraphy, palaeontology, photogrammetry and cartography, geochemistry, hydrogeology, engineering geology, and economic and mining geology. The environment and water resources research is focused on water chemistry, water resources, aquatic and microbiology, water bacteriology, solid wastes, high pressure sewage treatment, air pollution, environmental systems and oceanography. Research on energy resources is concerned with fossil fuels, geothermal sources, solar energy, generation and transmission of electricity, nuclear energy, nuclear techniques and research reactors. Metrology and standards research is carried out in materials testing, chemical testing, non-destructive testing, statistical services, and computer interface and testing techniques. The institute is still being developed, and when fully developed it is expected to rank second, after the National Centre for Science and Technology, among major Saudi research institutions.

The university publishes the *Arabian Journal of Science and Engineering* (bi-annual) which also contains abstracts in Arabic.

The King Abdul Aziz University was founded as a private institution by senior citizens of Jeddah in 1967. The university was taken over by the State in 1971. While the university is based in Jeddah, it also has colleges in Mecca and Medina. The College of Shariah and the College of Education in Mecca form the nucleus of a future university of Mecca.

The university has the following faculties for science, engineering and applied science, medicine and medical sciences, earth sciences, economics and administration, and arts and humanities. Attached to the university are the Institute of Meteorology and Arid Land Studies, the Institute of Oceanography and the Hajj Research Centre.

The College of Science has departments for physics, mathematics, chemistry, biology and astronomy. It carries out research in pure science aspects of these subjects.

The College of Engineering and Applied Science has departments for civil, mechanical, electrical, mining, nuclear and industrial engineering, architecture, planning, landscape architecture, applied science, mathematics and socio-technical studies. Its research programmes are concerned with building structures, transportation, sanitary engineering, desalination, production engineering, aeronautics, electronic and communications.

The College of Medicine and Medical Sciences has departments for chemistry and biochemistry, anatomy, preventive medicine, pathology, pharmacology, surgery, paediatrics, gynaecology and obstetrics, physiology, physics, biology, microbiology, parasitology, internal medicine, psychology, and ear, nose and throat medicine. It has an attached hospital that will eventually be turned into a 'medical city' which will be the second most sophisticated medical hospital in Saudi Arabia, after the King Faisal Medical City in Riyadh. Research at the college is concerned with local diseases, preventive medicine and child medicine. The college publishes the *King Abdul Aziz Medical Journal* (bi-annual).

The College of Earth Sciences was formerly the Institute of Applied Geology. It has departments of petroleum, hydrogeology, sedimentation and stratigraphy, petrology and mineralogy, engineering geology, structural geology and photogeology, geophysics, economic geology and geochemistry. The college has a massive programme of research on the geology of Saudi Arabia. It publishes a research *Bulletin* and reports of fieldwork.

The Institute of Meteorology and Arid Land Studies was established in 1976 as a teaching and research institution. It has research programmes on meteorology, hydrology, arid regions and ecology and administration of water resources and pastures.

The Institute of Oceanography was established in 1978, as a teaching and research institute, in cooperation with the ALECSO. The institute is one of the networks of institutes around the Red Sea and the Gulf of Aden that ALECSO has promoted. It has departments for biological, chemical, physical and geological oceanography and a department of fishes and fisheries biology.

The Hajj Research Centre is an autonomous institute under the umbrella of the King Abdul Aziz University. It was established in 1975 to conduct research on the logistics and environment of *hajj* – the annual pilgrimage to Mecca – and the architecture, planning and cultural property of the holy cities of Mecca and Medina. It has carried out extensive surveys of pilgrim movements, transport and environmental problems and has studied the geology of Mecca and methods of conserving the cultural property of the holy cities and it has recommended many improvements in the organization and administration of *hajj* as well as in the environment and planning of the holy areas. The centre has extensive laboratory and computer facilities and acts as a consultant to government and private organizations.

The King Faisal University, at Dammam, was established in 1975. It has four colleges: the College of Architecture and Planning and the College of Medicine and Medical Sciences at Dammam; and the College of Agricultural Sciences and Foods and the College of Veterinary Medicine and Animal Health at Al Hasa.

The College of Architecture and Planning has departments for architectural design, history and theory, building technology and construction, engineering sciences, interior design, landscape architecture, urban and regional planning and mathematics and computer science. Research at the college concerns indigenous housing, the use of local raw material in construction and Islamic architecture.

The College of Medicine and Medical Sciences has departments for anatomy, biology, chemistry, community medicine, pathology, pharmacology and clinical clerkships.

The College of Agricultural Sciences and Foods has departments for agricultural economics and extension, agricultural engineering, aquatic wealth, crops and forage, food and dairy technology, horticulture, plant protection, poultry and animal production, soil and water, and chemistry and water. The college has farms in Al Hasa Oasis and offers consulting services in plant protection, food technology, marine resources, poultry and animal production, farm mechanization, land reclamation, irrigation and drainage, rural sociology, breeding and production of crops, fruits and vegetables and landscape horticulture to government and private institutions.

The College of Veterinary Medicine and Animal Health has departments for anatomy, physiology and biochemistry, parasitology, microbiology, pathology, medicine and therapeutics, preventive medicine and public health, animal resources, surgery, obstetrics, gynaecology and artificial insemination, pharmacology, toxicology and forensic medicine, clinical practice and mathematics and basic sciences. The college provides consultancy services to agricultural enterprises and to nomads and small farmers with camel, sheep and goat herds.

Agricultural Science and Research

Besides the College of Agriculture of the King Saud University and Colleges of Agricultural Science and Foods and Veterinary Medicine and Animal Health, considerable agricultural research is conducted at the Ministry of Agriculture and Water Resources. The planning unit of the Ministry supervises and coordinates the research efforts of the various departments of the ministry and departments for agricultural research and development, project implementation, land management and water management all have research programmes in their specific areas.

The Agricultural Research and Development Department has the following divisions:

1. Plant Production Division – which carries out research and experiments directed towards efficient agricultural practices.

2. Agricultural Statistics and Economics Division responsible for collection, interpretation and publication of information relating to production and consumption, and the coordination of agricultural planning.
3. Plant Protection Division which studies entomology, plant pathology, pest and disease control.
4. Animal Husbandry Division which is concerned with the protection and improvement of domestic animals and poultry.
5. Fishery Division – which carries out fisheries research, studies on water pollution, and all matters relating to fisheries.

The Research and Development Department cooperates with other national and international research organizations to support its research results.

The Organization Planning and Budget Department provides organization and management improvement studies for the ministry; prepares agricultural and water economic studies; prepares development plans and prepares, executes, and follows up the ministry's budget.

The Projects Implementation Department is actively engaged in building dams, and is concerned with the construction of agricultural facilities; it also supervises the operation and maintenance of agricultural projects.

The Land Management Department carries out long-range plans for afforestation; studies problems associated with moving sand dunes; carries out experiments in the planting of trees and the establishment of green belts to combat moving dunes; and conducts arid land analyses with a view to improvement. Its activities cover land reclamation and distribution; range, forests, wildlife and national parks management.

The Water Resources Department undertakes the development of water resources and studies the capacity and location of existing resources. It also determines the usage of various sources of water. The Water Services Department maintains a drinking water supply and services, and supervises the operation and maintenance of drinking water facilities throughout the Kingdom. The Water Conservation Department plans the proper use and maintenance of water resources; implements the water resources development plan; and authorizes well-drilling undertaken under the plan.

The Extension and Services Department is concerned with policy planning, publication and dissemination of information, advice and assistance to farmers on all aspects of agriculture and animal development; and administration of locust controlling policies.

The ministry also has a Training Department which studies manpower needs in agriculture and prepares and implements training programmes to fulfil these needs.

Medical Science and Research

The King Faisal Specialist Hospital in Riyadh is the most sophisticated medical research institution in the country. It is the nucleus of a future medical city which will provide a core for the planned nationwide uplift of health services. Established in 1975, the hospital has a vast array of advanced medical equipment including LARC (to count white blood cells), SMACK (to perform twenty different analyses on each of 150 separate blood specimens in an hour), a nuclear accelerator for treating cancer, and a total body scanner. The hospital also has a cancer therapy centre and facilities for open heart surgery. The hospital has satellite links with universities and medical institutions in the United States. Research at the hospital is focused on cancer, diabetes, viral hepatitis and diseases of the liver and heart.

Besides the King Faisal Specialist Hospital, medical research in the Kingdom is carried out at the College of Medicine of King Saud University, the College of Medicine and Medical Sciences of King Abdul Aziz University and the College of Medicine and Medical Sciences of King Faisal University. King Abdul University Medical City is being built on a 1.2 million m² site in Jeddah, and when completed in 1985, it will be the second largest and most advanced research and training hospital in Saudi Arabia.

Industrial Science and Research

The main organization concerned with industrial research in the Kingdom is the Industrial Studies and Development Centre (ISDC) which was conceived as a United Nations Development Programme Special Fund Project and established in 1967. The centre is an autonomous body governed by a board of directors with the director-general as the chief executive. It has its head office in Riyadh and there are branch offices in Jeddah and Dammam.

The centre has five departments: industrial research, technical services, information and documentation, evaluation and follow-up, and administration. It has an industrial laboratory and a well-equipped workshop in the Riyadh Industrial Estate with the capacity to design, manufacture and repair press tools, moulds, jigs and fixtures and various other spare parts. Research at the centre is concentrated on feasibility studies on industries which are important for Saudi Arabia.

The General Petroleum and Minerals Organization (PETROMIN), the Saudi Basic Industries Corporation (SABIC), the Saudi Arabian Standards Organization and the Directorate General of Mineral Resources (DGMR) also conduct some research in their particular areas.

Solar Energy

Saudi Arabia has an extensive solar energy research programme. The programme is carried out under the aegis of the Technical Cooperation Agreement with the United States in the Field of Solar Energy (SOLERAS). The technical objectives of the SOLERAS programme are to advance the development of solar technology and facilitate the transfer of solar technology to Saudi Arabia in four broad areas:

1. Rural and agricultural application.

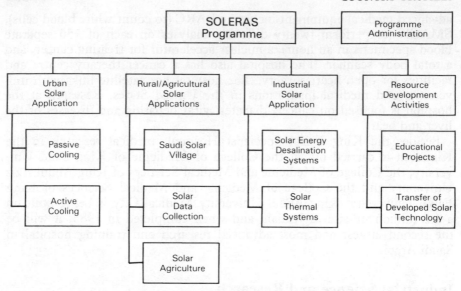

Fig. 3.8 Breakdown structure of SOLERAS Programme

2.   Urban applications.
3.   Industrial applications.
4.   Resource development activities.

The breakdown of the SOLERAS programme is given in Figure 3.8. The five-year programme started in 1977, and involved a total cost of US$100 million contributed equally by each party. Under the programme an operating agent, the Solar Energy Research Institute (SERI) located in Colorado, United States, has been created and two programme directors, one Saudi and one American, have been appointed.

In the rural/agricultural area, SOLERAS has initiated the Saudi solar village project designed to demonstrate the ability of solar energy to provide the electricity needed to make rural life more attractive and thereby slow the migration from rural to urban areas. The site of the project, about 50 km north-west of Riyadh, is located between the villages of al-Uyaynah and al-Jubaylah. The project involves the installation of a 350 kW peak DC photovoltaic power system. A solar controlled environment agricultural project has also been initiated.

In the area of urban application, two separate cooling projects have been initiated: an engineering field test of active solar cooling systems and establishment of solar cooling test facilities at the University of Petroleum and Minerals, King Saud University, King Abdul Aziz University and King Faisal University. The objective of the engineering field tests is to stimulate the development of advanced active solar cooling systems for conditions typical to the hot-arid and hot-humid environments of Saudi Arabia and the United States. The solar cooling laboratories at the four major Saudi universities will be equipped to conduct design, analysis, system integration and experimentation on new or advanced cooling concepts.

In the industrial applications area, a solar energy water desalination project was initiated in 1980. The objective of the project is to advance the technical and economic feasibility of large-scale solar powered desalination of both brackish water and seawater.

In the resource development area, a solar data collection project and an educational project were started in 1980. The solar data collection project provides solar radiation monitoring and meteorological measurements for the solar village project site. The educational project consists of student tours and seminars and workshops at Saudi universities.

The major Saudi universities have their own solar energy research programmes. The University of Petroleum and Minerals has a long history of solar energy research. The Department of Electrical Engineering started work in 1969 on heliohydroelectric power generation, solar energy simulated evaporators, solar energy storage and direct conversion of solar energy into electricity. In addition to this work, the department is now working on solar housing, process heat production, hydrogen production, collectors, water heating and desalination. The research institute of the university is building a major solar energy laboratory with facilities for thermal testing of flat plate solar collectors and monitoring of solar energy radiation.

The College of Engineering of the King Saud University has a major solar energy research programme concerned with solar desalination, water heating, collectors, solar concentration, storage, cooling and solar housing.

The College of Engineering of the King Abdul Aziz University has joint solar energy programme with the German Ministry of Research and Development. Research is concerned with the variation of spectral distribution of daylight at various geographical locations in the Mecca region and studies on biomass, semiconductors and superconductors.

The College of Architecture of King Faisal University is working on the use of passive solar energy systems in building design.

Scientific and Technological Information Services

The National Centre for Science and Technology Information of SANCST is responsible for the provision of scientific and technological information in the Kingdom. The centre is still being developed but its on-line search service, which uses satellite links to information networks in the United States, has been operating since 1979. The centre is now working to:

1. Develop Saudi Arabian science and technology data bases. Six data bases are being developed:

   (a) *Research in progress* – with summaries of research sponsored by SANCST and other organizations throughout the Kingdom as well as foreign projects of interest to Saudi Arabia;

   (b) *Science and technology publications* – with abstracts and descriptive information of publications by Saudis, Saudi Arabian organizations, published in Saudi Arabia or prepared for Saudi Arabian organizations by foreign organizations, as well as selected foreign publications of particular significance for Saudi Arabia;

(c) *Libraries and information centres* – with descriptions of their holdings and services and similar information for foreign libraries and scientific information centres of interest to the Kingdom;

(d) *Science and technology manpower* – with descriptions of education and work experiences of persons involved in activities in or on behalf of Saudi Arabia;

(e) *Laboratory, research and data processing facilities* – with descriptive information about their goals, activities and accomplishments;

(f) *Major equipment* – of the preceding organizations with descriptive information, including availability to researchers from other organizations.

2. Establish a scientific and technological data analysis unit to provide indices and studies of domestic and international science and technology developments.

3. Establish the National Science and Technology Library.

4. Facilitate the development of national, specialized network for accessing and transferring information among libraries and information centres within Saudi Arabia and between them and foreign information networks.

When fully developed, the centre will have the following divisions:

1. *Data communications*, which will be responsible for establishing, maintaining and administering a communications network that will link the centre with other scientific organizations both inside and outside Saudi Arabia.

2. *Research and development*, which will conduct research on information science in Saudi Arabia. The unit will work on such problems as development of multi-lingual science and technology lexographic data bases with emphasis on English-to-Arabic equivalences, development of software in Arabic and standardization of bibliographic records and text in Arabic.

3. *Data analysis*, which will analyse national and international trends of importance to Saudi science and technology.

4. *Information handling services*, which will be responsible for data base design; acquisition of information from internal and external sources; and processing of information.

5. Computer services.

6. *Support services* such as reprography, audio-visual aids and publications.

7. On-line searching services.

8. Library and National Library services.

The organization of the centre is shown in Figure 3.9.

Besides the National Centre for Science and Technology Information, information services are also offered by the libraries of the King Saud University, King Abdul Aziz University and the University of Petroleum and Minerals.

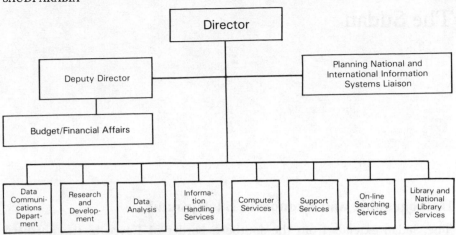

Source: 'Research Plan', SANCST, Riyadh, 1980.

Fig. 3.9 Organizational structure of the National Centre for Science and Technology Information

Scientific Societies and Associations

The Saudi Arabian Natural History Society is the oldest scientific society in the Kingdom. It is based in Jeddah and publishes a quarterly journal.

A number of professional associations such as the Saudi Arabian Biological Society and the Saudi Arabian Information Science Society, which publishes the *Arab Journal of Librarianship and Information Science* (quarterly), have either been recently formed or will be formed in the near future.

The King Faisal Philanthrophic Foundation was founded in 1976 and supports a wide range of scientific projects from solar energy, desalination, agriculture and housing to iceberg studies. It awards a number of annual prizes for distinguished work and scholarship.

The Sudan

Demographic and Economic Background

The Sudan extends from the southern border of Egypt to the northern border of Uganda, and from the Republic of Chad to the north-west border of Ethiopia. It covers 2.5 million km² and is the largest country in Africa. The White Nile travels through the entire length of the country from the swamps of the Sudd in the north to the Ugandan highlands in the south. The Blue Nile, originating in the Ethiopian highlands, joins it at Khartoum. The southern portion of Lake Nasser lies in Sudanese territory. Sudan's population is 17.9 million, with 46 per cent of the total population being under 14 years of age. Agriculture is the most important sector of the economy. The country has a cultivable potential of about 80 million ha of arable land, of which only 31 million ha are currently used for crop production and grazing purposes.

The current Six Year Plan for Economic and Social Development (1977/78–1982/83) of Sudan constitutes the first phase of a prospective plan for the period 1977/78–1994/95, whose objectives are to enable the economy to become regionally balanced, and to motivate self-sustaining and self-reliant growth. The plan aims at achieving accelerated economic growth. Its main objectives are:

1. Raising the per capita income in real terms of US$310 by the end of the plan.
2. Generation of more employment opportunities of a productive nature.
3. Improving the balance of payments position by expanding exports and producing import substitutes.
4. Encouraging the private sector to participate more effectively in the process of development.
5. Augmenting and mobilizing both public and private savings.
6. Encouraging rural development of underdeveloped areas through self-reliance.
7. Devoting more attention to improvement of development administration and training of qualified organizational administrative personnel.
8. Making regional planning the base for central development planning.
9. Raising the productivity of all sectors of the economy and improving the rate of implementation.

10. Interlinking development in all sectors with the agricultural sector, which will assume the leading role in the national economy.
11. Developing and modernizing the traditional agricultural sector and attaining self-sufficiency in certain food items and other agricultural commodities and inputs.
12. Conserving national resources.
13. Developing the industrial sector to complement the agricultural sector. Priority within this sector is to be given to agro-industries and import substitution.
14. Consolidating and expanding the basic infrastructure with special emphasis on transport and communication sectors.
15. Developing the cooperative movement and intensifying its activities so that it may contribute to mobilizing both human and financial resources for socio-economic development.
16. Providing more social services in the fields of culture, education, health, social welfare and training.

These objectives are pursued within a strategy that gives first priority to agricultural development and achieving self-sufficiency in certain food crops. The strategy also aims to diversify crop production to avoid dependence on one cash crop, cotton, which at present contributes 60 per cent of the country's foreign exchange earnings. Emphasis is on increasing production of oil seeds, sorghum and sugarcane. The industrial sector, which embraces manufacturing, mining, construction, and electricity and water, will also be expanded under the plan. Major industries in the Sudan are sugar, textiles, cement, leather, edible oil, fruits and vegetable processing, fertilizers and electricity. Of these textiles, sugar and cement industries will be further developed and limestone, molasses, canning, building materials, assembly and manufacturing of trucks and tractors, prefabricated houses, starch and glucose industries will be set up.

Science Policy and Organization

Sudan does not have an explicit science policy. Its research and development efforts are based on the strategy of the long-term prospective plan. Different sectors of the plan include explicit or implicit elements of science policy. This 'hidden' science policy is reflected in the organization of science and technology in the country and promotion of discipline-oriented research centres and institutes. However, the National Council for Research, after making a partial attempt in 1974, is preparing a detailed science and technology plan for the country.

Science and technology activities in Sudan face a number of serious obstacles. Sudan's national paper to UNCSTD identified eight obstacles impeding the indigenous development of science and technology in the country:

1. An apparent lack of appreciation of the role of science and technology in development by many production organizations in the Sudan. This

is primarily due to the indifference of many of the industrialists and entrepreneurs to quality control. This is coupled with absence of enforcement of quality-control measures. Moreover, industrialists and entrepreneurs are generally reluctant to be told by outsiders what to do, and usually try to avoid the extra cost of improvement innovations so long as they are making profit and are not confronted by competition.

2. Though the Sudan has the nucleus of a technological base and has managed to establish a good number of scientific research institutes in various disciplines, it has not been able to utilize these institutes effectively for development. This has been due to shortage of research scientists in terms of both number and specialization that are needed to handle various activities. Training of specialists and research workers started to take shape only in the mid-1950s after independence. Moreover the physical facilities and research equipment are minimal, spare parts for machinery are difficult to obtain and access to scientific and technological information has been very limited. As a result of these constraints most of the research workers, limited as their number is, are not working at full capacity.

3. The contact between indigenous research and development institutions and the users of their findings is rather weak and does not ensure the steady flow and application of research findings. This is particularly seen in the relatively new industrial sector, due to poor extension services.

4. With its ambitious long-term development plan the Sudan finds itself in great jeopardy and need for scientific and technological cadres at all levels. With its vast area of 2.5 million km^2 and 90 million ha of cultivable land, the Sudanese present potential of scientific and technological cadres is, to say the last, feeble. At present there are thirty-five agriculturists per million ha of cultivable land, and 200 engineers per million of the population and only about one-third of these numbers in respect of cadres of mid-level technicians. This situation has been imposed by the following constraints:

(a) Shortage of training personnel and expertise;
(b) High cost and lack of training facilities;
(c) Non-existence of a stimulating technological environment;
(d) A traditional zeal for learning which makes every citizen opt for the highest level of education, which makes difficult the building up of important mid-level cadres.

The distribution of training opportunities is biased more towards the higher level than the intermediate and lower levels. Technological training is mainly concentrated on the software side, which lacks the provision of scientific equipment and machinery to facilitate on-the-job training and full utilization of the software training.

5. During the last five years the already limited and scarce manpower resources of the Sudan have been exposed to a continuous drain. At present there are over 700 Sudanese physicians practising in England alone. Many high-level professionals and technicians have found their

way to various countries of the Arab world. This emigration of scientific and technological manpower has run through all levels from unskilled and skilled labour right to the top level of managerial and technological personnel.

6. Financing has in the vast majority of cases been a determining factor in the choice of technology. As the major part of the foreign currency needs of the development plans are financed through foreign loans or bilateral trade agreements, in most cases imported technology has come from the lender country, irrespective of its appropriateness to local needs and conditions.

7. All technology is often owned by private enterprises and companies having patent rights, trade secrets and not by governments or United Nations organizations, who, consequently, have no say in choice of technology.

8. There has been a tendency in the Sudan, as in most developing countries, to acquire the latest advanced technologies on grounds of prestige and a craving for glamour.

The National Council for Research was set up in 1970 to overcome these obstacles. The council is an autonomous corporate body responsible for policy, planning, programming and budgeting in science and technology. It is directly under the president and operates through a number of research units, centres and institutions, some of which belong to the council itself, and some of which belong to various ministries and government departments.

The governing body of the council is its board of directors, which consists of central and regional Ministers of Finance, Agriculture, Education and central Ministers of Health, National Planning, Industry and Public Service and Administrative Reform; leading Sudanese scientists from the universities and various research centres; and leading industrialists from private and public sectors. The president of the council is responsible for the day-to-day running of the organization.

The NCR operates through four specialized councils, which cover all the major research activities on the country:

1. The Agricultural Research Council.
2. The Economic and Social Research Council.
3. The Scientific and Technological Research Council.
4. The Medical Research Council.

The membership of these councils is honorary and technical committees run specific research projects.

The Agricultural Research Council has a veterinary division and an agricultural research division. Research at the council is concerned with irrigated agriculture, conservation of soil and moisture in rainland farming, farm mechanization, animal husbandry, high-yielding varieties and agricultural pests and diseases.

The Scientific and Technological Research Council has the following institutes:

1. Institute of Oceanography.
2. Institute of Energy Research, which has departments for (a) solar
    energy; (b) wind energy; and (c) biomass. Most of the research at the
    institute, however, is concerned with solar energy as the institute
    developed from the original Institute for Solar Energy Research. Re-
    search is concerned with solar pumping, solar refrigeration, water
    heating, water desalination, food drying, solar insulation and photo-
    voltaic conversion.
3. Centre Instrument Repair Workshop.
4. National Centre for Technology, which is responsible for organizing
    training courses to improve craftsmanship and local technical skills
    and provides consultation services to local industry on the choice and
    adaptation of suitable imported technology. The centre works in close
    collaboration with the Industrial Research and Consultancy Institute
    of the Ministry of Industry.

The council has joint programmes with the building and Road Research
Institute of the University of Khartoum and the Geological and Mineral
Resources Department of the Ministry of Energy and Mining.

The Medical Research Council has the following institutes: the Institute
of Tropical Diseases, which has an intensive research programme on the
control of bilharzia and malaria; and the Medical and Aromatic Herbs
Unit, which is concerned with traditional medicine, medicinal values of
local herbs and manufacture of pharmaceuticals based on local herbs.

The council also has joint programmes at the Medical Health Laboratories and the Hospital of Tropical Diseases, both of which belong to
the Ministry of Health and Social Welfare.

The General Secretariat of the National Council for Research has five
national committees and centres:

1. The Sudan Atomic Energy Commission, which is exploring the pos-
    sibilities of developing nuclear power in Sudan.
2. The National Computers Committee, which is promoting the develop-
    ment of a national computer network to rationalize the use of computer
    facilities in various sectors of the economy.
3. National Committee for Man, Environment and Development, which
    is responsible for environmental monitoring, developing environmental
    laws and advising the government on the transfer of technology and
    its environmental impact.
4. The National Remote Sensing Centre, where research is concerned
    with surveying national resources and identification and survey of
    size of pest and disease incidence.

Academic Science and Research

Sudan has five universities of which the University of Khartoum is the
oldest. The University of Gezira and the University of Juba were both
established in 1975. The Omdurman Islamic University, founded in 1912,

is purely a religious institution. The Khartoum Branch of the University of Cairo was founded by decree in 1955 and became an operative institution in 1959. It is financed by the University of Cairo.

The University of Khartoum was established in 1956, to supersede the University College of Khartoum, which had been founded in 1951. The university incorporated the Gordon Memorial College (founded in 1902), the Kitchener Medical School (founded in 1924), and the Shambat Agricultural Institute (founded in 1956). The university has faculties of arts, economic and social studies, law, engineering and architecture, agriculture, sciences, medicine, and veterinary sciences; it also includes the Natural History Museum, the university farm at Shambat, and hydrobiological and arid zone research units.

The Faculty of Agriculture has departments for agricultural botany, agricultural engineering, agronomy, animal production, biochemistry and soil sciences, crop protection, home sciences, horticulture, and rural economy. The Faculty of Veterinary Sciences has departments for anatomy and histology, animal husbandry, microbiology and parasitology, veterinary pathology, physiology and biochemistry, preventive medicine and veterinary public health, and for veterinary clinical studies and medicine.

The Faculty of Sciences undertakes teaching and research in departments for botany, chemistry, geology, mathematics, physics, and zoology. The professor of geology is also the director of the University's Arid Zone Research Unit, which undertakes studies into problems regarding the flora, fauna and geology of arid regions of the Sudan; the professor of zoology is the curator of the Natural History Museum.

The Faculty of Engineering and Architecture includes departments for architecture, civil engineering, electrical engineering, mechanical engineering, and engineering mathematics.

The Hydrobiological Research Unit is an autonomous unit in the University of Khartoum. It is under the supervision of a director and research projects are in the fields of hydrobiology and sedimentology in the River Nile, with emphasis on inland fisheries.

The Khartoum Technical Institute has institutes for civil engineering and architectural technicians, for textile engineering technicians, for agricultural engineering technicians, for laboratory technicians, for surveying technicians, and for mechanical engineering technicians.

Agricultural Science and Research

Besides the Agricultural Research Council, the Ministry of Agriculture, Food and Natural Resources has research departments for agriculture and forests. The Department of Agriculture has divisions for horticulture, plant protection (which is interested in controlling insect pests and plant diseases, especially desert locust and water hyacinth), plant propagation, soil surveys, agricultural engineering, and education and extension services. The department also controls the Agricultural Production Corporation, the Agricultural Development Corporation, the Agricultural Reform Corporation, the Agricultural Mechanical Corporation, and the Agricultural Research Corporation.

The Department of Forests has sections for timber technology, and for forest botany; there are silvicultural research stations at Khartoum (arid zone forestry), at Wad Medani for Eastern Sudan, and at El Obeid for Western Sudan. There is also a Gum Research Station at El Obeid. The Department of Forests maintains a college for forest rangers and controls the Forest Research and Education Institute.

The Agricultural Research Corporation carries out its work in sections for agronomy and plant physiology, botany and plant pathology, entomology, soil sciences, cotton breeding, cereals breeding and horticulture. The main agricultural research station is at Wad Medani and there are others at Ed Damer, Abu Naama, and Yambio. Sub-stations for research and experimental work are at Shambat, Khashm-el-Girba, Kadugli, Guneid, and Sennar.

The Forest Research and Education Institute, in Khartoum, conducts and coordinates research in the forestry and forest products field; it develops facilities and programmes for training personnel in silviculture; studies forest economics; and works on the production, processing and marketing of products. Particular attention is paid to work designed to mitigate against 'desert creep'; efforts are made to prevent deforestation in rural areas when such areas are subjected to intensive agriculture for up to four or five years and then abandoned for more fertile areas. Such cleared areas are especially subject to being covered by sand dunes as the desert makes its steady advance. The Forest Department of the Ministry and the Forest Research and Education Institute have a particularly difficult task in preventing this gradual erosion of potentially fertile land, since most of the agricultural workers are nomadic by nature and are difficult to educate.

The Ministry of Animal Resources has a Research Division with the following sections: the veterinary research section studies virology, bacteriology, biological products, animal pathology, entomology, trypanosomiasis, parasitology, and biochemistry. The animal health section is concerned with prophylactic and curative medicine; it supervises the quarantine regulations; and carries out inspection of meat products. The animal production section has a department for livestock improvement which works at five experimental stations throughout the country; a dairy sciences department, which carries out research and development work in government dairies; and other departments which deal with poultry, hides and skins, hair and wool production, animal nutrition, and marketing of products. The range management and pasture research section is concerned with the improvement, management and rehabilitation of both cultivated and natural range land; with the conservation of natural resources; with the establishment of range and pasture land through artificial and natural reseeding; with forage production; and with the settlement of the nomadic pastoral population. There is also an extension, education and training section which controls the Omdurman Training School for Stockmen, the Hides and Skins Institute, and the Kuku Veterinary and Animal Husbandry Institute.

Medical Science and Research

Most of the medical research in Sudan is conducted by the Medical Research Council whose activities are described above. However, the Ministry of Health and Social Welfare controls the Central Medical Laboratories and Hospital of Tropical Diseases which carry out research work and public health services. Most of the research work is concerned with tropical medicine; the laboratories contain the official government analyst's office, which is concerned with pharmaceutical quality control, foods, nutrition, water control and sewage.

Syria

Demographic and Economic Background

Syria is in the Levant and covers an area of 184,479 km². It is bounded in the north by Turkey, in the east by Iraq, in the south and south-east by Jordan, and in the west by Israel, Lebanon, and the Mediterranean Sea. It has a population of 8.6 million. Agriculture is the major contributor to the Syrian economy, accounting for at least one-fifth of GNP and employing two-thirds of the labour force. Cotton and wheat are the most valuable crops. Large textile industries are located in Aleppo and Damascus; the food processing industry is also important. Oil has been discovered in the north-east of Syria and has been exported since the late 1960s; indirect revenue accrues from oil, in the form of transit fees from Saudi Arabia and Iraq, whose pipelines cross Syria on their way to the Lebanese coast.

The fifth development plan (1981–85) is committed to a restraint in public spending and increased private sector investment in industrial projects. Agricultural development in particular is to be pushed ahead by the government, and the textile industry will be completely overhauled.

Science Policy and Organization

Syria has a science plan prepared by the Supreme Council of Sciences in cooperation with the Ministry of Planning but this plan is not incorporated in the country's development plan. The plan focuses on agriculture and industrial projects, and stipulates the manpower, equipment and other facilities needed for the implementation of these projects. The overall emphasis in Syrian research is on agriculture; but industrial research is also receiving increasing attention, in particular, textiles, electronics and industrial chemistry are receiving support from the government.

The principal science policy and planning body in Syria is the Supreme Council of Sciences, which was established in 1958. The council is attached to the Ministry of Higher Education and its main functions are:

1. The supervision of scientific activities in government departments and universities.
2. Manpower planning and formulation of science policy of government departments.

3. Granting awards and providing support services for scientific and technological institutions.

The main body of the council is the Supreme Committee of Sciences, which is responsible for the scientific affairs of the council. The scientific sections of the council are: physical and mathematical sciences; geological and mineralogical sciences; chemical sciences; biological sciences; civil engineering sciences; agricultural sciences; and medical sciences. In addition, the council has seven commissions responsible for specific tasks in their area:

1. The Commission of Scientific Research.
2. The Commission for Science Personnel.
3. The Commission of Scientific Instruments.
4. The Commission of Scientific Publications.
5. The Commission of Scientific Relations.
6. The Commission of Atomic Energy.
7. The Commission for Man and Environment.

An administrative council, headed by the secretary-general, is responsible for the day-to-day running of the council.

Academic Science and Research

There are four universities in Syria, of which the University of Damascus is the oldest and most established university and the University of Aleppo has the most extensive facilities for scientific research. The University of Tichreen in Lattakia is a much smaller university with faculties for sciences, agriculture, engineering and medicine but research at the university is limited. Al-Baath University was only established in 1979; it is a technological university with faculties for chemical and petroleum engineering, veterinary science and medicine.

The University of Damascus was established in 1903 when the Medical Institute, which included a School of Medicine and a School of Pharmacy, was founded. This institute was transferred to Beirut for the duration of the First World War, and Turkish was the language of instruction. In 1919 two institutes of law and medicine were re-founded in Damascus and the language of instruction became Arabic. Both institutes remained attached to the Syrian Ministry of Education as independent bodies until 1923, when they were merged under the name of the Syrian University. In 1946 four new faculties were established, for sciences, letters, education, and for engineering (in Aleppo). In 1955 a faculty for Islamic jurisprudence was created, and in 1958 the university was retitled the University of Damascus. In the same year the Dental School became a faculty, a Faculty of Commerce was formed from a department of the Faculty of Law, and a new Faculty of Engineering was established – the one in Aleppo now becoming the foundation for the new University of Aleppo. In 1962 the Department of Pharmacy of the medical faculty achieved faculty status of its own; in 1963 the Institutes of Fine Arts and Agriculture, originally run by the Ministry of Education became faculties in the university; and in 1971 the Technological Institute, formerly attached to the Ministry of Higher Education, was given faculty status within the University of Damascus. Today, the university has thirteen faculties, in addition to five intermediate institutes.

The university is administered by the rector, two vice-rectors, the university council, the Supreme Council of Universities, and a secretary.

The Faculty of Agriculture is organized into departments for plant production, animal production, soil and plant nutrition, food sciences, and plant protection. Special interests include insect control, weed control, and soil sciences (including the use of fertilizers).

The Faculty of Dentistry has departments for oral surgery, oral medicine, prosthodontics, and for dental and oral anatomy, pathology and histology.

The Faculty of Engineering is divided into sections for civil engineering and for architecture. The civil engineering section has departments for basic sciences, irrigation and hydraulics, construction engineering, and public works.

The Faculty of Electrical and Mechanical Engineering was formerly the Technological Institute attached to the Ministry of Higher Education; it became a faculty of the university in 1971. The Department of Mechanical Engineering carries out teaching and research in fields such as internal combustion engines, heating and refrigeration engineering, air-conditioning, hydraulic control, and production engineering. The Department of Electrical Engineering is concerned with electrical power systems, and with electronic engineering.

The Faculty of Medicine has departments for anatomy, physiology, health, pathology, laboratory medicine, internal medicine, dermatology and venereal diseases, surgery, ophthalmology and otorhinolaryngology, paediatrics, gynaecology and obstetrics, and for physical medicine. Attached to the faculty are a School of Midwifery and Nursing, and three hospitals – the National Hospital, Al Muwassat Hospital, and the Maternity Hospital.

The Faculty of Pharmacy has departments for pharmacology, analytical chemistry and toxicology, pharmaceutics, and pharmaceutical chemistry.

The Faculty of Science has departments for mathematics, physics, chemistry, botany, zoology, and geology. The Department of Mathematics is interested in real and complex analysis, differential equations, mechanics, algebra and abstract analysis, fluid mechanics, celestial mechanics, mathematical statistics, and the theory of probability. The Department of Physics is interested in physical mechanics and vibrations, electricity and electronics, optics and spectra, thermodynamics and statistical physics, quantum mechanics, solid-state and atomic physics, nuclear and corpuscular physics, nuclear technology, atmospheric thermodynamics and radiation; and practical and applied meteorology. The Department of Chemistry is concerned with radiochemistry, structural and coordinate chemistry and crystallography, the chemistry and biochemistry of natural products, colloidal and macromolecular chemistry, industrial organic and inorganic chemistry, petrochemistry and fuels, chemical technology and mineralogy, as well as the more usual branches of chemistry. The Department of Geology carries out studies in structural geology, mineralogy, petrography, palaeontology, stratigraphy, hydrogeology, petroleum geology, micro-palaeontology, and geochemistry and geophysics. The Department of Zoology is interested in genetics and evolution, histology and comparative anatomy, animal metabolism, animal nervous systems and senses, parasitology, systematic zoology, and embryology and developmental biology. The Department of Botany studies angiosperms and plant geography, archaegoniatae, thallophytes, genetics and morphogenesis, microbiology and enzymology, plant ecology, and plant taxonomy. The Faculty of Science also offers all the premedical courses necessary for entry into the Faculties of Dentistry and Pharmacy.

The University of Aleppo was established from the engineering faculty of the University of Damascus in 1960. The university is governed by the University Council which is composed of the rector, the two vice-rectors, the deans of the faculties, a professor representing the University Teachers' Union, three students, one member representing the Ministry of Higher Education, and the secretary-general of the university.

Scientific research is undertaken in the laboratories of the Faculty of Engineering on: strength of materials, geodesy, soil mechanics, geology, hydraulics, electrical communication and electrical machines, electronics, fuels, metrology, machine design, and workshop technology. New laboratories have been established for the study of industrial hydraulics, aerodynamics, electrical engineering, refrigeration and air-conditioning, water machines, materials testing, hydrodynamics, water analysis, high-voltage research, measuring instruments, glass pipes, automatic control, and heat transformation. Particular emphasis is being placed on research into the properties of stabilized sand; the influence of testing stabilized sand with bitumen emulsion; and the effect of time and temperature factors on the shear strength of stabilized sand with cationic bituminous emulsion.

The Faculty of Agriculture has laboratories for general, analytical, organic, and inorganic chemistry; soil chemistry and physics; plant physiology, crop production, food technology, horticulture, animal microbiology, geology, and agricultural machines. There is an agricultural research centre at Muslimieh. The faculty participates in regional and international research programmes such as the Arid Zones Institute, and UNESCO programmes. It undertakes research projects on behalf of other government departments such as the Euphrates Basin project. Special research projects include studies on the ecology of pine forests; hormone treatment of grape vines; ecological studies of natural pasture ranges in Syria; entomological studies on insects affecting olive crops; and studies on insects affecting stored food on behalf of the food preservation industry.

The Faculty of Medicine has laboratories for biochemistry, histology, pathology, pharmacology, psychology, and microbiology. Special research projects include the microsurgery of the ear; a new method of total laryngectomy; facial palsy; skin cancer; and the past and present situation of cutaneous leishmaniasis in Syria.

The Faculty of Science has laboratories for general, inorganic, organic,

analytical and physical chemistry; general and modern physics; electricity
and light; and thermodynamics. Special attention is being paid to the extraction of protein from oil.

The Faculty of Veterinary Sciences has laboratories for animal husbandry,
parasitology and physiology.

The Faculty of Economic Sciences carries out studies on the strategic
importance of heavy industries in the economic development of Syria; on
the feasibility of establishing an iron and steel industry in Syria; and comprehensive studies on small-scale industries that could be established in
Syria.

Attached to the university, is the Institute for the History of Arabic
Science which was established in 1976. The institute has three departments – basic sciences, medical science and applied sciences – and offers
postgraduate qualifications on the history of Arabic and Islamic science.
Research at the institute is directed towards understanding the place of
science in medieval Islamic civilization; the history of algebra, mathematics and Islamic medicine; and the process of transmission of Islamic
science to Latin West. A number of classical Muslim scientific treatises –
such as *al-Muadilat* of Sharaf al-Din al-Tusi, *al-Jabr* of Umar al-Khayyam,
the geohistorical encyclopaedia *Masalik al-Absar fi Mamalik al-Amaar* by
Ibn Fadl Allah al-Umari al-Dimashqi and the famous formulary of the
twelfth-century writer Badr al-Din al-Qalanisis, *The Aqrabadhin of al-
Qalansisi* – are being translated and edited at the institute.

Agricultural Science and Research

The Ministry of Agriculture and Agrarian Reform has an Agricultural
Research Department which undertakes the major part of agricultural
research, apart from that carried out by the universities. The Ecology and
Useful Plants Section of the department carries out work in plant classification, ecology, plant physiology and nutrition, biochemistry, harmful
grasses, crop rotation, and industrial plants. The Horticulture Section is
interested in fruit trees, vegetables, vineyards, and ornamental plants;
it also carries out studies in processing and storage. The Field Crops Section is concerned with rhizomes, legumes, oleic crops, sugarbeet, fibres, and
cereals technology. The Lands Section studies soil microbiology, fertility,
chemistry, minerals and ores, and is also concerned with land reclamation
studies. The Entomology Section studies insect ecology and physiology,
bees and silkworms, insect classification, and insecticides and methods of
biological control. The Diseases Section studies fungal, microbial, viral,
and parasitic diseases, and plant medicine. The Dairy and Agricultural
Industries Section studies microbiology; food chemistry, analysis and conservation; oleic juices and gaseous liquors; fermentation and distillation
processes; and dairy products. There is also a Laboratory Section which
conducts experiments and analyses required by all the other sections.

The Ministry has an Agricultural Affairs Department with sections for
agricultural investment, plant protection and quarantine, horticulture, field

crops and multiplication, land utilization and water use, and agricultural coordination and extension services.

The Cotton Bureau, in Aleppo, is a directorate of the Ministry of Agriculture and Agrarian Reform which is responsible for the supervision of cotton-growing and for conducting research. The bureau was established in 1952. Two other cotton organizations are established in Syria; the Cotton Marketing Organization is a commercial organization responsible for seed preparation, ginning and packing. The Agricultural Cooperative Bank buys cotton seed from the Cotton Marketing Organization and distributes it to farms by means of licences granted by the Ministry of Agriculture and Agrarian Reform.

The Cotton Bureau is the sole institution in Syria with responsibility for cotton-breeding and research; its activities are carried out in ten stations throughout the country; four of the stations are leased from private cotton farmers, the other six are in government agricultural stations. The Cotton Bureau has been responsible for perfecting the variety of cotton known as Aleppo 1, which has a very high yield and is practically immune from *Verticilium wilt*, the most prevalent cotton disease. Ninety-seven per cent of cotton grown in Syria is of the Aleppo 1 variety, the remaining 3 per cent is the Aleppo 4 variety, which was also developed by the Cotton Bureau. The following are the main fields of research:

Breeding and propagation research – is carried out by securing pure cotton seeds appropriate to the local environment and resistant or tolerant to prevailing diseases; by improving the characteristics of Aleppo 1 variety by hybridization research, which has been carried on since 1970 in order to:

1. Increase its tolerance to *Verticilium wilt*.
2. Lengthen its fibres.
3. Transfer resistance or immunity to black arm disease to Aleppo 1 by crossing with Turkish Acala SJ 1 and by crossing with some African varieties.
4. Transmit a glandless character to Aleppo 1 by crossing with Acala 4–42 glandless variety.

By the end of the fourth five year plan (1976–80), most of the cotton growing area was producing Aleppo 1 glandless cottons, which are capable of being used for the production of seed cakes for human and animal nutrition; the plant protein obtained in this way will make a valuable contribution to Syrian nutrition since leguminous crops are rarely grown and animal production is not yet sufficient for local consumption.

Experimental agricultural methods research – is being conducted to introduce mechanization into planting and ploughing methods in Syria. This is an important issue in Syria where traditional methods are still largely in operation. Effort is being made to apply modern farming methods, in particular the expansion of application of chemical and organic fertilizers. A survey has been made of Syrian soils and a pedological map has been made.

Plant protection research – breeding of improved varieties tolerant to damping-off, and intensive investigations on insecticides, fungicides and herbicides. Advances have been made in pest control methods and research has been conducted on the most important insects affecting cotton. Wilt and damping-off are the main diseases affecting cotton production. The entomological research has concentrated on the following insects, which have been arranged according to their appearance through the life cycle of the cotton plant: cut-worm, thrips, aphid, green worm, jassids, red spiders, spiny boll-worm, American boll-worm, pink boll-worm, and white fly.

The Cotton Bureau issues a twice-monthly report on the cotton situation in Syria, and readily makes its research results available to all interested organizations.

Arab Centre for the Study of Arid Zones – ACSAZ

The ACSAZ is a regional centre set up by ALECSO in 1970. Based in Damascus, the centre studies problems of aridity in the Arab world including water use and resources, soil classification and fertility, soil/water relationship and conservation, fruit trees and crop production, sheep pasture and range management, desertification, soil degradation and watershed management.

International Centre for Agricultural Research in the Dry Areas – ICARDA

ICARDA is an autonomous regional institution set up in 1976 by the Consultative Group on International Agricultural Research (CGIAR). ICARDA also has experimental stations in Iran and Lebanon. It has been designated as the world international centre for barley, lentils and broad beans, and serves, in cooperation with the International Maize and Wheat Improvement Centre and the International Crops Research Institute for the Semi-Arid Tropics, as a regional centre for the improvement of wheat and chickpeas, respectively. In addition, ICARDA's research activities include the study of environmental systems in the region, the establishment of principles on which to base the development of farming strategies and research into socio-economic constraints that limit the actual potential of existing farming systems.

Other Research

The Centre for Industrial Research and Development in Damascus is concerned with electronics, industrial management and operational research, and material science, and provides testing and pilot plant facilities to Syrian industry.

The Centre for Scientific Studies and Research is attached to the Ministry of Defence and conducts military research.

The Centre for Nuclear Energy and Research is in the process of being set up. The Nuclear Medicine Centre in Damascus conducts research on the use of radioisotopes in medicine.

The Marine Research Centre in Lattakia is concerned with oceanographic research and pollution monitoring.

Scientific Societies and Associations

The Arab Society for Plant Protection was established in 1979. It is a regional organization based at the Faculty of Agriculture of the University of Aleppo. The society's objective is to 'assist and participate in the co-ordination of studies and research in the field of plant protection in the Arab countries'.

Tunisia

Demographic and Economic Background

Tunisia is one of the Maghrib countries situated between Algeria to the east and Libya to the west, its northern boundary being the Mediterranean Sea. It has an area of 160,000 km² and a population of 6.2 million, which is increasing by 2.1 per cent annually. While the economy is based on agriculture, Tunisia does have some oil, a rapidly developing industry, and increasing tourism. In 1979, the GDP was US$6.07 billion.

The country's sixth five year development plan (1982–86) will tackle Tunisia's major problem – growing unemployment – which in 1981 reached 16 per cent, and involved the investment of US$17.5 to US$22.5 billion in the economy. The government's main strategy is to shore up agriculture and push hard at industrialization, particularly in the electro-mechanical field. Manufacturing industry, which has provided 42 per cent of the jobs since 1972, is earmarked as the key area of development. Among the big projects due for implementation in the 1982–86 plan are a new US$250 million refinery near Bizerta; expansion of phosphate capacity, bringing output from 5.1 million to 9 million tonnes by the end of the decade and boosting local refining capacity; development of the Miskar field and six or seven small oilfields; and the construction of sugar and cement plants. In the agricultural sector, cereal production yields will be greatly improved and a series of dams will be constructed along the Medjerdah Valley. The project will bring 32,000 ha of new land under irrigation. Tourism also has a big priority under the new plan. In 1979, Tunisia played host to 1.36 million tourists. The government plans to increase this number substantially by new tourist developments, notably in North Sousee, and by attracting Gulf money for tourist developments at Monastir and North Tunis.

Science Policy and Organization

The responsibility for science policy and planning in Tunisia is shared between the *Ministère de l'Enseignement Supérieur et de la Recherche Scientifique* (Ministry of Higher Education and Scientific Research), the *Ministère de l'Éducation Nationale* (Ministry of National Education) and the *Ministère de l'Agriculture* (Ministry of Agriculture). Major national research projects are carried out under the auspices of the Ministry of National Education and coordinated by the Ministry of Higher Education and Scientific Research, which was established in 1978. The bulk of the research is carried out at the various institutes of the Ministry of Agriculture and the research centres and institutes attached to the *Université de Tunis* (University of Tunis).

Academic Science and Research

There is only one university in Tunis, the University of Tunis, which was founded in 1960. It incorporates an existing institute of higher studies which had been founded in 1945, the Islamic University, as well as other institutions. It is an autonomous State institution governed by the University Council and financed by the State. It has scientific faculties for mathematical, physical and natural sciences, and for medicine.

The Faculty of Mathematical, Physical and Natural Sciences has institutes concerned with mathematics, physics, and chemistry; a laboratory dealing with animal biology; and a marine biology department.

The Faculty of Medicine has departments and clinics for anatomy, biochemistry, physiology, histology and embryology, biophysics, pathological anatomy, forensic medicine, bacteriology, virology and immunology, parasitology, preventive medicine, hydrological therapy, experimental medicine and pharmacology.

Attached to the university are the *Institut de Recherche Scientifique et Technique* (Institute of Scientific and Technical Research), and the *Institut National des Sciences de l'Éducation* (National Institute of Education Sciences).

The Institute of Scientific and Technical Research was established in 1969 and was originally the Atomic Energy Centre. It is dependent on the Directorate of Higher Education and Scientific Research of the Ministry of National Education. The institute has civil and financial autonomy. The original emphasis on nuclear research has now shifted to solar energy with extensive projects on desalination, water heating and space cooling. The institute's principal laboratories are:

1. The Laboratory of Plant Physiology, at the Arid Zone Research Centre, which studies the different aspects of the influence of salinity on the physiological behaviour of plants. Particular interest is taken in the effect of salt on growth characteristics; mineral nutrition (absorption, migration, and accumulation of elements); water economy; and nitrogen metabolism of sensitive plants (such as haricot beans and citrus trees) and tolerant plants.
2. The Laboratory of Soil Physics studies the problems of heat and mass transfer in porous media – problems of irrigation, evaporation of pure and saline water, and diffusion of salts in the interior of porous media.
3. The Chemistry Laboratory carries out research on crystallography and studies on the solid state. The analytical chemistry and applied electro-

chemistry section of the laboratory studies long-chain organic compounds.

4. The Institute of Scientific and Technical Research has an Ornithological Research Station, at Rades, which was established in 1966. The principal activities consist of ringing birds with the object of studying their migration patterns and behaviour.

The National Institute of Education Sciences was recently established to carry out research in secondary and undergraduate science education.

Agricultural Science and Research

The Ministry of Agriculture is responsible for and controls the National Agronomic Research Institute, the National Veterinary Research Institute, the National Forestry Research Institute, the National Scientific and Technical Institute for Oceanography and Fisheries, the Arid Zone Research Institute, the Rural Engineering Research Centre and the Water and Forest Service.

The *Institut National de la Recherche Agronomique de Tunisie* (National Agronomic Research Institute of Tunisia) has responsibility for all agricultural research carried out in the country. The institute's aim is to increase agricultural production and this is achieved through soil and climate studies, the selection of species most suited to the climate and giving the greatest yield, improved agricultural practices, and pest control studies. The institute is responsible for animal as well as plant production.

Research activities are organized into four major sections: plant improvement, improvement of cultural practices, crop protection, and animal husbandry and improvement. The following laboratories are grouped under plant improvement: genetics, horticulture, forage crops, fruit and viticulture, cereals technology, and fruit and vegetable technology. The cultural practices section has divisions for agricultural chemistry, agronomy, and bioclimatology. Crop protection studies are carried out under four headings, namely, phytopathology, entomology, virology, and phytopharmacy. The activities of the animal husbandry section fall under the two headings of species improvement and nutritional studies. Laboratory work is complemented by experimental work undertaken in field stations situated in the country's principal agro-ecological regions. The institute publishes its research findings in *Annales*, and *Documents Techniques*.

The *Institut National de Recherches Vétérinaires* (National Veterinary Research Institute) has laboratory and administrative facilities in Tunis. It is a public institution under the State Secretariat of Agriculture and research is undertaken in all aspects of veterinary medicine and sciences.

The *Institut National de Recherches Forestières* (National Forestry Research Institute), at Ariana, undertakes studies in sections for reafforestation, forest ecology and nutritional physiology, improvement of forest plants, techniques of reafforestation, forest pasture lands, biometry and silviculture, wood technology, and forest entomology. Studies are undertaken over the whole of Tunisia; the institute controls forty-one arboretums, six experimental stations, nine plots of land for practical work, two forests for management studies, one pilot zone for reafforestation studies, and one pilot zone for pasture land management. The institute regularly publishes its research results.

The *Institut National Scientifique et Technique d'Océanographie et de Pêche* (National Scientific and Technical Institute for Oceanography and Fisheries), at Salammbô, near Carthage, is a public organization which undertakes applied research in fisheries, including fish stocks and population dynamics, plankton, benthos, and algae.

The Arid Zone Research Institute in Tunis has laboratories for soil physics and plant physiology, an experimental station at Tozeur, and is particularly active on solar water pumping and its application to irrigation in arid zones.

The *Centre de Recherches du Génie Rural* (Rural Engineering Research Centre) in Ariana was founded in 1960 and its main activities are in the field of irrigation techniques, hydro-agricultural management and the use of saline and brackish waters for irrigation. The centre has established an inventory of traditional Tunisian agricultural hydraulic techniques and it has promoted the rehabilitation and improvement of local and traditional irrigation methods such as irrigation systems using buried pottery jars, local collection systems for run-off waters and water tanks. The centre has also developed ten different types of animal-drawn implements, some 500 units of which have been industrially manufactured and has revived a traditional cotton sheller.

The *Service des Eaux et Forêts* (Water and Forest Service) of the Ministry of Agriculture, is responsible for the creation of animal reserves, the prevention of extinction of rare species, and the building-up of certain species of game stock. The National Forestry Research Institute comes within the jurisdiction of this department of the Ministry of Agriculture.

Industrial and Solar Energy Research

Most of the industrial research is carried out at the *Laboratoire Central du Ministère de l'Industrie des Mines et de l'Énergie* (Central Laboratory of the Ministry of Industry and Energy), the *Laboratoires de l'Office des Mines* (Laboratories of the Office of Mines) and at the *Centre National des Études Industrielles* (National Centre for Industrial Studies).

Most of the industrial research is on solar energy and its commercial applications. The *École Nationale d'Ingénieurs de Tunis* (National School of Engineering in Tunis) is the leading solar energy research and development establishment in Tunis. It is working on photovoltaic cells, production of Cu/Cu_2O photocells, production of Si/SnO_2 Schottky diodes, production of silicon monocrystals, theoretical modelling of photovoltaic plants and solar heating and air-conditioning.

The *Entreprise Tunisienne d'Activités Petrolières* (Tunisian Enterprise for Petroleum Activities), a government institution, is responsible for advising

on energy policy, including the option offered by solar energy. It is studying the use of collectors for water and space heating, possible fabrication of
collectors from local materials and subsidies needed for encouraging the
production of solar technology in the country. The State utility company,
the *Société Tunisienne de l'Électricité et du Gaz* (Tunisian Society for Electricity and Gas) has set up an experimental solar energy complex at
Hamman Biadha; it plans to set up similar complexes throughout the rural
areas in Tunisia.

The *Association pour le Développement et l'Animation Rurale* (Association for Rural Development and Animation) in Tunis was created in 1975
under the sponsorship of the Ministries of Agriculture and Social Affairs.
It is an independent, non-profit centre that carries out integrated development projects for poor rural families. It has been involved in small-scale
poultry industry, the rehabilitation of the traditional weaving handicrafts,
and self-help housing, and has conducted surveys on traditional agricultural
tools and implements and sought to identify the social and technological
obstacles to their wider use.

Scientific and Technical Information Services

The *Centre de Documentation Nationale* (National Documentation Centre),
established in 1966, has a Science and Technology Division and provides
literature for Tunisian scientists. It publishes *Documentation Tunisienne* and
Bulletin d'Information.

Turkey

Demographic and Economic Background

Turkey forms a link between Europe and Asia at the Bosphorus Straits. The major portion of Turkey is in Asia, and the Asian part is bordered by the Soviet Union and Iran in the east, and by Iraq and Syria in the south. The European portion is bordered by Greece and Bulgaria. The interior of the Asian part suffers from extremes of climate, while the European portion has a typical Mediterranean climate – mild winters and hot summers. Turkey covers a total area of 779,452 km².

In 1979, Turkey's population was 44.2 million, growing at the annual rate of 2.5 per cent. Some two-thirds of the population lives in the rural areas and is employed in agriculture. In 1979, Turkey's GDP was US$56.46 billion, 23 per cent of which was generated by agriculture, 29 per cent by industry and 21 per cent by the manufacturing sector.

Turkey is traditionally an agricultural country although much of the land is mountainous and barren. Of the total crop acreage, 90 per cent is devoted to cereals, more than half of which is wheat. The Central Anatolian Plateau is the chief wheat cultivation area. Barley is the second most important cereal and others include maize, rye, oats, rice and millet. Olives, vines, hazelnuts and figs are also important agricultural products, Turkey being the world's largest producer of sultanas. Tobacco of very high quality is grown on the Aegean coast in the Black Sea area and in the Marmara–Thrace region. Cotton is grown in the very fertile Cilian Plain. The growing and production of opium has now been prohibited.

Turkey has a relatively large industrial sector with established petrochemicals and iron and steel industries. But the largest industry is textiles, which provides 20 per cent of the total industrial output. Artificial fibres, knitware and cotton-spinning are the fastest-growing industries and cotton yarn and clothing exports have increased over the last five years. The Turkish Iron and Steel Corporation has three mills – at Karabuk and Enegli and a new plant built with the assistance of Soviet Union at Iskenderun – which produced 2 million tons in 1979. The output of these mills is expected to increase to 6 million tons in 1982. Turkey also has a developing investment goods industry producing metal products, machinery, road vehicles, electronic goods, railways, and a relatively developed shipping industry. The country's intermediate goods industries produce forest products, pulp and paper, hides and leather, plastics, chemicals, cement, glass, ceramics and rubber.

Turkey is also relatively rich in mineral resources. Coal, copper, iron ore and chromium are mined in good quantities. Lead, zinc, alum, antimony, boracite, asbestos, manganese, mercury, molybdenum and tungsten are also mined.

The tourist industry is also well developed. Turkey has natural tourist attractions in the coastal areas of the Black Sea, the Sea of Marmara and the Aegean Sea. An estimated 2.5 million tourists visit Turkey every year.

Since 1978, Turkey's economy has been on the verge of collapse, with inflation running at over 70 per cent and unemployment approaching 25 per cent. The country also faces a massive debt repayment problem. Internal debts have also been increasing rapidly. Government-run industries – half of Turkey's industrial base – lost US$2 million in 1979, a burden which had to be met by the deficit-ridden treasury.

In January 1980, the Turkish government initiated a new economic stabilization programme to give the Turkish economy a major reorientation. The programme is based on obtaining international assistance to pursue a tight monetary policy, establishing a relatively high rate of exchange, eliminating the black market on oil products, devaluing the Turkish lira, introducing an export levy on agricultural products, reducing the prices of basic foodstuffs and boosting the industrial and services sector. The underlying philosophy of the initiative is described and explained in a document entitled 'Economic Stabilization Programme of Turkey' prepared by the State Planning Organization in the following words:

1. The existing chronic inflation taking the Turkish economy in its grips is clearly associated with and largely caused by the monetary expansion. The main aim of the operation is, first of all, to put out the inflationary flame by attacking it at the source. The role of the public sector deficits in generating and maintaining inflationary pressures cannot be stressed enough. Subsidies on domestic prices of petroleum products and on the products and services of State Economic Enterprises should be eliminated.

2. Introducing the new principle that the State Economic Enterprises prices should be determined by their management, guided by the market mechanism, ensures that after the initial correction [which] places them on the right track, the deviations from it will not be allowed to build up in the future. . . .

3. All price-controlling activities regarding the private sector should also be lifted. This will eliminate the black market and under-the-counter dealings in every corner of the economic scene; unregistered profits and resources will be channelled to efficient users at the sources of production, also making them taxable. . . .

4. For the whole system, the fulcrum of the operation is the correctly set rate of exchange and effective exchange rate policy to eliminate the general severe rationing of foreign currency. Exports and all foreign-currency earning activities (workers' remittances, private foreign invest-

ment, tourism, transfer of accumulated savings abroad) will be encouraged by an initial above-equilibrium rate of exchange policy.

5. In the markets for basic goods, domestic equilibrium prices will be established in line with and approaching the world prices.

6. Optimal trade oriented policy will remove bias against exports. The guiding theme will be to introduce promotionary measures in addition to the general liberalization policy, in order to reduce friction, to increase efficiency and to achieve speedy results.

7. The banking system will be fully utilized in this operation.

8. Medium-term results are expected from: private foreign capital and petroleum exploration and domestic oil production operations, with the help of newly introduced clear guidelines.

9. For this operation to succeed, it is imperative that a unified and coherent set of decisions are taken and the implementation of these decisions should be followed up systematically and consistently. All the related government bureaucracy should have the same enthusiasm for the success of the measures taken and should be fully in tune so that there are no inefficiencies and unnecessary red tape in implementation.

   To this end, under centralized guidance by the prime minister, a Coordinating Committee, a Money and Credit Committee, an Investment and Export Promotion and Implementation Department and a Foreign Investment Promotion Department have been set up.

10. The Money and Credit Committee will continually establish dynamic guidelines, review performance closely, keeping a firm hand on the workings of the operation, monitoring and correcting deviations from planned financial objectives where necessary.

11. Finally, the key to success lies in gaining the lost confidence of local entrepreneurs and international circles; only then can the latent potential of the Turkish economy be fully activated to pull through this period of economic crisis onto the mid-term path of viable growth and stability.

Science Policy and Planning

The State Planning Organization of the prime minister's office is the main body responsible for planning in Turkey. Science planning is carried out in conjunction with the Ministry of Finance, the Ministry of Industry and Technology, the Ministry of Agriculture and the Ministry of Health and Social Security, with the State Planning Organization coordinating the planning process. The Science Policy Unit of the Scientific and Technical Research Council of Turkey (TUBITAK) also prepares policy guidelines for various ministries.

Turkish science policy emphasizes technology much more than science. There is great emphasis on the transfer of technology, and 'technological progress' and 'socio-economic objectives of national economy' are seen purely in terms of transferring and securing Western technology. The main features of the science policy formulated by the State Planning Organization under its new 'Economic Stabilization Programme' are:

1. Strengthening the ability of the national economy for creating, absorbing and adopting contemporary technologies and securing compatability between technological progress and socio-economic objectives.
2. Securing the latest technologies in selected fields.
3. Taking measures to enable industry to create and develop new technologies of its own so that it acquires a competitive strength and establishing new research and development units working with close links with industry and acting as catalysts in increasing industrial production.
4. Encouraging scientific and technological research, surveys, engineering and other industrial studies and improving cooperation among public institutions, scientific and educational bodies and private research establishments.
5. Increasing technological cooperation with other developing countries.
6. Developing labour intensive technologies where it is economically feasible.

Science Organization

The main scientific and research institution in the country is TUBITAK. Created in 1963, TUBITAK is an autonomous body responsible for developing, promoting, organizing and coordinating basic and applied research. The council is attached to the office of the Prime Minister.

The functions of TUBITAK, as set out in Article 2 of the Establishment Law, are:

1. To carry out, promote and encourage basic and applied research in positive sciences and to set up institutes to work in this field.
2. To assist the government in formulating the national policy to be pursued in the field of fundamental and applied research in positive sciences.
3. To formulate basic principles and procedures for education and research in the fields of positive sciences and to give advice to the institutions concerned.
4. To make recommendations at the request of public institutions, provincial governments, municipalities, and other organizations and individuals in the field of scientific and technical research.
5. To provide means of training and advancement for scientists and researchers in the fields of basic and applied sciences. To follow up young people who have demonstrated a high degree of talent and success during the course of their education, postgraduate work and career, and to help them in their training and development; for this purpose to provide scholarships within the country and abroad, to organize competitions, and to produce publications.

6.   To supply the government with necessary information for the prepara-
     tion and negotiation of international agreements on subjects related to
     the field of activity of the council.
7.   To establish contact and to cooperate with domestic and foreign
     research institutions and researchers and to follow their activities
     closely.
8.   To organize and to help in the organization of courses, conferences,
     and seminars in order to propagate the concept of research.
9.   To publish or sponsor the publication of material related to the fields
     of activity of the council, and to establish a documentation centre.

The organizational structure of TUBITAK is: the Science Board, the
Advisory Board, the General Secretariat, the Research Groups, the Research
Units and the Marmara Scientific and Industrial Research Institute and
the Building Research Institute. The complete organizational structure of
TUBITAK is shown in Figure 3.10.

The Science Board. The Science Board consists of eleven members and
the secretary-general. Five members are elected from among scientists who
are distinguished for their oustanding research activities, publications or
discoveries in basic sciences; four members are similarly qualified in applied sciences. Of the remaining two members, one is elected from the
State Economic Enterprises, and the other from private industry. Duration of membership of the Science Board is four years; members may be
re-elected for one additional consecutive period.

The functions of the Science Board, which is the supreme decision-
making organ of the council, are stated in the Establishment Law:

1.   To determine the principles and prepare the programmes for the activi-
     ties of the council.
2.   To set up research groups, institutes and other institutions.
3.   To elect members of the executive committee of research groups.
4.   To elect and appoint the secretary-general from among well-known
     scientists of the country within or outside the council by the absolute
     majority of its total members.
5.   To supervise the activities of the council and of its organs, to prepare
     regulations for these activities and to approve the council's budget
     proposals.

The Advisory Board. The Advisory Board consists of members elected
by the Science Board from the universities, ministries, public institutions,
and professional associations. The Science Board may establish new mem-
berships as the need arises. Duration of membership of the Advisory Board
is two years.

The functions of the Advisory Board are: to give advice on basic policy
concerning the work of the council; and to make recommendations on the
annual activity report, annual budget, and work programmes of the
council.

The Secretariat-General. The Secretariat-General is the executive organ of
the council and is composed of a secretary-general and the necessary
personnel.

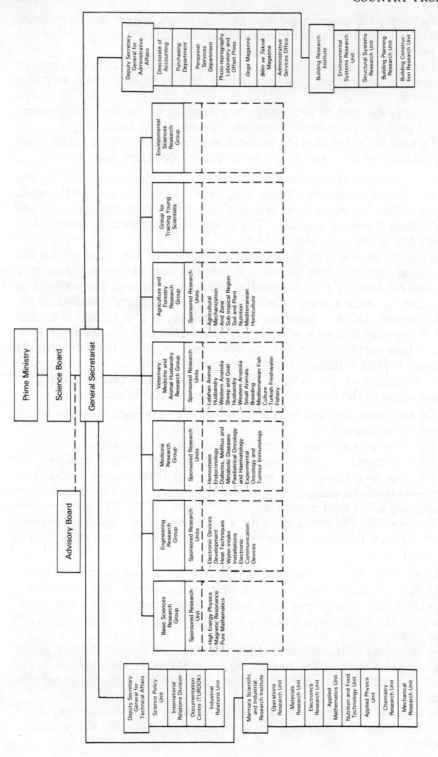

Fig. 3.10 Organizational structure of the Scientific and Technical Research Council of Turkey

The secretary-general is nominated by the Science Board from among well-known scientists of the country and is appointed by decree of the prime minister and the president of the republic. There are two main departments of the Secretariat-General: Deputy General Secretariat for Administrative Affairs, and Deputy General Secretariat for Technical Affairs.

The units within the framework of the General Secretariat for Administrative Affairs are the Directorate of Accounting, the Directorate of Administrative Affairs, the Services Department, the Purchasing Department, and the unit responsible for the publication of the *Journal of Science and Technology*. The units within the framework of the Deputy General Secretariat for Technical Affairs are the Science Policy Unit, the International Relations Division, the Turkish Scientific and Technical Documentation Centre, the Industrial Liaison Unit, and the Environmental Pollution Research Unit. The units of the latter department are more fully described below.

The secretary-general is responsible for carrying out all the administrative work of the council, which includes taking necessary measures for the implementation of decisions made by the Science Board and executive committees; preparing the drafts of regulations required for the activities of the council; preparing the budget and reports to the Science Board on the implementation of programmes; and organizing liaison between the Science Board and other organs of the council.

Research groups. Research groups are the units directed to develop, promote and coordinate research studies in their fields of activity. Each research group consists of an executive committee with five members, the secretary of the committee, and various institutes and institutions.

The Basic Sciences Research Group was established in 1964 and its fields of activity are basic sciences such as mathematics, physics, chemistry, and biology. The group sponsors the Mathematics Research Unit.

The Engineering Research Group was established in 1964 to deal with basic and applied engineering sciences. Affiliated units of the group are: Polymer Chemistry Unit (established 1969), Electronic Devices Development Unit (1970), Heat Techniques Research Unit (1971), Water-intake Installations Unit (1972), and the Unit for Electronic Communication Devices (established in 1974).

The Medical Research Group was established in 1964, and its fields of activity are basic and applied medicine, pharmacy, and dentistry. The units affiliated to the group are the Haemostasis Unit (established in 1971), the Endocrinology Unit (1973), and the Unit for Diabetes Mellitus and Metabolic Diseases (1974).

The Veterinary Medicine and Animal Husbandry Research Group was established in 1965 and its fields of activity are basic and applied veterinary medicine and animal husbandry. Affiliated units of the group are the Lalahan Animal Husbandry Research Unit (established in 1972), the Milking Sheep Research Unit of Western Anatolia (1972), and the Turkish Freshwater Research Unit (1974).

The Agriculture and Forestry Research Group was established in 1964 and is concerned with basic and applied sciences in its field. Affiliated units of the group are the Agricultural Mechanization Unit (established in 1971), and the Arid Zone Research Unit (1972).

The Group for Training Young Scientists was also established in 1964 and it cooperates with other research groups and makes studies of training and of the development and selection for training of research scientists needed in the country.

The functions of the research groups are to determine the fields of research, development and training which they consider necessary and to prepare research projects on these subjects, or to arrange for their preparation. The groups either examine such proposals or refer them to outside experts for approval or rejection.

The research groups organize and promote symposia, seminars, congresses, conferences, and competitions related to research in their fields of activity and also participate in these meetings held in Turkey and abroad. Courses on education are organized by the Group for Training of Young Scientists.

The groups make proposals to the Science Board for the establishment of research institutes, stations, and laboratories in their fields of activity, and prepare the work programmes for such establishments. The groups also make recommendations to the Science Board on measures to be taken with regard to research activities for national development in scientific, technological, and economic fields.

The Group for Training of Young Scientists determines and proposes to the Science Board the basic principles and methods for education and research studies in positive sciences. It is also the function of this group to follow up and select young people of ability and to provide them with scholarships, and also to cooperate with other organizations which provide scholarship funds in order to train young scientists.

Research sponsoring activities:

1. *Sponsored research projects.* The purpose of the programme is to sponsor researchers in the universities and other higher education sectors, in public institutions and in the industrial sector, who are in need of resources; to help in the development of research activities; and to solve the scientific and technical problems of the country.

   Project proposals are submitted by the researchers to the secretariat of the group executive committees. The proposals are examined by the executive committee of the related research group, who consider the following priorities in selecting projects which are compatible with scientific standards, methods, and materials.

   (a) Projects which will contribute to science and technology;
   (b) Projects which will help to achieve the targets set in the current development plan;
   (c) Projects which lead to the training of research workers;
   (d) Projects which lead to coordination between various research institutions and scientists;

Table 3.3

Some research projects of TUBITAK's main research groups for 1979–80

Basic Science Research Group

1. Investigations on the species of *Grylidae* (orthoptera) and their habitats and taxonomic distinctions in Central Anatolia

2. The petrology and geology investigation of Gavur Dagi (Yozgat)

3. An investigation on the hormonal control of Senescence in flower petals

4. The Lambda calculus and its feature in the function evaluation and programming languages

5. A qualitative and quantitative study of algae of Marmara and Aegean Sea

6. Qualitative and quantitative studies of the seasonal changes in the vertical and horizontal distribution of the phytoplankton in the Kurtbogazi water reservoir

7. Radioisotope X-ray fluorescence analysis

8. Geomorphology of the Eldivan Dagi and Terma ayn basin

9. The genetic and petrographic study of perlite occurrences in Western Anatolia

10. A study of plant ecology and sociology based on the vegetation of Tiryal Mountain

Engineering Research Group

1. Systematic study on rotor-cascades in radial turbomachinery

2. Improvement of forms of fishing boats suitable for Turkish waters

3. Mathematical simulation of a Rotary kiln

4. Evaluation of Turkey's seismicity from a probabilistic point of view

5. An investigation into water pollution in Cark-suyu channel

6. Investigation of the effects of water and reagents in the control of dust produced during rock drilling

7. A preliminary study for determination of the capabilities of the Ankara wind tunnel

8. A study of the behaviour of boran-epoxy composites

9. The growth kinetics of vanadium nitride precipitates

10. Periodical fluorine determination in drinking water sources of Istanbul

Medical Research Group

1. The screening of congenital amino acid metabolism disorders in newborn infants

2. A study of the twenty-four hour excretion pattern of oestrogen fractions in the urine of Turkish girls of nine to twelve years of age and the relation of oestrogen levels to clinical signs of puberty

3. Experimental investigation on the glandular suprarenalis and adrenal system diseases

4. The evaluation of the efficiency of various physical training methods by the oxygen transport system parameters

5. Relation between zinc deficiency and serum somatomedin levels during pregnancy

6. Human alpha-fetoprotein purification and clinical implications

7. The screening for diabetes mellitus in western and south-eastern Turkey

8. A sensitive and specific method for measurements of immuno-complex in leukaemia-induced mice by using radioactive ^{51}Cr

Table 3.3 – *cont.*

9. Frequency-response characteristics of the normal and the epileptic cortical neutron and their correlation with electro-corticographic activity

10. Quality control and safety studies on the commercial shampoos, soaps, conditioners, hair-setting gels and hair tonics and the necessity of cosmetic regulations in Turkey

Agricultural and Forestry Research Group
1. Preliminary studies on some aspects of Turkish Delight technology

2. Investigation into the rice-seeding method suitable to Aegean region

3. An investigation into the insect pests of west Black Sea coast and central regions of Turkey

4. Nutritional and economical utilization of whey in Turkey

5. The spacing effect on the early growth in Eucalyptus plantations

6. Timing studies with tomatoes and cucumbers grown in heated glasshouses

7. Studies on the selection of walnut in the eastern Anatolia and eastern Black Sea

8. The biology of mugwort and investigations on its control in hazelnut and tea plantations

9. Investigation on cadmium, nickle, copper, zinc, manganese, iron, chromium and mercury in Turkish tobacco

10. Mechanization and determination of the best cultivars of ground peanut in Aegean region

Veterinary Sciences and Animal Husbandry Research Group
1. The relation of different production characteristics and genotype of Ankara goats bred in various regions in Turkey

2. A study of ageing in Ankara goats by examination of eruption and wear of teeth

3. Toxoplasmosis in cats in Aegean region

4. Changes in lipids during frozen storage of fish

5. Urea as a protein supplement in the food rations of lactating cows

6. Studies in the preparation of starter cultures for Turkish butter

7. Domestication and inbreeding of the Anatolian hamster

8. Limnological survey of Lake Golbasi

9. A study of defence mechanism of the uterus against infection during the different phases in the oestral cycle of sheep

10. Genetic parameters of selected meat quality traits and the relationship with carcass composition and feed-lot in Friesian cattle

(e) Projects which are based on the outcome of the projects sponsored by TUBITAK and which may lead to new discoveries;
(f) Projects which are not carried out by other institutions.

The executive committees of the research groups approve these projects, in line with the accepted criteria, which are within the allocation limits set by the Science Board. The research groups inform the

Science Board of any reasons for approval or rejection of proposed projects, so that the Science Board may supervise and comment on the activities of the groups. After it has been decided to sponsor a particular project, an agreement is made between the secretary-general and the project director, and the project is then carried out according to the principles of the agreement. A final report covering the scientific and technical aspects of the project is submitted to TUBITAK within two months of the conclusion of the project.

2. *Oriented research projects.* These are determined by the related research groups – if necessary in collaboration with other groups – by considering the targets of the development plan and taking into account the value of the research from technical, economic, and social points of view.

Oriented research projects are prepared by the project director or by a group of research workers selected by the executive committee of the relative research group. In assembling a research team great care is taken to assure the participation and collaboration of those organizations which are most likely to apply the results of the project, and so ensure that oriented research results are purposeful and applicable.

3. *Sponsored research units.* TUBITAK sponsors and supports research units in the universities, in government ministries, and in the industrial sector in order to increase the research potential and efficiency of these units and to develop specific disciplines of science. A unit can obtain the support of TUBITAK only if it has the necessary research potential and can offer opportunities for the training of research workers.

Units attached to the secretariat-general:

1. The Science Policy Unit (established in 1965) makes various surveys of the institutions, research workers, and resources allocated for research activities in fundamental and applied sciences, in order to determine the research potential of Turkey. The unit also carries out research, collects data, and prepares documents on science policy, as required by the decision-making organs of the council.

2. The International Relations Division (established in 1968), acts as liaison between the council and international and national organizations and scientists, both in Turkey and abroad, and cooperates with them and follows up their activities. Because of the importance of international cooperation in scientific research activities, the council also acts as an adviser to the Ministry of Foreign Affairs.

3. Turkish Scientific and Technical Documentation Centre (TURDOC) was established in 1966 to provide documentation services for supporting and contributing to the activities of the council. It soon became evident that nationwide documentation services were urgently needed, so TURDOC soon expanded to act as the National Documentation and Information Centre. The main objectives of TURDOC are to facilitate the use of scientific and technical information produced within and outside Turkey in the fields of pure and applied sciences, in-

cluding industrial management; and to promote, encourage, and co-ordinate documentation and information activities in the country. In order to achieve these objectives, TURDOC:

(a) Provides and maintains services to meet the information and/or documentation requirements of government organizations, scientists, research workers, and industrial establishments of the public and private sectors;

(b) Conducts research on the methods of transfer of scientific and technical information in response to the specific needs of different user categories;

(c) Acts as a referral centre when necessary;

(d) Publicizes the importance of documentation and information activities;

(e) Contributes to the training of manpower in information sciences;

(f) Carries out research programmes for promoting and improving information services and information handling techniques;

(g) Assists and advises on the establishment of new information units;

(h) Participates in overall provision of library and information services in the country.

TURDOC's activities are carried out in six units: the Information Unit carries out searches, compiles bibliographies, prepares evaluated reports and technical publications, and provides a technical consultancy service; the Follow-Up Unit carries out user studies and evaluates the information services provided; the Training-Publicity Research Unit organizes courses, provides on-the-job training, provides advisory services on the establishment of new information units, conducts research in information sciences, and publicizes the services and activities of TURDOC in particular and information services in general; the Library and Photocopy Unit is in charge of selection, acquisition and organization of library materials, photocopying services, and translation services; the Publication Unit issues the following publications: *Current Titles in Turkish Science* (in Turkish and English), and *National and International Meetings on Science and Technology* (monthly); it also assists in publishing subject bibliographies, technical publications, papers on various aspects of information activities and handling techniques, brochures, accession lists, and catalogues of scientific and technical periodicals. TURDOC's objectives and services are supported and promoted by the State Planning Organization, which has authorized TURDOC to act as the national coordination body in this field.

4. The Industrial Liaison Unit was established in 1969 in order to study the problems of organizations which apply the results of research in positive sciences in the areas of technology. The unit disseminates the findings of research projects carried out both within TUBITAK and outside, by putting them in a form which can be made available to applying organizations.

5. The Environmental Pollution Research Unit. The first studies on air

pollution in Ankara had already commenced when the council joined the International Air Pollution Project (NATO–CCMS) by the decision of the Turkish government. Studies on the air pollution problem in Ankara continued after the termination of this project, and in 1973 the Environmental Pollution Research Unit was established and carried out these studies. At present the fields of activity of the unit are expanding to cover all pollution problems.

Marmara Scientific and Industrial Research Institute

The Scientific and Industrial Research Institute was established in 1966 with a mandate to identify and solve problems of Turkish industry within the framework of the country's development goals. The basic objectives of the institute are:

1. To create competence in particular disciplines in Turkey.
2. To undertake research in the development of new materials, products, processes, methods, technological systems and managerial skills.
3. To adopt and accelerate the transfer of technology to the country.
4. To provide research and development services to industry.

The institute is organized in research units in specific scientific and industrial areas. The research units of the institute are:

1. The Operations Research Unit.
2. The Materials Research Unit.
3. The Electronics Research Unit.
4. The Applied Mathematics Unit.
5. The Chemistry Research Unit.
6. The Applied Physics Unit.
7. The Mechanical Research Unit.

Building Research Institute

The Building Research Institute was established in 1969 to determine the research requirements of the building industry, to solve scientific and technical problems within the industry and ensure that research results are utilized within the framework of the national development plan. The institute provides consultancy services to the building industry and promotes new building technologies in Turkey. It has four research units:

1. The Environmental Systems Research Unit.
2. The Structural Systems Research Unit.
3. The Building Planning Research Unit.
4. The Buildings Construction Research Unit.

Academic Science and Research

Turkey has seventeen universities, but research is carried out largely at

Ankara University, the Technical University of Istanbul, and the Middle East Technical University in Ankara. Five universities – 19 May University in Samsun, Selcuk University in Konya, Inonu University in Malatya, Firat University in Elazig and Bursa University in Bursa – were founded in 1975 and are essentially teaching institutions. Kayseri University was founded in 1978 and has yet to develop into a fully-fledged institution.

Ankara University was established in 1946 and is one of the biggest universities in Turkey. In science and technology, it has faculties for agriculture, veterinary science, medicine, pharmacy and science.

The Faculty of Agriculture in Ankara has departments for research and teaching in agricultural crafts, agricultural economics and management, agricultural implements and machinery, agricultural microbiology, agricultural policy, animal food plants, agricultural power machinery, animal technology, culture technology, fermentation technology, fruit-growing and improvement, genetics and statistics, home economics, industrial plants, landscape architecture and reafforestation, milk and milk products, nutrients and animal nutrition, plant breeding and improvement, plant nutrition, plant protection, radiophysiology and soil productivity, slaughterhouse products, soil sciences, and vine and vegetable growing. A second Faculty of Agriculture at Adana, has departments for agricultural economics, agricultural machinery, animal husbandry sciences, crop agriculture, culture technology, food science and technology, landscape architecture, plant protection, soil sciences, and vegetable cultivation.

The Faculty of Veterinary Medicine in Ankara has departments for anatomy, animal food and nutrition, animal husbandry and managerial economics, animal technology, bacteriology and epidemiology, biochemistry, histology, the history of veterinary medicine, general and experimental pathology, internal diseases, nutrition control and hygiene, obstetrics and gynaecology, parasitology and helminthology, pathological anatomy, pharmacology and toxicology, physiology, protozoology, statistics and planning of veterinary services, surgery, virology, and water products and fisheries. There is an attached Graduate School on Animal Breeding and Health Sciences, an Institute for Research on Animal Health, and an electron microscopy laboratory. A second Faculty of Veterinary Medicine at Elazig has departments for anatomy, histology and embryology, economics of animal husbandry, animal nutrition and nutrients, animal technology, biochemistry, breeding and artificial insemination, food control and nutrients, internal medicine, microbiology and preventive medicine, obstetrics and gynaecology, parasitology and protozoology, pathological anatomy and experimental pathology, pharmacology and toxicology, physiology, surgery, and water products, fisheries and game.

The Faculty of Medicine in Ankara has clinics and research laboratories for anaesthesiology, anatomy, histology and embryology, biochemistry, botany, chest diseases, chest surgery, dermatology and venereal diseases, gastro-enterology, genetics, history of medicine, hygiene and protective medicine, infectious diseases, internal medicine, medical jurisprudence and social medicine, microbiology and parasitology, neurology, neurosurgery, obstetrics and gynaecology, ophthalmology, orthopaedics and traumatology, otorhinolaryngology, paediatrics, pathological anatomy, pharmacology, physical therapy and hydrology, physics, physiology, physiopathology, psychiatry, radiology, surgery, urology, and zoology. A second Faculty of Medicine at Diyarbakir has departments for biochemistry and chemistry, biology, internal medicine, medical physics and radionuclear medicine, morphology, obstetrics and gynaecology, pathology, physiology and pharmacology, psychiatry and geriatrics, medical jurisprudence, public health and preventive medicine, and surgery; there is also a newly organized department for pure sciences. The Faculties of Medicine have an attached School of Dentistry and a College of Nursing and Health Services.

The Faculty of Pharmacy has departments for analytical chemistry, biochemistry, Galenic Pharmacy, hygiene, medicinal sciences, microbiology and food analysis, pharmaceutical botany, pharmaceutical chemistry, pharmacology, pharmacognosy, and toxicology.

The Faculty of Science has departments for botany, analytical chemistry, applied chemistry, general chemistry, industrial chemistry, physical chemistry, geology, algebra and geometry, astronomy, mathematics, physics, general zoology, and systematic zoology.

The Technical University of Istanbul was established in its present form in 1944 having had its origins in an institution of the eighteenth century. It is one of the oldest technological universities in the world. It has faculties for civil engineering, architecture, mechanical engineering, electrical engineering, mining engineering, chemical engineering, naval architecture and ocean engineering, metallurgy and management engineering.

The Faculty of Civil Engineering carries out teaching and research in: descriptive geometry and technical drawing, higher mathematics, surveying and geodesy, technical mechanics and strength of materials, statics of structures, hydraulics and water power, soil mechanics and foundation engineering, construction materials, reinforced concrete and advanced strength of materials, construction elements and machines, construction administration, steel and timber structures, highways and traffic engineering, railroads and earthworks, hydraulic structures, urban sanitation, and economics and administrative law.

The Faculty of Architecture studies architectural design and architectural construction. Special emphasis is laid on town and country planning. Other departments within the faculty deal with advanced mathematics, statics and reinforced concrete and the history of architecture.

The Faculty of Mechanical Engineering has teaching and research departments for advanced mathematics, mechanics and fluid mechanics, technology, machine elements and design, thermodynamics and thermal turbomachinery, internal combustion engines, hydraulic machines, machine tools and industrial engineering, heat techniques (heat engineering), nuclear energy and heat transfer, aircraft elements and engines, aircraft design, naval architecture, textile machines, and agricultural machines.

The Faculty of Electrical Engineering has departments for electrical engineering and electrical metrology, electrical machines and power plants, power transmission, applications of electricity in industry, telecommunications, and high-frequency techniques.

The Faculty of Mining Engineering has departments for physics, geology, mineral deposits and mineralogy, the exploitation of mineral deposits, mining machinery, geophysics, petroleum prospecting and exploitation, ore-dressing, and general and physical metallurgy.

The Faculty of Chemical Engineering has departments for inorganic chemistry, physical chemistry, analytical chemistry, chemical engineering, industrial chemistry, and physics.

Attached to the university are the Institute of Computer Science, Institute of Nuclear Energy and the newly established Institute of History of Science and Technology.

The Institute of History of Science and Technology was established in 1979 to conduct research on the history of Turkish–Islamic science and technology. The institute is working on an inventory of the vast collections of Turkish museums, libraries and archives on Turkish and Islamic science and technology and establishing a science museum in Istanbul. The institute specializes in the history of water supply systems, bridges, roads, aqueducts and building technology. Current projects at the institute are on Ottoman water-pumping equipment, water supplies and fountains of Istanbul, Urartuian water engineering, automatic control in machines of Banu Musa and al-Jizari, and evaluation of engineering manuscripts of Ottoman origins.

The Middle East Technical University was established in 1956 as an independent institution of higher education and research. Although the university conducts some basic research, the emphasis is on applied research within the framework of the national development plan. The Ankara campus of the university consists of four faculties: administrative sciences, architecture, arts and sciences and engineering. The Ankara campus also has an independent Department of Computer Science and a Department of Marine Sciences. The Gaziantep campus consists of a Faculty of Engineering and a School of Languages.

The Faculty of Architecture has departments for architecture, city and regional planning (with a special section devoted to regional planning), and for the restoration and preservation of historic monuments.

The Faculty of Arts and Sciences includes scientific departments for chemistry, mathematics, physics, and theoretical chemistry.

The Faculty of Engineering has main departments for chemical engineering, civil engineering, computer sciences, electrical engineering, engineering sciences, geological engineering, industrial engineering, mining engineering, metallurgical engineering, and mechanical engineering. The last-named department has laboratories for heat engineering; heating, air-conditioning and refrigeration; heat, power and solar energy; fluid mechanics and fluid machinery, production and metrology, internal combustion engines and gas turbines, agricultural machinery, automotion, dynamics and automatic control, mechanics and strength of materials, and nuclear engineering. The civil engineering department has the largest hydraulics laboratory in the region, and thus undertakes research in conjunction with government agencies on the development of water resources. Harbour and coastal engineering is an important area of research, particularly with respect to the effects of wave conditions in the Mediterranean, Marmara and Black Seas on harbour design and water-cooling intake for power plants. The civil engineering department also undertakes research into building, in particular, studies of the clay of the Anatolian Plateau as a substrate for buildings and road construction. The electrical engineering department has close contacts with Etibank, Turkey's power generation and distribution concern, which is one of the State Economic Enterprises.

Istanbul University was originally founded as long ago as the fifteenth century; it was reorganized in 1927 and 1933 and again in 1948. Its scientific faculties include those for science, forestry, medicine, pharmacy, dentistry, chemistry, and business administration. There is a second faculty of medicine at Cerrahpasa. The Faculty of Science has an attached Hydrobiological Research Institute which has two main sections for marine and for freshwater research. The faculty publishes two periodicals: *Review of the Faculty of Science of the University of Istanbul*, a quarterly journal in English, French and German and which appears in three sections – mathematics, biology–geology, and physics–chemistry; and *Hydrogeology*, which appears in two series, one in Turkish, and the other in English, French and German.

Hacettepe University, on the outskirts of Ankara, was established in 1967. Its Faculty of Sciences includes main departments for earth sciences, biological sciences, physics, statistics and mathematics.

The Eskisehir Faculty of Medicine, the most developed of the faculties, has clinics and laboratories for anaesthesiology, anatomy, cardiology, cardiovascular surgery, community medicine, dermatology, haematology, histology, internal medicine, microbiology, medical technology, neurology, neurosurgery, obstetrics and gynaecology, ophthalmology, orthopaedics, otorhinolaryngology, paediatric pathology, paediatric radiology, paediatric surgery, paediatrics, pathology, physical medicine and rehabilitation, physiology, psychiatry, psychology, radiobiology, radiology, surgical research, surgery, thoracic surgery, and urology. There is an attached *Cocuk Sagligi Enstitüsü* (Institute of Child Health), where research is carried out in clinical paediatrics including paediatric subspecialities: cardiology, haematology, endocrinology, metabolism, nephrology, allergy, neurology, psychiatry, adolescence, paediatric surgery, social paediatrics; and basic and applied research in all paediatric subjects.

Other scientific faculties in Hacettepe University include those for engineering, chemistry, dentistry, pharmacy, health sciences, and the Gevher Nesibe Faculty of Medicine.

The Aegean University, at Izmir, was founded in 1955. It is a technological university with faculties for agriculture, medicine, food science, textile science, earth science, chemistry and civil engineering.

The Faculty of Agriculture has departments for agricultural economics and management sciences, agro-ecology and general plant breeding, agronomy and genetics, dairy technology, entomology and agricultural zoology, farm machinery and tools, feeds and animal nutrition, fibre technology, food and fermentation technology, fruit and vine cultivation and improvement, land irrigation and rural construction, landscape architecture, phytopathology and agricultural botany, soil sciences, vegetable cultivation and improvement, and zoo technology.

The Faculty of Medicine has clinics and laboratories for public health and preventive medicine, morphology, internal medicine, paediatrics, surgery, ophthalmology, neurology, obstetrics and gynaecology, physical therapy, microbiology and infectious diseases, physiology, radiology, dermatology, urology, chest diseases, gastro-enterology, parasitology, orthopaedic surgery and traumatology, pathology, pharmacology, otorhinolaryngology, psychiatry, and paediatric surgery.

The Faculty of Science was founded in 1961 and has departments for astronomy, general and analytical chemistry, general botany, general physics, general zoology, general and applied mathematics, organic chemistry, physical chemistry, systematic botany, systematic zoology, and theoretical mathematics. Two external foundations are under the control of the Faculty of Science – the Marine Biology Investigation and Practice Laboratory, and an Observatory Station on the Nif Mountain. In addition, the faculty also administers the Aegean University Botanical Garden, the Herbarium Centre, and the Nuclear Research and Education Institute.

Attached to the university are a Genetic Institute and Medical and Agricultural Drugs Research Institute.

The Ataturk University, in Erzurum, was founded in 1957. Its Faculty of Basic Sciences is divided into three main departments for biological sciences, physics and mathematical sciences, and chemistry. The Faculty of Agriculture has departments for animal sciences, soil sciences, plant sciences, agricultural economics and cultural techniques. The Faculty of Medicine has main departments for basic sciences, clinical pathology, community medicine, internal medicine and surgery. There is also a Faculty of Dentistry. There is an Institute of Fur Animals and Handicrafts attached to the Faculty of Agriculture.

The Bosphorus University was formerly Robert College (the American College of Istanbul). The change of status took place in 1971. The university has schools for administrative sciences, engineering, and arts and sciences. The Bosphorus University Research Centre carries out studies in engineering, science and economics. In the engineering section research is undertaken in earthquake engineering, measurement of air pollution, classification of air-odour standards; water filtration studies; feasibility studies for new industries to be developed in Turkey; and fuel cells. Scientific research includes studies in nuclear quadrupole resonance, polarography of norbornyl compounds; behaviour of a nuclear reactor under rapid transient condition; and quality test methods for rose oil.

Agricultural Science and Research

Besides TUBITAK's Agriculture and Forestry Research Group and Veterinary Medicine and Animal Husbandry Research Group, extensive agricultural research is done by the Ministry of Agriculture. The ministry is organized into a number of directorates, including general agricultural affairs, veterinary affairs, forestry, agricultural supply, plant protection and plant quarantine, the milk industry, cotton, soil conservation and farm irrigation and the Government Meteorological Office. The animal feed industry and the wool and mohair industry are State Economic Enterprises under the Ministry of Agriculture.

The Cotton Directorate undertakes general administration and coordination of cotton breeding and research work in its two regional cotton research institutes. The Regional Cotton Research Institute at Adana is concerned with cotton-breeding fibre technology, and spinning tests; the institute at Nazilli carries out cotton-breeding research and studies the technology of cotton production.

The Directorate of Plant Protection and Plant Quarantine carries out general research work in entomology and phytopathology, which includes nematology, fruit and vine pests, weed control, and biological control.

There are also a large number of institutes, experimental stations and stud farms under the aegis of the Ministry of Agriculture. The location and interests of each is given below:

1. Altindere State Stud Farm, Erics-Van – animal breeding and husbandry (pure-bred and half-bred Arab, eastern red cattle, brown Swiss cattle, native Akkaraman sheep and merinos).
2. Cifteler State Stud Farm, Mahmudiye-Eskisehir – animal breeding and husbandry (pure-bred and half-bred Arab, half-bred native grey cattle, Karakul Angora goat).
3. Karacabey State Stud Farm, Bursa-Karacabey – animal breeding and husbandry (Swiss brown cattle, pure-bred and half-bred Arab, pure-bred and half-bred merino sheep).
4. Karakoy State Stud Farm, Bafra – animal breeding and husbandry (pure-bred and half-bred Arab, native black cattle, Jersey cattle, Karakaya sheep).
5. Konya State Stud Farm, Konya – animal breeding and husbandry (pure-bred Arab, native black cattle, Jersey cattle, Aberdeen Angus cattle, merino and Akkaraman sheep).
6. Sultansuyu State Stud Farm, Akcadag-Malatya – animal breeding and husbandry (pure-bred Arab, eastern red cattle, Swiss brown cattle, merino and Akkaraman sheep).
7. Lalahan Institute of Veterinary Research, Lalahan, Ankara – animal breeding, feeding, and management.
8. Agricultural Research Institute, Ankara – research on cereals and vegetables, cytogenetics, food technology.
9. Agricultural Research Institute, Antalya – cotton, sugarbeet, alfalfa, barley, peanuts, oats, rice, poultry, sericulture, animal husbandry.
10. Agricultural Research Institute, Diyarbakir – wheat, cotton, peanuts, hybrid maize, legumes, pulses, vegetables, forage crops.
11. Plant Research and Introduction Centre, Izmir – wheat, barley, hybrid

maize, tobacco, cotton, tomatoes, aubergine, pepper, water melon, melon, fruits, apiculture.

12. Agricultural Research Institute, Yesilköy – wheat, barley, oats, hybrid maize, rice, sunflowers, tobacco, soya beans, pasture and forage crops, vegetables, animal husbandry.

13. Seed Improvement and Experiment Station, Adapazari – wheat, maize, potatoes, fibres, crops, cow vetch.

14. Seed Improvement and Experiment Station, Eskisehir – wheat, barley, oats, hybrid maize, forage crops.

15. Seed Improvement and Experiment Station, Samsun – hybrid maize, wheat, soya beans, fibre crops.

16. Experimental Station, Edirne – wheat, barley, hybrid maize, sunflowers, rice, rotation trials on forage crops.

17. Experimental Station, Corum – soya beans, wheat, barley, oats, rye, forage crops.

18. Experimental Fields Substation, Ordu – improvement and production of wheat, maize, soya beans, beans.

19. Regional Experimental Station on Varieties, Ankara – field trials of crop varieties.

20. Soil and Fertilizer Research Institute, Ankara – fertilizer trials on cereals, cotton, potatoes, rice, sunflowers, tobacco, grapes, vegetables, forage crops; improvement trials; fertility testing; bacterial isolation.

21. Topraksu Research Institute, Eskisehir – meteorological and phenological investigations, adaptation of wheat and vegetables, fertility and fertilizer trials, reclamation of land by irrigation, trials on forage crops.

22. Irrigation Research Institute, Menemen – meteorological observations, irrigation, reclamation of soils, rotation trials on cotton and forage crops, yield of rice varieties, fertility and fertilizer trials.

23. Irrigation Research Institute, Tarsus – soil irrigation trials, reclamation of soils, rotation and adaptation trials.

24. Irrigation Experimental Station, Cumra – meteorological observations, irrigation, reclamation of salty soils, rotation trials on forage crops, fertilizer trials.

25. Agricultural Research Institute, Konya – fruit and crop production.

26. Forage and Pasture Crops and Animal Breeding Research Institute, Ankara – pasture and forage crops, animal breeding, viticulture.

27. Seed Production and Animal Breeding Experimental Stations – Adana, Afyon, Kayseri, and Kars – all engaged in regional experiments in seed production and animal breeding.

28. Pasture and Forage Crops Production and Animal Breeding Station, Mus – regional experiments in pasture and forage crops and animal breeding.

29. Viticulture Station, Tekirdag – viticulture, fruits and poultry.

30. Horticulture Station, Soguksu – viticulture, olives, fruits, and poultry.

31. Vines Nursery, Bilecik – viticulture, fruits, hops.

32. Viticulture and Poultry Station, Canakkale – viticulture, fruits, poultry.

33. Viticulture and Poultry Station, Kilis – viticulture, olives, poultry.

34. Vines Nursery, Erenköy – viticulture.

35. Viticulture Institute, Manisa – viticulture, fruits.
36. Viticulture Station, Nevsehir – viticulture.
37. Horticultural Research Institute, Antalya – citrus production and research.
38. Regional Horticultural Research Station, Icel – fruit trees.
39. Hazelnut Research Institute, Giresun – hazelnuts and poultry.
40. Tea Research Institute, Rize – tea, citrus fruits.
41. Horticulture Research Station, Malatya – fruit.
42. Horticulture Institute, Egridir – fruit.
43. Horticulture and Poultry Institute, Arifiye – poultry, fruit.
44. Horticulture and Poultry Institute, Aydin-Erbeyli – figs, poultry.
45. Horticulture Research Institute, Iskenderun – citrus fruits.
46. Horticulture and Poultry Institute, Kastamonu – fruit, poultry.
47. Horticulture and Poultry Institute, Tokat – fruit, poultry.
48. Nursery and Poultry Stations, Duzce and Nigde – fruit and poultry (other nursery stations for fruit production are at Alanya, Afsin, Artvin, Bartin, Elâzig, Odemis, Sultanhisar, Yahyali, Van, Afyon, Bingöl, Konya-Eregli, Konya-Karaasli, Siirt-Basur, Sinop-Ahmetyeri, Sivas-Susehri, Tunceli-Sihenk, Urfa-Siverek, Urfa-Bozova, and Sebin-harahisar-Giresun).
49. Horticulture Research and Training Centre, Yalova – vegetables and ornamental plants.
50. Vegetable Station, Antalya – vegetables, ornamental plants.
51. Seed Production Centre, Balikesir – seed production projects.
52. Preservation Research Institute, Bursa – fruit and vegetable technology.
53. Extension Station for Technological Research on Agricultural Products, Canakkale – fruit and vegetable juice preservation.
54. Sericulture Institute, Bursa – silkworms.
55. Poultry and Bees Institute, Ankara – poultry, bees, rabbits (other stations concerned with similar interests are at Kütahya, Bigadic, Sinop, Denizli; apiculture institutes are at Mugla, Ardahan and Bingöl).
56. Olive Institute, Bornova, and the Olive Station at Edremit, are both concerned with olive production.
57. Regional Viticulture and Horticulture Research Institute, Gaziantep – particularly concerned with growing pistachio nuts.

Medical Science and Research

Besides the Medical Research Group of TUBITAK, medical research is conducted at the Refik Saydam Central Institute of Hygiene which is under the Ministry of Health and Social Security. The institute is concerned with laboratory diagnosis of infectious diseases; control of pharmaceutical and biological preparations, foods and beverages; and with the production of vaccines and sera. The institute has nine major departments which carry out studies in bacteriology, virology, production of vaccines and sera, preparation of human blood derivatives, chemical analysis, toxicological and pharmacological analysis, and the control of pharmaceutical and biological substances.

Research in the Department of Bacteriology has included work on the effects of bile and bile salts on vibrio cholera, and surveillance of causative agents of enteric infections. The Laboratory of Parasitology has completed work on the treatment of larva migrans with thiabendazol and is carrying out comparative studies on the effects of different anthelmintics. The Virology and Virus Vaccines Department is particularly interested in laboratory studies on influenza. The Department of Drug Control carries out quantitative experiments with various pharmaceutical formulae containing steroids and volatile oils, using gas chromatography techniques; microbiological studies have been developed with biotin and inositol in pharmaceutical preparations; and a laboratory has been established to analyse and control the plastic containers used for pharmaceutical products. The Department of Pharmacology has carried out research which includes histamine tests on antibiotics; determination of biological activity of digitalis preparations; visible absorptiometric determination of antimony in industrial wastewaters; and colourimetric determination of arsenic in food materials and other different media. The Department of Chemistry carries out research which includes work on food additives; the determination of diethyl pyrocarbonate in wines; vitamins A and D in fats, oils, and baby foods; and thymol tubidity tests in hepatitis and other disturbances of the liver. The Reference and Research Laboratory of Tuberculosis coordinates drug-susceptibility testing by laboratories participating in cooperative studies on the chemotherapy of tuberculosis (in collaboration with the Turkish National Antituberculosis Association).

The production activities of the institute include bacterial vaccines to combat typhoid, cholera, tetanus, and diphtheria; viral vaccines to combat rabies, smallpox, and influenza; antigens and allergens; blood grouping sera; and antitoxins and other sera – among the latter special emphasis is placed on anti-anthrax serum, and on scorpion anti-venom. The analysis and control activities of the institute constitute a major part of the work: bacteriological examinations and analysis are made on various cultures, with particular emphasis on tuberculosis; chemical analysis and control is carried out in many fields, with special emphasis on foods and biochemical analysis; drug control activities cover the whole field of medical preparations, with special attention being given to antibiotics, narcotics, hypnotics, antipyretics, analgesics and expectorants; strict control is exercised over unauthorized preparations. The Refik Saydam Institute also specializes in breeding laboratory animals.

The services of the institute are available throughout Turkey at fees which are fixed by the Turkish government.

Industrial and Building Science and Technology

The work of the leading institutes in these fields, the Marmara Scientific and Industrial Research Institute and the Building Research Institute of

TUBITAK has already been described. In addition, industrial research is carried out at the State Economic Enterprises, the Standards Institute of Turkey and the Mineral Research and Exploration Institute of Turkey – all three are under the Ministry of Industry and Technology (see p. 261). Building research is carried out at the Building and Building Materials Research Department, the Highway Technical Research Board, the Electrical Resources Survey Division and the General Directorate of State Hydraulic Works, all being part of the Ministry of Public Works. The Ministry of Reconstruction and Resettlement has an Earthquake Research Institute in Ankara carrying out research on built structures in disaster areas.

The Mineral Research and Exploration Institute of Turkey has departments for geology, geophysics, petroleum and geothermal energy, metallic minerals, radioactive minerals and coal, industrial raw materials, drilling technology and laboratories for mineralogy, petrography, analytical chemistry, spectrochemistry, fuels and geochemistry. The institute has the following ongoing projects:

1. Metallic mineral project for the exploration of iron, copper, lead, zinc, mercury and antimony.
2. Prospecting for industrial raw materials.
3. Energy and combustibles project – coal, petroleum, radioactive minerals, and geothermal energy exploration; prospecting and exploration for bituminous schists.
4. Developing geological and tectonic maps of Turkey and surveying regional geophysical features.
5. Basic Research Project – neogene palaeogeography, geological correlation studies, studies on melanges, the earth's crust, palaeomagnetism, micro-earthquakes, seismotectonic maps, measurement of earth deformations, coastal geomorphology, volcanology, and environmental geology.
6. Other projects – hydrogeology, scientific and technical research, construction, prospecting and study of placer deposits along the coasts, and prospecting, exploration and evaluation of offshore, shore and alluvial mineral deposits.

Nuclear Science and Research

The Turkish Atomic Energy Commission, established in 1956 and under the authority of the prime minister's office, is responsible for nuclear science and research in Turkey. The commission supervises and coordinates general scientific research and training in nuclear sciences. It provides financial support to the Mineral Research and Exploration Institute of Turkey and to university laboratories working on nuclear energy problems – mainly the Institute of Nuclear Energy of the Technical University of Istanbul, the Radiobiology Institute of the Faculty of Agriculture, and the Radiobiology Institute of the Faculty of Medicine in Ankara University, the radioisotope laboratories of the Faculties of Agriculture and

Medicine and the Nuclear Research and Education Institute of the Aegean University. In cooperation with the Turkish Electricity Authority, the commission is supervising the construction of a 600 MW nuclear power station at Akkuya, near Silifki. The commission plans to build eight more power plants by the year 2000.

The commission promotes all kinds of health physics services throughout the country, including a film badge service. It arranges the supply of radioactive isotopes to hospitals and laboratories.

There are two nuclear research centres administered by the commission. The *Cekmece Nükleer Arastirma ve Egiti, Merkesi* (Cekmece Nuclear Research and Training Centre) is situated in Istanbul and has a 1 MW swimming-pool type reactor. Research is carried out in nuclear physics, nuclear engineering, plasma physics, chemistry, radiation protection, radiobiology, electronics, metallurgy, and applications of nuclear energy in agriculture.

The other research centre is in Ankara and has a sub-critical assembly. Research is conducted in nuclear analysis, radioactive isotopes, applications of nuclear energy for industry, applied physics, nuclear chemistry, electronics, and applications of nuclear energy in agriculture. Close contact is maintained with the Institute of Radiobiology of Ankara University.

Scientific Societies and Associations

The Turkish Biological Society was formed in 1949 to promote biological research. It publishes *Turk Biyoloji Dergisi* three times a year.

The Turkish Pharmaceutical Association maintains professional standards and publishes the bi-monthly *Turk Ecxacilars Birligi Mecmuasi.*

The Turkish Microbiological Society was established in 1931 in Istanbul and publishes the quarterly journal, *Turk Mikrobiyoloji Cemiyeti Dergisi.*

The Turkish Neuro-Psychiatric Society was established in 1914 in Istanbul and publishes the quarterly *Noro-Psikiyatri Arsivi.*

The Turkish Society of Pure and Applied Mathematics was founded in 1948 in Istanbul.

The Turkish Medical Society was established in 1856 in Istanbul and publishes a quarterly journal.

The Turkish Medical History Society was founded in 1938 and operates from Istanbul University.

The Turkish Veterinary Medicine Association was founded in 1930 in Ankara.

The Turkish Society of Mental Hygiene was established in 1930 in Istanbul.

The Turkish Geological Society was founded in Ankara in 1946. It publishes the journals *Turkiye Kurum Bulteni* twice a year, *Yeryuvarive Insan* (quarterly) and *Tuytek Bulteni* (bi-monthly).

The Chemical Society of Turkey was established in 1919 in Istanbul and publishes *Kmya ve Sanayi.*

Yemen Arab Republic

The Yemen Arab Republic, or 'North Yemen', is a mountainous country, with a long Red Sea coastline, in the south-west part of the Arabian peninsula. It has borders with Saudi Arabia to the north and east and the People's Democratic Republic of Yemen to the south and east. The country covers an area of approximately 195,000 km² and in 1979 had an estimated population of 5.7 million. The economy is mainly based on agriculture which employs 90 per cent of the population. Chief crops are cereals and fruits, while coffee is an important export crop. There is virtually no industry in the Yemen Arab Republic: a Chinese-built textile plant utilizes some of the locally produced cotton and small workshops are based on locally produced hide and tobacco. The country receives considerable foreign aid which is concentrated on building roads, sewage systems and a new airport and on improving irrigation and grain storage facilities. The country faces considerable shortage of skilled and unskilled manpower; some 15 to 18 per cent of the population is working abroad, mainly in Saudi Arabia. The 1976–81 development plan was devoted to improving agriculture and health services.

Research and Development

Very little research is carried out in the Yemen Arab Republic. There is only one university and the government ministries do not have research facilities. Sana'a University was founded in 1970 as a State-controlled institution. It is run with financial support from Kuwait and Saudi Arabia and has a Faculty of Science. The country also has a military academy, an agricultural school and colleges concerned with aviation and radiotelecommunication.

In its national paper to UNCSTD, the Yemen Arab Republic listed the following obstacles to the development of science and technology in the country:

1. The low technological awareness of the planners of industrial projects.
2. Absence of plans for the development and transfer of technology.
3. Absence of incentives that encourage industrial management and effective technology transfer.

4. Shortage of trained manpower.
5. The brain drain.
6. The difficulty of selecting technologies that are suitable to local conditions and satisfy the needs of the country.

People's Democratic Republic of Yemen

The People's Democratic Republic of Yemen is on the southern coastline of the Arabian peninsula and has borders with Saudi Arabia in the north, the Yemen Arab Republic in the north-west, and Oman in the east. The total area is 290,000 km². In 1979, the country had a population of 1.9 million. Some 95 per cent of population is employed in agriculture. Arable land represents only 2 per cent of the total area of the country. Some 300,000 acres are now being cultivated. The major crop, cotton, was only introduced in the country in 1940 and by 1960 it accounted for more than half of the country's exports. Industry consists of only thirty factories concentrated in Aden. In recent years, considerable efforts have been made to expand the fishing industry of the country. Japanese and Soviet–Yemani companies have been formed to exploit the fish resources and a fish-processing plant is being constructed near Nishtun Port with aid from Iraq and Abu Dhabi.

Research and Development

Little research is carried out in the People's Democratic Republic of Yemen. The country has only one institution of higher learning, the University of Aden. The university has faculties for agriculture, medicine, engineering and technology. Some locally oriented research is carried out in the faculties of medicine and agriculture.

Appendix

Directory of Major Establishments in the Middle East

Afghanistan

Afghan Cartographic and Cadastral Surveys Institute
Address: Pushtunistan Wat, Kabul, Afghanistan

Afghanistan Water and Soil Survey Authority
Address: Kabul, Afghanistan

Atomic Energy Commission
Address: Pushtunistan Wat, Kabul, Afghanistan

Department of Mines and Geology
Address: Ministry of Mines and Industries, Kabul, Afghanistan

Institute of Public Health
Address: Ansari Wat, Kabul, Afghanistan

Kabul University
Address: Kabul, Afghanistan

Research and Extension Department
Address: Ministry of Agriculture, Kabul, Afghanistan

University of Nangrahar
Address: Jalalabad, Afghanistan

Algeria

Centre National de Recherches et Expérimentations Forestières
(National Forestry Research and Experimentation Centre)
Address: BP 156, Petit-Atlas, Algiers, Algeria

Conseil National de la Recherche Scientifique
(National Council for Scientific Research)
Address: 27 Rue Si Arezki Abri, Hydra, Algiers, Algeria

Ecole Nationale Polytechnique
(National Polytechnic)
Address: El-Harrach, Algiers, Algeria

Institut d'Etudes Nucléaires d'Alger
(Algiers Institute of Nuclear Studies)
Address: BP 1147, Algiers, Algeria

Institut de Recherches Agronomique Tropicales et des Cultures Vivières
(Institute for Research on Tropical Agriculture and Food Crops)
Address: Station Expérimentale, El-Khemis Miliana, Algeria

Institut Nationale Supérieur Agronomique
(National Institute of Agronomy)
Address: Avenue Pasteur, El-Harrach, Algiers 10, Algeria

Institut Pasteur d'Algérie
(Algerian Pasteur Institute)
Address: Rue de Docteur Laveran, Algiers, Algeria

Ministère de l'Enseignement Supérieur et de la Recherche Scientifique
(Ministry of Higher Education and Scientific Research)
Address: Algiers, Algeria

Organisme National de la Recherche Scientifique,
(National Organization for Scientific Research)
Address: 27 Rue Si Arezki Abri, Hydra, Algiers, Algeria

Service Géologique de l'Algérie
(Algerian Geological Service)
Address: Boulevard Colonel Amirouche, Algiers, Algeria

Université d'Alger
(University of Algiers)
Address: 2 Rue Diddouche Mourad, Algiers, Algeria

Université d'Oran
(University of Oran)
Address: Oran-Senia, Algeria

Université de Constantine
(University of Constantine)
Address: Ain el-Bey, Constantine, Algeria

Egypt

Academy of Scientific Research and Technology
Address: 101 Kasr El Eini Street, Cairo, Egypt

Ain Shams University
Address: Kasr-el-Zaafran, Abbasiyah, Cairo, Egypt

al-Azhar University
Address: Cairo, Egypt

Alexandria Institute of Oceanography and Fisheries
Address: Kayed-Bey, Alexandria, Egypt

Alexandria Medical Association
Address: 4 G. Carduci Street, Alexandria, Egypt

American University in Cairo
Address: 113 Shaira Kasr El Aini, Cairo, Egypt

Atomic Energy Establishment – AEE
Address: 101 Kasr El Eini Street, Cairo, Egypt

Building Research Institute
Address: Dokki, Giza, Cairo, Egypt

Egyptian Agriculture Organization
Address: P.O. Box 63, Exhibition Grounds, Gezira, Cairo, Egypt

Egyptian Horticulture Society
Address: P.O. Box 46, Cairo, Egypt

Egyptian Medical Association
Address: 42 Shaira Kasr El Aini, Cairo, Egypt

Egyptian Society of Engineers
Address: Sharia Hahdet Misr, Cairo, Egypt

Egyptian Society of Medicine and Tropical Hygiene
Address: 2 Sharia Fouad I, Alexandria, Egypt

General Organization for Housing, Building and Planning Research
Address: P.O. Box 1770, El Tahreer Street, Dokki, Cairo, Egypt

Geological Survey and Mining Authority
Address: Ministry of Petroleum and Mineral Wealth, Abbassiya, Cairo, Egypt

Hydrological Research Station
Address: Kanater-al-Khaiyria Barages, Cairo, Egypt

Institut d'Egypte
(Egyptian Institute)
Address: 13 Sharia Sheikh Rihane, Cairo, Egypt

Institute of Astronomy and Geophysics
Address: Egyptian Observatories, Helwan, Cairo, Egypt

Institute of Freshwater Biology
Address: 10 Hassam Sabry Street, P.O. Gezira, Cairo, Egypt

Institute of Oceanography and Fisheries
Address: Al-Ghardaqa, Egypt

Medical Research Executive Organization
Address: Al-Tahrir, Dokki, Cairo, Egypt
    Drug Research Institute
    Industrial Health Research Institute
    Ophthalmological Research Institute
    Bilharziasis Research Institute
        Address: Imhala, Giza
    Medical Research Institute
        Address: Alexandria

Memorial Institute for Ophthalmic Research
Address: Giza, Cairo, Egypt

Metallurgical Research Centre
Address: c/o Helwan Steelworks, Helwan, Cairo, Egypt

Middle East Regional Isotopes Centre for the Arab States
Address: Cairo, Egypt

Mining and Water Research Executive Organization
Address: Dokki, Cairo, Egypt

Ministry of Scientific Research
Address: Cairo, Egypt

National Chemical Research Centre
Address: c/o Industrial Research Executive Organization, Dokki, Cairo, Egypt

National Information and Documentation Centre
Address: al-Tahrir Street, Dokki, Cairo, Egypt

National Institute of Standards
Address: Dokki, Cairo, Egypt
    National Physical Laboratory for Metrology
    Central Laboratory for Metrology and Materials Testing

National Research Centre
Address: Al-Tahrir Street, Dokki, Cairo, Egypt
    Physics Department
    Applied Inorganic Chemistry Department
    Applied Organic Chemistry Department
    Chemical Industries Department
    Engineering Department
    Petroleum and Minerals Department
    Biology and Agriculture Department
    Medicine and Pharmacy Department

Ophthalmological Society of Egypt
Address: Dar El Hekma, 42 Sharia Kasr El Aini, Cairo, Egypt

Petroleum Research Institute
Address: Medinat Nasser, Cairo, Egypt

Public Health Laboratories
Address: Ministry of Public Health, Sharia Sheikh Rehan, Cairo, Egypt

Remote Sensing Centre
Address: 101 Kasr El Eini Street, Cairo, Egypt

Research Institute and Hospital for Tropical Diseases
Address: 10–12 Sharia Kasr El Aini, Cairo, Egypt

Serum and Vaccine Institute
Address: Agouza, Cairo, Egypt

Société Entomologique d'Egypte
(Egyptian Entomological Society)
Address: 14 Sharia Ramses, P.O. Box 430, Cairo, Egypt

Textile Research Centre
Address: Alexandria, Egypt

University of Alexandria
Address: 12 Al-Gueish Avenue, Shatby, Alexandria, Egypt

University of Assiut
Address: Assiut, Egypt

University of Cairo
Address: Orman, Giza, Cairo, Egypt

Gulf States

Centre for Documentation and Research
Address: Abu Dhabi, United Arab Emirates

Gulf Technical College
Address: Isa Town, Bahrain

University of Abu Dhabi
Address: Abu Dhabi, United Arab Emirates

Iran

Atomic Energy Organization
Address: Karin Khan Avenue, Tehran, Iran

Baluchistan University
Address: Zahedan, Iran

Centre for Scientific and Industrial Research
Address: Tehran, Iran

Department of Environment
Address: Ustad Nijatullahi Avenue, Tehran, Iran

Gilan University
Address: P.O. Box 401, Rasht, Iran

Institute for Research and Planning in Science and Education
Address: P.O. Box 11-1387, 46 Inqelab Street, Tehran, Iran
    Centre for Scientific and Educational Planning
    Iranian Documentation Centre
    Centre for Science and Research Policy

Isfahan University
Address: Isfahan, Iran

Jundi Shapur University
Address: Ahwaz, Khuzestan, Iran

Ministry of Science and Higher Education
Address: Ustad Nijatullahi Avenue, Tehran, Iran

Tehran University of Technology
Address: Azadi Avenue, Tehran, Iran

University of Mashhad
Address: Mashhad, Iran

University of Shiraz
Address: Shiraz, Iran

University of Tabriz
Address: Tabriz, Iran

University of Tehran
Address: Inqelab Avenue, Tehran, Iran

Iraq

al-Mustansiriya University
Address: Baghdad, Iraq

Department of Scientific and Industrial Research
Address: Directorate-General of Industry, Baghdad, Iraq

Foundation of Scientific Research
Address: Jadiriyah, Baghdad, Iraq
  Agriculture Research Centre
    Address: Tudhaliyah, Baghdad
  Biological Research Centre
    Address: Adhamiyah, Baghdad
  Building Research Centre
    Address: Baghdad
  Dates and Palm Research Centre
    Address: Baghdad
  Institute of Applied Research on Natural Resources
    Address: Abu Chraib, Baghdad
  Petroleum Research Institute
    Address: Shalijah, Baghdad

Iraqi Atomic Energy Commission
Address: Baghdad, Iraq

Ministry of Higher Education and Scientific Research
Address: Baghdad, Iraq

National Library
Address: Waziriyah, Abu Talib Street, Baghdad, Iraq

Nuclear Research Institute
Address: Iraq Atomic Energy Commission, Tuwaitha, Baghdad, Iraq

University of Baghdad
Address: Baghdad, Iraq

University of Basra
Address: Basra, Iraq

University of Mosul
Address: Baghdad, Iraq

University of Sulaimaniya
Address: Sulaimaniya, Iraq

Jordan

Bethlehem University
Address: P.O. Box 9, Bethlehem, West Bank, via Israel

Birzeit University
Address: P.O. Box 14, Birzeit, via Israel

Directorate of Research and Agricultural Extension
Address: P.O. Box 226 and 2178, Amman, Jordan

Royal Scientific Society
Address: P.O. Box 6945, Amman, Jordan

University of Jordan
Address: P.O. Box 1682, Amman, Jordan

Yarmouk University
Address: c/o P.O. Box 20184, Amman, Jordan

Kuwait

Agricultural Experimental Station
Address: c/o Agricultural Department, Ministry of Public Works, Kuwait

Kuwait Foundation for the Advancement of the Sciences
Address: Kuwait City, Kuwait

Kuwait Institute for Scientific Research
National Scientific and Technical Information Centre
Address: P.O. Box 16009, Kuwait City, Kuwait

University of Kuwait
Address: P.O. Box 5969, Kuwait City, Kuwait

Lebanon

American University of Beirut
Address: Beirut, Lebanon

Arab Physical Society
Address: P.O. Box 11-7142, Beirut, Lebanon

Beirut Arab University
Address: Tarik el-Jadidé, P.O. Box 5020, Beirut, Lebanon

Bibliothèque Nationale du Liban
(National Library of the Lebanon)
Address: Place de l'Etoile, Beirut, Lebanon

Office de la Recherche Scientifique et Technique d'Outre-Mer
(Overseas Scientific and Technical Research Office)
- *Address:* Mission ORSTOM, Laboratoires de Fanar, Jdeideh el-Metn,
Tel Amara, Rayak, Lebanon

Université Libanaise
(Lebanese University)
Address: Bir Hassan, Beirut, Lebanon

Université Saint-Joseph
(St Joseph University)
Address: BP 293, Beirut, Lebanon

Libya

Al Fateh University
Address: P.O. Box 13040, Tripoli, Libya

Arab Development Institute
Address: Tripoli, Libya

Ministry of Agriculture and Natural Resources
Address: Research Department, Benghazi, Libya

University of Gar Younis
Address: P.O. Box 1308, Benghazi, Libya

Morocco

Bureau de Recherches et de Participations Minières
(Office of Mining Research)
Address: 27 Avenue Urbain Blan, Rabat, Morocco

Centre National de Coordination et de Planification de la Recherche Scientifique et Technique
(National Centre for Coordination and Planning of Scientific and Technological Research)
Address: Rabat, Morocco

Centre Universitaire de la Recherche Scientifique
(University Centre of Scientific Research)
Address: Université Mohammed V, Rabat, Morocco

Direction de la Recherche Agronomique
(Agricultural Research Directorate)
Address: BP 415, Rabat, Morocco

Direction des Services Techniques
(Technical Services Directorate)
Address: Ministry of Public Health, Rabat, Morocco

Division de la Géologie
(Geology Division)
Address: Ministry of Commerce, Industry, Mines and Merchant Marine, Rabat, Morocco

Institut Agronomique et Vétérinaire Hassan II
(Hassan II Agricultural and Veterinary Institute)
Address: BP 704, Rabat-Agdal, Morocco

Institut des Pêches Maritimes
(Institute of Marine Fisheries)
Address: Rue de Tiznit, Casablanca, Morocco

Institut National d'Hygiène
(National Institute of Health)
Address: Avenue Moulay Chérif, Rabat, Morocco

Institut Pasteur
(Pasteur Institute)
Address: BP 415, Tangier, Morocco

Institute Scientifique Chérifen
(Moroccan Scientific Institute)
Address: Avenue Moulay-Chérif, Rabat, Morocco
  Seismology Observatory, Averroës, Berrechid
  Station de Recherches Presahariennes (Sahara Research Station,
    Aouinet-Torkoz)
  Seismology Station, Ifrane
  Seismology Station, Tiouine

Laboratoire Public d'Essais et d'Etudes
(Public Testing and Research Laboratory)
Address: 25 rue d'Azilal, Casablanca, Morocco

Office Chérifien des Phosphates
(Moroccan Phosphates Office)
Address: Rabat, Morocco

Office de la Recherche Scientifique et Technique d'Outre-Mer
(Overseas Scientific and Technical Research Office)
Address: BP 432, Rabat, Morocco

Société d'Horticulture et de l'Acclimatation du Maroc
(Moroccan Horticultural and Acclimatization Society)
Address: BP 854, Casablanca, Morocco

Société des Sciences Naturelles et Physiques du Maroc
(Moroccan Society of Natural and Physical Sciences)
Address: Avenue Moulay Chérif, Rabat, Morocco

Université Mohammed V
(Mohammed V University)
Address: Avenue Moulay Chérif, Rabat, Morocco

Pakistan

Appropriate Technology Development Organization
Address: 1-b, 47, F-7/1, P.O. Box 1306, Islamabad, Pakistan

Gomal University
Address: D. I. Khan, North West Frontier Province, Pakistan

Hamdard National Foundation
Address: Hamdard Centre, Nazimabad, Karachi 18, Pakistan

Institution of Electrical Engineering
Address: 4 Lawrence Road, Lahore, Pakistan

Irrigation, Drainage and Flood Control Research Council
Address: 84-D Satellite Town, Rawalpindi, Pakistan

Mehran University of Engineering and Technology
Address: Nawabshah, Pakistan

NED University of Engineering and Technology
Address: University Road, Karachi 32, Pakistan

Pakistan Agricultural Research Council
Address: P.O. Box 1031, Islamabad, Pakistan
  National Agricultural Research Centre
  Arid Zone Research Centre
  Cereal Diseases Research Institute
  Locust Research Station

Pakistan Association for the Advancement of Science
Address: 14 Shah Jamal Scheme, P.O. Ichhra, Lahore 12, Pakistan

Pakistan Atomic Energy Commission
Address: P.O. Box 1114, Islamabad, Pakistan
  Pakistan Institute of Nuclear Science and Technology
    Address: P.O. Nilore, Islamabad
  Atomic Energy Agricultural Research Centre
    Address: Tandojam, Pakistan
  Nuclear Institute for Agriculture and Biology
    Address: Faisalabad, Pakistan
  Institute of Radiotherapy and Nuclear Medicine
    Address: Peshawar, Pakistan

Pakistan Council for Scientific and Industrial Research
Address: Press Centre, Shahrah-e-Kamal Ataturk, Karachi 1, Pakistan

Pakistan Medical Association
Address: P.M.A. House, Garden Road, P.O. Box 7267, Karachi 3, Pakistan

Pakistan Medical Research Council
Address: Jinah Postgraduate Medical Centre, Karachi, Pakistan

Pakistan Science Foundation
Pakistan Scientific and Technological Information Centre
Address: 63 School Road, Shalimar 7/4, Islamabad, Pakistan

Quaid-i-Azam University
Address: P.O. Box 1090, Islamabad, Pakistan

Scientific Society of Pakistan
Address: University of Karachi, Karachi 32, Pakistan

Sind Agriculture University
Address: Tandojam, Sind, Pakistan

University of Agriculture
Address: Faisalabad, Pakistan

University of Baluchistan
Address: Sariab Road, Quetta, Pakistan

University of Engineering and Technology
Address: Grand Trunk Road, Lahore 31, Pakistan

University of Karachi
Address: University Campus, Karachi 32, Pakistan

University of Peshawar
Address: Peshawar, North West Frontier Province, Pakistan

University of Punjab
Address: 1 Shahrah-e-Al Biruni, Lahore 2, Pakistan

University of Sind
Address: Jamshoro, District Dadu, Pakistan

Saudi Arabia

Industrial Studies and Development Centre
Address: P.O. Box 1267, Riyadh, Saudi Arabia

King Abdul Aziz University
Address: P.O. Box 1540, Jeddah, Saudi Arabia

King Faisal Specialist Hospital
Address: King Faisal Medical City, Riyadh, Saudi Arabia

King Faisal University
Address: P.O. Box 1982, Dammam, Saudi Arabia/P.O. Box 380, Al Hasa, Saudi Arabia

King Saud University
Address: P.O. Box 2454, Riyadh, Saudi Arabia

Saudi Arabian National Centre for Science and Technology
Address: P.O. Box 6086, Riyadh, Saudi Arabia

University of Petroleum and Minerals
Address: Dahran, Saudi Arabia

The Sudan

Agriculture Research Corporation, Ministry of Agriculture
Address: P.O. Box 126, Wad Medani, The Sudan

Cairo University, Khartoum Branch
Address: P.O. Box 1055, Khartoum, The Sudan

Forest Research and Education Institute
Address: P.O. Box 658, Khartoum, The Sudan

Geological Survey Department
Address: P.O. Box 410, Khartoum, The Sudan

Industrial Consultancy Corporation
Address: P.O. Box 268, Khartoum, The Sudan

Institute of Industrial Research
Address: P.O. Box 268, Khartoum, The Sudan

National Council for Research
Address: P.O. Box 2404, Khartoum, The Sudan
    Agricultural Research Council
    Medical Research Council
    Scientific and Technological Research Council

Sudan Medical Research Laboratories
Address: P.O. Box 287, Khartoum, The Sudan

University of Khartoum
Address: P.O. Box 321, Khartoum, The Sudan

Syria

Arab Centre for the Study of Arid Zones
Address: P.O. Box 2440, Damascus, Syria

Centre for Industrial Studies and Scientific Research
Address: P.O. Box 4470, Damascus, Syria

Cotton Bureau
Address: Aleppo, Syria

International Centre for Agricultural Research in the Dry Areas
Address: P.O. Box 5466, Aleppo, Syria

Ministry of Agricultural and Agrarian Reform
Address: Damascus, Syria

University of Aleppo
Address: Aleppo, Syria

University of Damascus
Address: Damascus, Syria

University of Tichreen
Address: Lattakia, Syria

Tunisia

Centre de Recherches du Génie Rural
(Rural Engineering Research Centre)
Address: BP 10, Ariana, Tunisia

Institut Artoing (veterinary research)
(Artoing Institute)
Address: Tunis, Tunisia

Institut de Recherches Scientifiques et Techniques
(Scientific and Technical Research Institute)
Address: Tunis-Carthage, Tunisia

Institut National de la Recherche Agronomique de Tunisie
(National Agronomic Research Institute of Tunisia)
Address: Ariana, Tunisia

Institut National de Nutrition
(National Nutrition Institute)
Address: 12 rue de Rome, Tunis, Tunisia

Institut National de Recherches Forestières
(National Forestry Research Institute)
Address: Ariana, Tunisia

Institut National de Recherches Vétérinaires
(National Veterinary Research Institute)
Address: Tunis, Tunisia

Institut National Scientifique et Technique d'Océanographie et de Pêche
(National Scientific and Technical Institute of Oceanography and Fisheries)
Address: Salammbö, Tunisia

Institut Pasteur
(Pasteur Institute)
Address: 13 place Pasteur, Tunis, Tunisia

Ministère de l'Enseignement Supérieur et de la Recherche Scientifique
(Ministry of Higher Education and Scientific Research)
Address: Tunis, Tunisia

Université de Tunis
(Tunis University)
Address: 94 Boulevard du 8 Avril 1938, Tunis, Tunisia

Research

Turkey

Ankara Universitesi
(Ankara University)
Address: Tandogan Meydani, Ankara, Turkey

Ataturk Universitesi
(Ataturk University)
Address: Erzurum, Turkey

Atom Enerjisi Komisyonu
(Atomic Energy Commission)
Address: 12 Ziya Gokalp Caddesi, Ankara, Turkey
      Ankara Nuclear Research Centre
      Cekmece Nükleer Arastirma ve Egitim Merkezi
      (Cekmece Nuclear Research and Training Centre)
          Address: PI 1 Hava Alani, Istanbul, Turkey

Bogazici Universitesi
(Bosphorus University)
Address: PK 2, Bebek, Istanbul, Turkey

Cukurova Universitesi
(Cukurova University)
Address: Balcali Campus, Adana, Turkey

Diyarbakir Universitesi
(Diyarbakir University)
Address: Diyarbakir, Turkey

Ege Universitesi
(Aegean University)
Address: Bornova, Izmir, Turkey

Hacettepe Universitesi
(Hacettepe University)
Address: Hacettepe Parki, Ankara, Istanbul, Turkey

Istanbul Teknik Universitesi
(Istanbul Technical University)
Address: 389 Taksim, Taskisla, Istanbul, Turkey

Istanbul Universitesi
(Istanbul University)
Address: Bayazit, Istanbul, Turkey

Karadeniz Teknik Universitesi
(Black Sea Technical University)
Address: Trabos, Turkey

Maden Tetkik ve Arama Enstitüsü
(Mineral Research and Exploration Institute of Turkey)
Address: PK 116, Ankara, Turkey

Orta Dogu Teknik Universitesi
(Middle East Technical University)
Address: Ismat Inonu Bulvari, Ankara, Turkey

Pamuk Isleri Müdürlügu
(Cotton Directorate)
Address: Necati Bey Caddesi 98, Ankara, Turkey
    Bölge Pamuk Arastirma Enstitüsü Müdürlügu
    (Regional Cotton Research Institute)
        Address: Adana, Turkey
    Bölge Pamuk Arastirma Enstitüsü Müdürlügu
    (Regional Cotton Research Institute)
        Address: Nazilli, Turkey

Refik Saydam Merkez Hifzissihha Enstitüsü
(Refik Saydam Central Institute of Hygiene)
Address: Ankara, Turkey

Seker Enstitüsü Kütüphanesi
(Sugar Beet Research Institute)
Address: Etimesgut, Ankara, Turkey

Seluloz ve Kagit Fabrikalar Isletmesi
(Pulp and Paper Enterprise)
Address: Izmit, Turkey

Seyir ve Hidrografi Daire Baskanligi
(Navigation and Hydrography Department of the Turkish Navy)
Address: Cubuklu, Istanbul, Turkey

Tarim Bakanligi
(Ministry of Agriculture)
Address: Ankara, Turkey

Türk Kanser Arastirma ve Savas Murumu
(Turkish Cancer Research and Control Association)
Address: Tuna Caddesi Atac Sokak 21, Yenisehir-Ankara, Turkey

Türk Kardiyoloji Cemiyeti
(Cardiology Society of Turkey)
Address: Lamartin Caddesi 11/1, Taksim, Istanbul, Turkey

Türkiye Bilimsel ve Teknik Arastirma Kurumu – TUBITAK
(Scientific and Technical Research Council of Turkey)
Address: Bayindir Sokak 33, Yenisehir, Ankara, Turkey
    Mathematical, Physical and Biological Research Group

Engineering Research Group
Medical Research Group
Veterinary Medicine and Animal Husbandry Research Group
Agriculture and Forestry Research Group
Group for Training Young Scientists
Marmara Scientific and Industrial Research Institute

Türkiye Bilimsel ve Teknik Dokumantasyon Merkezi – TURDOC
(Turkish Scientific and Technical Documentation Centre)
Address: Bayindir Sokak 33, Yenisehir, Ankara

Türkiye Jeoloji Kurumu
(Turkish Geological Society)
Address: PI 464, Kizilay, Ankara, Turkey

Türkiye Kimya Cemiyeti
(Chemical Society of Turkey)
Address: PK 829, Istanbul, Turkey

Yeraltisulari Dairesi Baskanligi
(General Directorate of State Hydraulic Works)
Address: Gulhane, Ankara, Turkey

Zirai Mucadele ve Zirai Karantina Genel Müdürlügü
(General Directorate of Plant Protection and Plant Quarantine)
Address: Necatibey Caddesi 98, Ankara, Turkey

Yemen Arab Republic

Sana'a University
Address: P.O. Box 1247, Sana'a, Yemen Arab Republic

Yemen, People's Democatic Republic of

University of Aden
Address: Airport Road, Khormaksar, Aden, People's Democratic Republic of Yemen

Regional Organizations

Arab Bureau of Education for the Gulf States
Address: Riyadh, Saudi Arabia

Arab League Educational, Cultural and Scientific Organization
Address: P.O. Box 1120, Tunis, Tunisia

Conference of Ministers of Arab Member States Responsible for the Application of Science and Technology to Development
Address: c/o Division of Science and Technology Policy, UNESCO,
7 Place de Fontenoy, 75700 Paris, France

Islamic Foundation for Science and Technology for Development
Address: P.O. Box 178, Jeddah, Saudi Arabia

Union of Arab National Research Councils
Address: Baghdad, Iraq

Index of Establishments

Subject Index

This index covers the subject matter and geographical location of scientific and technological research and development. The terminology used is based on ROOT, *the British Standards Institution thesaurus (1981).*

Index by Ann Edwards